METABOLIC
AND
ENDOCRINE
PHYSIOLOGY

METABOLIC AND

JAY TEPPERMAN, M.D.
Professor of Experimental Medicine, Department of Pharmacology
State University of New York Upstate Medical Center, Syracuse

ENDOCRINE PHYSIOLOGY

An
Introductory Text

SECOND EDITION

YEAR BOOK MEDICAL PUBLISHERS INCORPORATED

35 EAST WACKER DRIVE, CHICAGO

For
HELEN
and for
JEAN, KATHY *and* JIM

Preface to the Second Edition

THE RECEPTION of the first edition of this book was gratifying. Although various errors were quickly called to the attention of the author and although a few people considered my literary style inappropriate for the presentation of a serious scientific subject, there were many more who seemed to find the book entertaining as well as informative.

In presenting this second edition, I would like to reiterate the fact that the selection of material for a monograph of this kind is extremely arbitrary. The literature on the subject continues to accumulate at an exponential rate, so that no author, especially one who has continuing teaching, administrative and research duties, can read more than a small fraction of it. The fact that I have seen as much of it as I have is more to the credit of my wife, Helen, than to me, for she has called to my attention many interesting new developments and has helped me to understand the historical significance of ideas I would have ignored. Again, she has read all the new material critically and has prevented me from making a number of egregious mistakes.

My selection of material for inclusion has been influenced by my chance encounters with many seminar speakers and by my participation in a number of conferences, symposia and other meetings. While this form of education is not very systematic, I am sure it has contributed much to the set of associations I bring to the task of writing these essays.

One of the main criticisms of the first edition was my failure to document specific statements in the text. I thought that I had made it very clear that the book was not intended to be an encyclopedic review but was rather a narrative account of the subject aimed at the beginning student. I did not anticipate that it would be interesting to workers in the field or to beginning research fellows. Since it has proved to be so, I have tried to be a little more careful about attributing ideas to individual investigators. It would be easy to fill a book of this size with nothing but bibliographic citations. I have, therefore, tried to save space by referring to authors by names and, parenthetically, the year of publication so that any interested reader with access to a cumulative index can quickly locate the original sources. The references added are usually to review articles, published symposia or to a few original articles.

Possibly the most important pedagogical idea advanced since 1961 is that of the *cept,* a happy invention of a Princeton undergraduate student. A *cept* is simply an idea, but by supplying the proper prefix one can give some sort of quantitative expression to the relative importance of the idea. At one end of the scale are *megacepts* and *kilocepts,* while at the other end one finds *microcepts* and, possibly, even *picocepts.* The one *megacept* in endocrinology during the past five years or so has been the widespread and vigorous attempt to apply the ideas and methods of molecular biology to the problem of the mechanism of action of hormones. This *cept* has been so prominent that I have rearranged the book to include a new chapter on Hormones and Protein Synthesis. Another *cept,* discussed in the first edition, has now assumed the proportions of a *megacept,* i.e., Sutherland's "second messenger" or "molecular deputy" theory of hormone action. Accordingly, I have expanded the discussion of 3', 5' cyclic AMP. In addition, I have added material on the following subjects: radioimmunoassay of hormones in blood; the pineal gland; hormones and brain organization in the infant rat; thyroid-stimulating hormone; hormones and lysosomes; regulation of aldosterone secretion; a biochemistry of hope and despair; glucagon; the glucose fatty acid cycle; obesity and energy balance; parathyroid hormone and thyrocalcitonin.

Acknowledgments

Many investigators have responded sympathetically to my requests for help in making this revision. I am especially grateful to the following for their kindness and generosity: I. S. Edelman, J. Gorski, L. Peachey, L. G. Raisz, A. Moses, S. Segal, S. Glick, S. Berson, G. Mueller, L. Garren, R. Schimke, A. Korner, J. O. Davis, A. Leaf, R. Gustafsson, S. Reichlin and J. Larner.

JAY TEPPERMAN

Preface to the First Edition

THE TIME has long since gone when anyone could presume to say to the beginning student: "Here are the facts of physiology which you must learn in order to prepare yourself to be a physician." Every attempt to describe the state of development of a field of physiology at present must involve arbitrary selection of material, emphasis colored by the personal experience and limitations of the author, and the occupational risk of offending the sensibilities of one's colleagues and fellow authors. This is not to be regarded as a plea for sympathy, since my choice to write a review of endocrine physiology was a free one, but the reader should reflect, for a moment, about the problems involved in constructing such a review.

In the first place, the preparation or (in the educationist's patois) the "readiness" of our first-year medical students in this area is quite variable. I have seen students who have been exposed to excellent undergraduate courses in endocrinology on the one hand and some who were quite virginally innocent of any knowledge about the glands of internal secretion on the other. The future application of this information by individual students may be equally variable; some of our students have elected to become specialists in this field and have devoted their lives to study, teaching and research in it, while others have chosen to work in some branch of medicine which they manage to visualize as nonmetabolic (although it is difficult to understand how they contrive to do this). In the intermediate zone there is a whole spectrum of professional activities, which range from internal medicine and gynecology through general practice to psychiatry, in which the facts and concepts of endocrinology and metabolism are not merely pertinent but crucial in the diagnosis of disease and the management of sick people.

These variations in educational origin and professional destination of our students are confusing enough, but when one adds to this the nature of the material to be presented, the confusion is compounded. The rate at which new knowledge is accumulating in the field of endocrinology cannot be appreciated by anyone who has not been obliged to try to keep up with some of it. These essays are beads drawn on rapidly moving targets.

This, then, is one author's account of the current state of knowledge of endocrinology as he understands it, and it is directed to an imaginary undifferentiated, totipotential first- or second-year medical student (I would not be desolate, however, if a colleague or fellow-teacher were to experience an occasional "shock of recognition" in these pages). Some students, like the little girl who wrote the review of a book on penguins, may find more here than they care to know. Others may find much less, and for them I have included key references (mainly to monographs, symposia and recent review articles) which were selected to guide the reader back to original sources. I intend to indicate, wherever possible, how the physiological idea is applied in the clinic, for I do not subscribe to the view that a physiological insight that has practical application is necessarily less interesting or beautiful than one for which there is as yet none. This is not to be construed as a promise to omit mention of concepts which may not yet have been applied to the practice of medicine or public health, or to refrain from discussing certain theories and speculations. It seems to me that the fantasies and daydreams of physiology are an important part of the art, and that they do no harm if they are clearly identified. The good ones will one day be validated by experiment and the bad ones will be punctured and discarded in due time.

It is assumed that by the time the student attempts to read this account he will have acquired some information about the gross and microscopic anatomy and embryology of the endocrine glands, and that he is familiar with the broad outlines of carbohydrate, fat and protein metabolism. No attempt will be made here to recapitulate in detail material which is readily available in any standard textbook of histology or biochemistry.

The selection of illustrative experiments from our own experience is not intended to convey the impression that the data cited have any special significance or originality. It often indicates merely that the material was more readily available to me than other similar data would have been. It is obviously impossible to give more than a very small sample of the kinds of data on which statements made in the text are based. In fact, it would be unfair to both the reader and the data to attempt too broad a reporting of more or less original information. Therefore, in the few examples I have used, I have tried consciously to include samples taken from every wavelength of the biological research spectrum from the molecular to the epidemiological.

There are two widely used methods of drawing diagrams of the endocrine system: in one, the endocrine organs, kidneys, gastrointestinal tract, etc., are represented by more or less faithful cartoons of their gross anatomic structure (the "Giblet School"); in the other, the related structures are rendered simply as engineers' "black boxes" (the "Mondrianesque School"). Many of the diagrams to be presented herein are in the latter category, and they are intended both as guides to and summaries of the discussion. The encircled numbers represent subsections of the text which are identified by the corresponding numbers in the text. These diagrams have been designed to show the structures and hormones to be discussed and some of their interrelationships.

No one can really understand any subject unless he has some knowledge of the historical development of the modern idea. When I have

attempted historical accounts of some of the subjects to be covered in this section in lectures, I have noticed a certain restiveness on the part of students who appeared to be impatient to reach topics that seemed more likely than Minkowski's dogs to be included in an examination. While I have been unable to permit myself the luxury of extended historical treatment of the subject, I could not bring myself to present this inventory without giving some indication that the intellectual edifice of physiology was built over many years by patient and devoted individuals to whom we and those who follow us owe a great debt. Therefore, I have included abbreviated chronologies of some subjects at the beginnings of most chapters. In addition to serving as a small tribute to our professional ancestors, these chronologies illustrate beautifully the interchange of information between clinic and experimental laboratory that has occurred mainly in the past century, and promises to be even more fruitful in the future.

Acknowledgments

There is no doubt that this enterprise could not have been completed without the help of my wife, Dr. Helen Tepperman. In addition to teaching me most of the material in Chapters 5 and 11 and helping in the collection and evaluation of much source information for all other chapters, she read every word of this account in three successive drafts, criticized gently but firmly, and made many valuable suggestions for improving the final product.

I am grateful, too, to Dr. Alfred Farah, Chairman of the department in which I work, for his encouragement and help in many ways. I have requested and received welcome help from each of the following: D. Tapley, R. Barrnett, G. Sayers, M. Karnofsky, J. L. Kostyo, H. Rasmussen, R. C. Haynes, Jr., D. Sabbatini, D. H. P. Streeten, M. Voorhess, L. Gardner, A. Moses and L. Raisz.

I owe a special debt to Nicolas Apgar and Julia Hammack for the great care and skill with which they prepared the illustrations, and to Shirley Martin for expert secretarial help. I am grateful, too, to the publishers for their understanding cooperation.

JAY TEPPERMAN

Table of Contents

1

Introduction

LIVING THINGS, including people, go to a considerable amount of trouble to stay alive. Some of the work and effort involved in staying alive is expended at the level of consciousness, but fortunately much of it is carried on autonomically under the direction of the two great communications systems of the body—the nervous system and the endocrine system. In any multicellular organism which consists of cooperative clusters of highly differentiated cells there are systems of signals and mechanisms for the transmission of messages from one part of the organism to another. The nervous tissues of the body, "voluntary" and autonomic, are analogous to an elaborate system of telegraphy in which there is a wire connection from the source of initiation of the message to the place where the reception of the message has its effect. The endocrine complex is a wireless communications system in which messages are carried in the blood stream in the form of highly specialized chemical substances which interact with cells which have differentiated in such a way as to be able to receive hormonal direction and act on it. Thus, over aeons of evolutionary time there has been a parallel development of hormone-producing cells, which we call endocrine glands, their hormonal products, the intracellular mechanisms that permit cells to respond to such products, and the auxiliary tissues which participate in regulating the function of the glands. The capacity of an end-organ cell to respond to a chemical substance in a characteristic way involves no less admirable a trick than does the production of this substance by a specialized cell type.

Interrelations of Nervous and Endocrine Systems

One of the most striking developments in endocrinology during the past 15 years has been the growing realization that the "wire" and the "wireless" communication systems of the body function in a closely coordinated way and that each is dependent on the other for its proper operation. A whole new subdivision of endocrinology—called "neuroendocrinology"—has been developed as a result of recent and older studies of the relationships between the central nervous system and the hypophysis. It is now clear that nervous influences play not only on the neurohypophysis but also on the adenohypophysis; later, some of these will be discussed in detail. It is equally clear that the function of the central nervous system itself is strongly influenced by such hormones as thyroxin, insulin, hydrocortisone and sex steroids. Thus, the total behavior of the organism is integrated by the constant circulation of neural and hormonal signals which are received, decoded and acted on by appropriate tissues. Moreover, the tissues which are responsible for the maintenance of this complex communications apparatus are themselves dependent on neural and hormonal stimuli, as well as on a proper supply of nutrients of the sort that all living cells must have. The cells which are so vital in integrating the living and breathing patterns of organisms are themselves living, breathing entities. In each cell are elaborate communications mechanisms which participate in the maintenance of a sort of "microhomeostasis."

Metabolism and Endocrinology

The phrase "metabolism and endocrinology" is an arbitrary and artificial designation and represents no more than a teaching convenience. It is merely a point of view, for everything in physiology is obviously metabolic or it would not be alive. Historically, the general area to be covered in this volume grew out of the preoccupation of clinicians with diseases of the pancreas, adrenals, thyroid, parathyroid, hypophysis, gonads, and so on, and it came to involve that part of physiology which was studied by means of chemical methods. This has ceased to be meaningful, for there is no aspect of physiology which is *not* studied by means of chemical methods at present. Moreover, endocrinologists do not restrict themselves to chemical methods in their analysis of the effects of hormonal deficits, replacement therapy, or hormonal excesses. Such biophysical methods as electrocardiography or electroencephalography can be applied with profit to the study of problems in endocrinology and metabolism. There are no such things as pure, disembodied action potentials in an animal.

Endocrine System as a Vehicle for Correlation of Medical Curriculum

Many medical students complain about the fact that they are inundated by great masses of information but that the interrelationships of knowledge obtained in different courses (or, in some curricula, in different "areas") are not often pointed out explicitly. Although a good case can be made for the view that the student can perform more meaningful feats of correlation than can his teachers and that, in any case, correlation is not something that is done by a "correlator" to a "correlatee," the study of endocrinology can be viewed as one long exercise in correlation. Anatomy, histology, biochemistry and histochemistry, microbiology, immunology, pathology, clinical medicine, public health and preventive medicine, genetics, and information theory all converge in reflections about the endocrine system. It is impossible to segregate pharmacology from endocrinology for two major reasons: first, many therapeutically important substances are of endocrine origin or represent molecular modifications of naturally occurring hormonal substances; second, chemical compounds which have sharply selective actions

have become extremely important tools for the analysis of endocrine function as well as for the treatment of certain endocrine disorders. Generally, pharmacology is defined as the study of the effects of chemical agents on living systems. In this sense, endocrinology has been referred to as "autopharmacology." For this reason, in the pages to follow, no attempt will be made to amputate certain pharmacological aspects of endocrinology from the main body of the subject. If it is of interest to mention that an adrenal steroid called "aldosterone" has the effect of facilitating the renal tubular reabsorption of sodium, it is of further interest that we now have synthetic steroids which function as "antialdosterones."

Shared Characteristics of Hormones

Although hormones belong to several different chemical classes (proteins, peptides, amino acid derivatives and steroids) certain general remarks can be made about all of them. *None is believed to initiate reactions in cells de novo.* In other words, the biochemical machinery of the cell responds to the presence of the hormone by either increasing or decreasing the *rate* at which a critical, rate-limiting reaction may proceed, but all of the necessary equipment for the performance of the reaction and for the response to the hormone is built into the cell during its differentiation. None of the postulated rate-limiting reactions of the cell have been identified with certainty, but a general discussion of the mechanism of action of hormones at the cellular level will be presented.

Another generalization that can be made about most hormones is the fact that *none of them is secreted at a precisely uniform rate.* Some of them, like the adrenal hormones, are secreted in a diurnal rhythm. Others, like the gonadotrophins and sex steroids in the female, are secreted in complicated cycles which are timed to coincide with such events as ovulation and menstruation or with pregnancy and lactation. Still others, like insulin, are produced at rates which depend on the carbohydrate content of the diet or, in the case of aldosterone, on its sodium content. Thyroid hormone output is closely related to environmental temperature. This variability in hormone output suggests that certain environmental or nutritional circumstances set up appropriate signals which "instruct" a hormone-producing cell to release and manufacture more or less of the required substance. Most of the time, these responses can be described in Cannon's famous phrase as "the wisdom of the body," but unfortunately there are circumstances in which the customary response of an endocrine gland to its usual stimulus may have a deleterious effect on the whole organism rather than a favorable one. A few such circumstances will be referred to in the chapters that follow, particularly in connection with aldosterone.

All of the hormones exert their effects in biocatalytic concentrations; in the case of certain hormones—particularly tri-iodothyronine and aldosterone—the effective dose is in the microgram range. Unlike inorganic catalysts which, by definition, are not influenced by the reactions they facilitate, *the hormones are continually lost to the body either by processes of metabolic inactivation or by excretion.* Some of the inactivation may occur in the very tissue on which the hormone exerts its effect (for example, thyroid-stimulating hormone is inactivated by the thyroid gland), while some of it may occur in an organ like the liver which we have no reason to think of as an end-organ for the hormone in question (i.e., the inactivation of vasopressin by the liver). The net effect of these losses by inactivation or excretion is the fact that all of the hormone-producing glands must continually produce a certain basal, finite quantity of material to make up for the loss and amounts more than this to fill the variable needs of the whole organism for the hormone. A knowledge of this point may be of some practical usefulness, for certain clinical conditions exist in which hormones may exert noticeable and physiologically inappropriate effects not because they are being overproduced, but because they are being metabolically inactivated at too slow a rate.

Integrative Functions of Hormones

The endocrine glands have a central role in all of the important life transactions of the organism: in the *reproduction* of the species and all of the functions associated with this elaborate enterprise; in *growth and structural and biochemical differentiation;* and in *adaptation* to environmental or nutritional circumstances that threaten life or health. Moreover, all of these activities are intricately interrelated with one another and with the nutritional condition of the animal and with its state of hydration. A disturbance in one specific function may have devastating effects on another that is many steps removed from the original difficulty (see, for example, the discussion of the pathophysiology of diabetic acidosis in Chapter 9).

Perhaps the best way to understand what the endocrine system accomplishes is to imagine that a technically skilled but fiendish surgeon has succeeded in performing the following operations on a human infant 6 months old: pancreatectomy, bilateral adrenalectomy, parathyroidectomy, and hypophysectomy. Judging from the experience with similarly operated animals, it would be possible to keep such an infant alive with devoted, round-the-clock nursing care and a small amount of adrenal cortical hormone substitution therapy.

Obviously, such an infant, even if it were possible to maintain it for 20 years, would be unable to reproduce because of the lack of hypophysial gonadotrophins and the secondary lack of sex steroids. It would be unable to grow because of the lack of hypophysial growth hormone, thyroid hormone, adrenal cortical hormones, and insulin, all of which participate in the processes of normal growth. Differentiation, particularly of the central nervous system, would not occur normally because of the lack of thyroid hormone. The capacity to adapt to infectious disease, trauma, toxic chemicals, even moderate fluctuations in ambient air temperature, transient hypoxia or other similar insults would be minimal because of the lack of adrenal cortical hormones, thyroid hormone, and possibly hypophysial growth hormone. There would be a marked inability to regulate serum calcium levels in the normal manner due to the lack of parathyroid hormone. There would be considerable difficulty in making an adaptation to abrupt changes in the carbohydrate content of the diet because of the insulin deficiency, although this would be compensated for in part by the absence of insulin antagonists. A water load that could be excreted by the intact individual with no great effort would produce water intoxication in this infant, especially if the cortisone were omitted from the regimen. In summary, it may be possible to live with only a fragmentary endocrine system, but the quality of life under such circumstances would approximate that of a feeble vegetable.

Lest botanists take umbrage at this remark it should be pointed out that healthy plants have hormones of their own.

Genetics and the Endocrine System

The remarkable advances that have been made in the field of biochemical genetics during the past two decades have stimulated much thought about genetics and endocrinology. In the beginning, each human being is little more (and nothing less!) than the coalescence of two small packages of DNA. All of the information required to produce an individual is encoded in the genetic material, and the code is "solved" by the developmental process. Clearly, morphological characteristics of individuals, such as height, body configuration, hair color, eye color, and so on, are hereditary in nature. Biochemical constitution is no less so.

There are many examples of inborn errors of metabolism in the endocrine system, some rare and others frequent. For example, the lack of a single enzyme in the cells of the adrenal cortex may produce a complicated disturbance which is characterized by an inadequate production of hydrocortisone and an overproduction of adrenal androgen (see Chapter 7). A number of different forms of hypothyroidism have been described which are the end result of hereditary biochemical defects in one or another locus in the reaction sequence by which thyroid hormone is produced (see Chapter 6). There is no doubt that the human disease, diabetes mellitus, is hereditary in nature and there is some evidence that susceptibility to hyperthyroidism may be familial. The inborn error may not be built into the hormone-producing tissue but rather may be present in the end-organ of a hormone as, for example, in the case of certain individuals whose renal tubules lack the ability to respond to antidiuretic hormone.

It is a mistake to think of genetics and the endocrine system only in relation to inborn errors which manifest themselves in overt disabilities and dysfunctions. Endocrine strength and resiliency is probably no less hereditary than is endocrine weakness and susceptibility to disease. Even those people who have no obvious endocrine disease doubtless have varying amounts of what might be called "endocrine reserve." Whether or not they eventually succumb to an endocrine disorder may depend largely on environmental factors. For example, a man with "weak" beta cells in his islets of Langerhans may avoid overt diabetes mellitus if he does not become obese. It is for this reason that a frank acknowledgment of the importance of heredity in metabolic and endocrine diseases is not defeatist, as some observers have asserted. In the future, increased methodological sophistication may make it possible to detect not merely malfunction of the endocrine glands but "borderline compensation" as well. Measures may then be devised which will make possible the prevention of manifest disease.

REFERENCES

Astwood, E. B. (ed.): *Clinical Endocrinology* (New York: Grune & Stratton, Inc., 1960).

Barrington, E. J. W.: *An Introduction to General and Comparative Endocrinology* (Oxford: Clarendon Press, 1963).

Best, C. H., and Taylor, N. B.: *The Physiological Basis of Medical Practice* (Baltimore: Williams & Wilkins Company, 1961).

Danowski, T. S.: *Clinical Endocrinology* (4 vols.; Baltimore: Williams & Wilkins Company, 1962).

Gardiner-Hill, H.: *Modern Trends in Endocrinology* (New York: Paul B. Hoeber, Inc., 1958).

Gorbman, A., and Bern, H. A.: *A Textbook of Comparative Endocrinology* (John Wiley & Sons, Inc., 1962).

Houssay, B. A.: *Human Physiology* (New York: McGraw-Hill Book Co., Inc., 1955).

Kupperman, H. S.: *Human Endocrinology* (Philadelphia: F. A. Davis Company, 1963).

Paschkis, K. E., Rakoff, A., and Cantarow, A.: *Clinical Endocrinology* (2d ed.; New York: Paul B. Hoeber, Inc., 1958).

Ruch, T. C., and Patton, H. D.: *Physiology and Biophysics* (Philadelphia: W. B. Saunders Company, 1965).

Stanbury, J. B., Wyngaarden, J. B., and Fredrickson, D. S. (eds.): *The Metabolic Basis of Inherited Disease* (New York: McGraw-Hill Book Co., Inc., 1966).

Turner, C. D.: *General Endocrinology* (Philadelphia: W. B. Saunders Company, 1966).

Williams, R. H.: *Textbook of Endocrinology* (3d ed.; Philadelphia: W. B. Saunders Company, 1961).

2

Methodology
and
the Levels of Metabolic Organization

It is beyond the scope of this chapter to present a detailed account of any of the myriad of methods and techniques that were used in collecting much of the information that will be described. Every branch of physiology has acquired its own methods and traditions and with the passage of time these have become progressively more precise and discriminating. It is only by attempting to use some of these methods in the laboratory that the student can appreciate their value and their limitations, and it is in the laboratory that detailed methodological instruction should be given. It is for this reason that no extended discussion even of such time-honored subjects as the basal metabolic rate will be attempted here.

In endocrinology, the historical development of new knowledge has followed a well-worn road. At first, observations were made in the clinic and correlated with findings at autopsy, gross and microscopic. When a certain anatomical structure was implicated in a disease, organ extirpation experiments were done in an attempt to find an animal model for the observed human disease. The gland suspected of producing a hormone was extracted and crude gland extracts were shown to ameliorate the disease produced in animals by gland removal. As better chemical methods became available, the gland extracts were progressively purified and chemically pure substances were obtained. Their chemical structures

were established and, in many cases, synthetic substances indistinguishable in biologic effect from the original were prepared. Meanwhile, the effects of overdoses of extracts in various stages of purification and of the pure substances were determined.

The recent revolution in neuroendocrinology has added a new dimension to the methodology of the subject. The Horsley-Clarke stereotaxic instrument, which is a sort of vernier-calibrated microscope mechanical stage in three dimensions, has made it possible for the experimenter to place either destructive or stimulating electrodes in certain parts of the brain; for example, in the hypothalamus. In the case of lesioned animals he may observe either diminished or increased endocrine function and, with his stimulating electrodes, he can sometimes find evidence of stimulation of an endocrine gland some distance away. Details of some of these experiments will be presented in appropriate chapters to follow.

In many cases, chemical agents with highly selective effects, such as thiouracil (Chapter 6) and alloxan and tolbutamide (Chapter 9), have been used as valuable experimental tools in the analysis of endocrine function.

Assay of hormone effect: It is often necessary, especially during the process of purification of a hormone, to obtain a quantitative estimate of the effect of an extract. Certain hormone-sensitive tissues, like androgen-dependent ventral prostate and seminal vesicles of the rat, or the capon's comb, can be used to detect the presence of minute amounts of hormone. With known amounts of hormone a standard dose-response curve can be prepared which resembles that of a photometric assay of a pure chemical substance. Any easily measured parameter can be used as an index of hormone effect: weight (as in the case of the prostate and seminal vesicles mentioned above), epithelial cell height (as in the seminal vesicle in response to androgen, or in the thyroid in response to thyroid-stimulating hormone), or a standard physiological response (such as blood sugar lowering by insulin in the rabbit, or incidence of convulsions in insulin-treated mice). Such bioassay methods will be described in discussions of individual hormones.

Chemical methods: It should be obvious that the development of the field of endocrinology has depended heavily on new developments in preparative and analytic chemistry, and endocrinologists have not hesitated to appropriate these whenever they have found uses for them. New chemical knowledge has proved to be important not only in hormone chemistry but in the analysis of the physiological effects of hormones and in their metabolism. The number and variety of chemical methods that have been used in endocrinology is beyond belief, but two comparatively recent methods have been used with especially good effect. These are *paper chromatography,* which has proved to be a particularly valuable tool in the analysis of problems which involve steroid and thyroactive hormones, and the use of *radioactive isotopes,* which has infiltrated all aspects of intermediary metabolism and has yielded especially outstanding results in the study of the thyroid gland and its hormonal products. In some experiments, particularly those involving studies of biotransformations of steroid or thyroactive hormones, the use of these methods in combination has produced exciting results.

Organization, Disorganization, and the Truth

Biologists are motivated by the compulsive desire to understand as much as they possibly can about the life process. In studying the endocrine system we would like to know the following: (1) The precise chemical structure and charac-

teristics of each hormone. (2) The most intimate chemical details of its biosynthesis, storage (if any), and release, including the nature of the signal that stimulates its release and the mechanisms by which its release may be inhibited. (3) The exact form in which it is transmitted in the blood stream and which proteins, if any, participate in its transport. (4) The chemical identity of the constituent of the cell with which it interacts at the molecular level, and the details of this interaction. (5) Exactly how the interaction of the hormone with its cell receptor causes an acceleration or deceleration of the metabolic activities of the target cell. (6) How this cellular effect fits into the vital economy of the whole organism, free-living in its environment.

We do not yet have all of this information for any hormone, although we have fragmentary knowledge about all of them. If one starts with a whole organism and studies smaller and smaller units of it, one progresses to lower and lower levels of organization (or higher and higher levels of disorganization). If one starts with a purified enzyme and, having characterized it as precisely as possible, tries to fit the enzyme conceptually into a cell organelle, or into a functioning cell, one is attempting to achieve understanding at a higher level of organization. Thus, there is a whole spectrum of wavelengths of legitimate scientific inquiry, from observations of behavior of intact organisms in their environment to studies of the interaction of molecules in reconstructed model systems. Insights obtained at any of these wavelengths may help us to understand our problem, but Nature has been careful to plant numerous booby traps to confound the unwary, for observations at any wavelength may mislead the experimenter, sometimes in particularly poignant ways. The blunt truth is that we cannot observe life without having our act of observation distort it or even destroy it. When Hippocrates said, "Art is long, life short," he said a Greek mouthful. We try to piece together information obtained at all wavelengths of the spectrum and we measure our progress in Ångstrom units.

Some experimenters may begin by making an observation at the level of organization of the whole animal and find themselves asking ever more pointed questions until eventually they are dealing with the original problem at the molecular level. Others may begin with a problem in cell metabolism or enzyme characterization and later cultivate an interest in the physiological implications of what may have started as an inquiry in "pure" chemistry. It is in this constant groping for the whole from the fragment and toward the molecule from the whole that significant interactions occur and new understanding comes.

Some of the levels of metabolic organization (or disorganization) at which endocrinologists work are discussed below.

THE WHOLE ANIMAL OR PERSON

The student of endocrinology has been interested in *behavior* ever since those first early amateur endocrinologists observed that eunuchs behaved oddly according to the standards of intact controls. The study of behavior itself ranges over a whole spectrum of activities from psychoanalysis to the observation of some such primitive behavior as web building in spiders. There are many ways in which hormones influence the operation of the central nervous system and thus affect behavior. We have already seen that hypothyroidism in childhood prevents the proper differentiation of the nervous system, and we will see in a later chapter how hyperthyroidism can produce states of extreme anxiety and apprehension. Hyperinsulinism, hyperepinephrinism and hyperadrenocorticism can all have striking effects on central and peripheral nerve function which result in behavioral changes. Although the behavioral approach has the advantage of the wholeness of the subject, the complexity of the intact, unfragmented organism and its responses renders cause and effect judgments especially difficult to make in this circumstance.

A variety of chemical techniques may be used for studying the intact human being or animal. Most frequently these involve measurements of the *respiratory gases* (oxygen consumption, CO_2 production) or the *chemical composition of the body fluids* (blood, urine, sweat, tears, gastric juice) under conditions that permit comparisons between the experimental subject and an appropriate control subject.

An especially useful technique employed in the study of whole animals is the *balance experiment*. The balance idea can be used in relation to total calories; specific nutrients, such as proteins; water, potassium, and sodium; calcium and phosphorus; and many other biologically important materials. The principle in all cases remains the same: A careful inventory of intake and outgo can permit conclusions concerning net loss or gain of the constituent under study. Important information about hormone deficits, replacements, and excesses can be gained from this simple method which has the great virtue of being possible to do in unanesthetized, unrestrained animals living in favorable laboratory environments, or in patients on metabolic wards.

Just as blood samples may be obtained from intact animals, small samples of certain tissues can be secured by punch biopsy with comparatively little trauma. These can be studied histologically, histochemically, or even biochemically, sometimes serially. Biopsy tissues have been obtained in this way from liver, kidney, adipose tissue, and testis among other tissues.

The blood may be regarded as a kind of tissue biopsy, particularly when examined for its formed elements. Moreover, in the case of certain damaged tissues, enzymes which normally are kept inside cells leak into the circulating blood where their activity can be measured. Much valuable information has accumulated on this point, particularly about acid phosphatase (Chapter 4), the transaminases and lactic dehydrogenase, and it is probable that further advances will be made in this field in the future.

ORGAN SYSTEMS

The effects of hormone lack or excess can be studied in diffusely distributed organ systems which do not lend themselves readily to isolation from the whole organism. Examples of these systems are the nervous system, the peripheral vascular system, the reticuloendothelial system, and the hematopoietic system. Interesting hormonal effects have been reflected, for example, in changes in the EEG, in the blood pressure, in phagocytic activity of RE cells, and in the blood picture and bone marrow histology.

INDIVIDUAL ORGANS AND TISSUES

It is not always easy to determine whether or not a certain hormone has an effect in a particular organ and, if it has, what the nature of the effect is. Sometimes it has been possible to make inferences about the function of an organ by studying an animal which has been deprived of it. It is often possible to attribute functions to an organ which are inferred from differences in the concentration of key substances in arterial and venous blood. It was from studies of this type that Claude Bernard discovered the contribution of glucose to the blood by the liver. The perfection of intravascular catheterization techniques in recent years has revived interest in this type of approach because the organ is studied under as nearly physiological conditions of blood perfusion and oxygenation as one can achieve.

Not quite as physiological, but nevertheless effective, are perfusion techniques in which the organ under study is removed from the animal and perfused with whole blood or a balanced salt solution. Skilled experimenters can perfuse livers, for example, for many hours during which bile production and many metabolic activities are maintained at respectable rates.

Another way of studying individual organs is by preparing slices of them which are sufficiently thin to permit oxygenation of the cells by diffusion. Slices of this sort often consume oxygen and eliminate CO_2 for many hours, and much valuable information can be gained from them although they are far removed from their natural physiological state and many of the cells on the surface of the slice are necessarily damaged during preparation. Not only can the respiratory gases be measured with great accuracy, but the rate of use of substrates and the accumulation of metabolic intermediates can also be studied by means of suitable microchemical methods. The great advantage of this technique is the ability of the experimenter to localize reactions in specific tissues and to attempt to relate his findings to other information gained at higher or lower levels of organization. Such attempts at correlation must be made with caution, for the observation of a phenomenon in a surviving slice does not necessarily mean that the reaction under study is quantitatively important to the whole animal.

The techniques of tissue and organ culture have also been used in the analysis of endocrine problems. These methods differ from the slice and mince approaches in that tissue fragments are incubated under sterile conditions over a period of days, and thus a longer time scale of observation is possible with them. Here, too, caution must be used in extrapolating results to the field of integrative physiology because many tissues tend to dedifferentiate on cultivation in

vitro and their biochemical characteristics may be quite unlike those of the tissue of origin.

THE CELL

Since the days of Schleiden, Schwann, and Virchow the cell has been the biologist's central preoccupation. If tissues are sufficiently homogeneous in their cell populations, much information about the biochemical transactions of cells can be obtained from the methods discussed in the preceding section. But in addition to these, the study of *cell morphology*—and particularly of *changes* in cell morphology that occur in response to various states of hormone deprivation or excess—has contributed enormously to our knowledge of the endocrine glands and their function. The light microscope and all of the histologist's staining skills have been used in the study of hormone effects; more recently, additional progress has been made with phase contrast, polarizing light, and fluorescence microscopy. Among the most exciting advances that have been made in recent years are those made with the *electron microscope,* which has added a whole new order of magnitude to our capacity to see. *Histochemistry,* which enables one to localize chemical substances and enzymatic reactions in specific parts of the cell, has been used with good effect and promises to be extremely important in the future, for this is one of the few methods we have of putting cells back together conceptually after they have been disrupted for the study of specific enzyme activities. Another modern method of localizing events and substances in cells is that of *autoradiography,* in which cells containing radioactive compounds take snapshots of themselves when they are placed on suitable photographic emulsions. One cannot repeat too often that structure and function cannot be separated from each other. It is quite beyond the scope of this volume to repeat in detail information about the gross and microscopic morphology of the endocrine system. It is suggested that the beginning student review pertinent aspects of this phase of the subject before he begins to read succeeding pages.

THE CELL ORGANELLE

The cell used to be the microcosm of the body; now it must be seen as a macrocosm in its own right, for more and more information is accumulating about intracellular events and their localization. Some of this information is morphological and histochemical in nature, but much of it is derived from the technique of *differential centrifugation,* which is based on the fact that when a homogenate of cells is prepared in a suitable grinding device and centrifuged, the structural components of the cell sediment at different centrifugal forces depending on their size and weight. The nuclei come down at quite low speeds; then, the mitochondria, followed by the microsomal fraction. What is left is usually called the "soluble" or "nonparticulate" fraction. There is a large body of literature on the subject of the metabolic activities of all of these fractions. Out of this kind of research has grown a whole new science of what we may call mitochondriology, for the mitochondrion is now being studied in much the way cells are studied, and problems of mitochondrial membrane permeability are as gravely discussed as are those of cell membrane permeability. Effects of hormone deficiency and replacement have been described on a variety of localizable biochemical processes within cells, i.e., on ribosomal function, nuclear function, lysosomal membrane stability, and on the permeability of various cellular and subcellular membranes to water and solutes.

Enzyme Systems and Metabolic Pathways

It is now widely recognized that cells are not merely bags stuffed with enzymes at random, but that enzymes occur in constellations, or teams, within cells and function in a systematic way. Some, like those involved in the process of electron transport and oxidative phosphorylation, appear to be bound in a sort of lattice arrangement so that they are in a fixed relationship to each other, an arrangement that Lehninger has called "solid state enzymology." Others have been localized at or near the cell surface. Still others, concerned with protein synthesis and various detoxification reactions, travel with the microsomes on differential centrifugation. The enzymes involved in the metabolism of glucose to the triose level are in the nonparticulate compartment of the cell, whereas the electron transport machinery, the Krebs cycle enzymes, and those involved in fatty acid oxidation are in the mitochondria. No attempt will be made to give a detailed review of the reaction sequences of carbohydrate, fat, and protein metabolism, although reference will be made to specific pathways in context. The student doubtless has available to him a modern textbook of biochemistry which contains as many metabolic maps as he is likely to need in order to understand the discussion to follow.

Individual Enzymes

In certain rare instances, individual enzymes which catalyze a single crucial reaction can be identified as particularly important in the understanding of a physiological mechanism or a pathophysiological condition. Most of the inborn errors of metabolism that will be referred to belong to this category and others will be cited.

Molecular Biology

In the first edition of this book, I included the following paragraph:

"With the reader's permission I would like to say a brief, dyspeptic word about the term 'molecular biology,' which has recently become chic in many quarters. The phrase has a large subjective component, and even a certain *mystique* about it. People who think of themselves as Molecular Biologists sometimes give the impression that their truths are somehow deeper and more meaningful than those of other biologists. Of course, all biology is ultimately molecular, but the study of the life process at the level of interaction between molecules of known structure is a fragment of total biology, and it gains in meaning when it is related to integrative physiology, to behavior, or even to epidemiology. There could be no 'molecular biology' without antecedent observations at higher levels of organization. It is quite honorable to work at any wavelength of the biological spectrum one finds interesting. A diagrammatic outline of the levels of biological organization will be found in Figure 2-1."

All sorts of interesting responses were elicited by these remarks. Some of my friends regarded them as not merely old-fashioned but subversive. Others, beleaguered by the New Wave, asked permission to quote the paragraph *in toto* in essays with titles like "The Indivisibility of Biology." I should explain that I am not anti-molecule; I am pro-integrative biology. Molecular biology is exciting, but it does not free us from the obligation

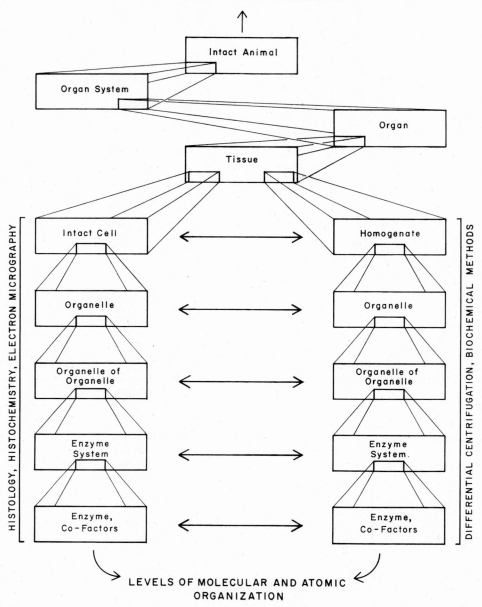

Fig. 2-1.—Levels of biological organization. This diagram can be read from top to bottom (progressive fragmentation) or from bottom to top (integration). Note that morphological and biochemical studies of the cell complement each other and that events at any level may be involved in observations at any other level.

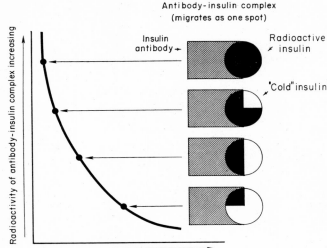

Fig. 2-2.—Schematic description of the principle of a typical Berson-Yalow radioimmunoassay. (See Berson, S. A., and Yalow, R. S., Diabetes 14:549-572, 1965 [Banting Lecture].)

to analyze biology in integrative terms; it only renders such analysis more interesting.

As a token of my regret for having offended some Molecular Biologists five years ago, I have written a new chapter (Chapter 12) on Hormones and Protein Synthesis for this edition.

HORMONES IN BLOOD

It is often convenient to be able to measure either the concentration of a hormone in blood at a particular instant in time or to measure changes in its concentration in relation to some experimental, therapeutic or diagnostic maneuver. The advent of chromatographic procedures has made it possible to estimate certain steroid hormones in blood with some success. Possibly the most widely used method of this sort is that for estimating blood levels of adrenal glucocorticoids. This method has proved to be particularly useful when adrenal vein effluent blood is analyzed under various experimental conditions. A discussion of thyroid hormone in the blood will be reserved for Chapter 6.

One of the most important advances in endocrinology during the past decade has been the introduction and widespread use of radioimmunoassay procedures for estimating blood concentrations of peptide and protein hormones. Berson and Yalow, the pioneers in this field, first devised such a method for the measurement of serum insulin levels. Their method depends on forming an antibody-radioactive insulin complex which migrates in paper electrophoresis systems as a single spot. After the complex is formed, known amounts of nonradioactive insulin are added as standards and the mixture of antibody-I^{131}-insulin complex and "cold" insulin is incubated at low temperatures. Some of the "cold" insulin displaces some of the radioactive insulin in the complex as illustrated in Figure 2-2. Electrophoresis is then performed and the region over the antibody-insulin complex is scanned for radioactivity. The more radioactive it is, the less "cold" insulin is present. Progressively increasing concentrations of "cold" insulin cause a diminished radioactivity, as illustrated in Figure 2-2. If an unknown is run parallel with standard solutions, a very accurate estimate of the amount of insulin can be made.

The remarkable success of the Berson-Yalow technique for insulin was only the prelude to the development of a large number of valuable immunoassay procedures. Similar tests have been devised for ACTH, TSH, somatotrophin, glucagon, parathyroid hormone, thyrocalcitonin and others. There is even some hope of applying the principle of this measurement to very small peptides the size of vasopressin, which contains only eight amino acids. Some of the surprising things that were discovered when these methods were applied under clinical and experimental conditions will be described in appropriate sections of the text.

REFERENCES

Green, D. E., and Hatefi, Y.: The mitochondrion and biochemical machines, Science 133:13–18, 1961.

Grobstein, C.: Levels and ontogeny, Am. Scientist 50:46–58, 1962.

Hayashi, T.: *Subcellular Particles* (New York: Ronald Press, 1961).

Kety, S. S.: A biologist examines the mind and behavior, Science 132:1861–1870, 1960.

Palade, G. E.: Structure and function at the cellular level, J.A.M.A. 198:815–25, 1966.

Simpson, G. G.: The status of the study of organisms, Am. Scientist 50:36–45, 1962.

3

The Neuro-Hypophysial
Relay Systems

The Adenohypophysis

NO DOUBT THE READER has already learned from his studies in anatomy, embryology, and histology about the development and morphological characteristics of the hypophysis. The neurohypophysis, or posterior hypophysis, is properly regarded as an anatomical and functional extension of the central nervous system. This view is based on the embryological origin of the structure and on the fact that there are clearly defined neural connections between certain hypothalamic cell clusters and the posterior lobe.

As short a time as 15 years ago, the adenohypophysis, or anterior hypophysis, was widely believed to be a comparatively autonomous organ which, having developed from an outpouching of the primitive foregut, somehow came to rest in the *sella turcica,* where it functioned in splendid isolation as the "leader of the endocrine orchestra." There was no reason to believe that it was getting any direction, or even any suggestions, from neighboring structures like the hypothalamus, for repeated attempts to demonstrate a neural connection between the brain and the adenohypophysis had failed. In fact, more recent attempts with the electron microscope have been equally unsuccessful. In retrospect, it is easy to find many recorded observations, made in both clinic and experimental laboratory, which suggested that there was *some* way for messages to travel from the central nervous system to the adenohypophysis. Now, of course, there is no longer any doubt that the adenohypophysis and the hypothalamus are parts of an integrated functional unit, an informational relay system. The anatomical location of the anterior pituitary just below the hypothalamus is not just a developmental coincidence; the physiological integrity of the gland depends upon its unique position in the body, and on an intact vascular connection with the brain immediately above it. The pituitary is no longer the "leader of the endocrine orchestra"; it is now more properly called the "concertmaster."

The early beginnings of our modern concept of hypothalamo-hypophysial information transfer occurred in a morgue. Rainer, a pathologist in Bucharest, in 1927 observed a plexus of vessels surrounding the pituitary stalk and noted that these were especially prominent in people who had died sudden and violent deaths. He pointed out these vessels to a medical student called Popa, and suggested that the hypothalamus and pituitary be removed en bloc, and that serial sections be prepared for study of the vascular connections. Popa took the bait and discovered that the vessels began as a plexus of capillaries in the tuber cinereum, passed down over the stalk and ended in the sinusoids of the anterior lobe. At about the same time Wislocki and his colleagues in Boston were describing similar vessels in the opossum and other species. These vascular connections, surely among the shortest and most important in evolutionary history, have been found in all species examined and, due to the

brilliant studies of Harris and his school and many others, they are now centrally involved in the development of a new subspecialty of endocrinology, namely, neuroendocrinology.

Just as it is essential to study the hypothalamus and the pituitary en bloc in order to understand the anatomical relationships of the structures, it is necessary to discuss them en bloc in order to emphasize their functional relationships. The hypothalamus can be visualized as an enormously complex switchboard compressed into a very small space. An incredible number and variety of messages pour into this switchboard from various monitoring devices all over the body. The messages are received, "decoded," and "decisions" are quickly made which are sent in the form of instructions over one or another outflow system. The incoming messages may be in the form of neural impulses or they may be brought as chemical substances by way of the blood stream. Similarly, the outgoing messages may be sent over "wired" connections via autonomic efferents or they may be humoral in nature.

The two main components of the hypophysis, the neurohypophysis and the adenohypophysis, can be meaningfully discussed only if they are related to the hypothalamic structures with which they interact. In the case of the posterior pituitary, two definite and fairly discrete constellations of cells, the supraoptic and paraventricular nuclei, clearly have neuronal connections with the gland. Two specific chemical substances, oxytocin and vasopressin, are synthesized in the hypothalamic nuclei, travel down the axon fibers attached to or enclosed by a carrier protein, and are secreted into the blood stream at the nerve endings in the gland.

The problem of the control of the adenohypophysis by way of the hypothalamus and suprahypothalamic structures is being vigorously explored in many research laboratories. Our knowledge of this subject is fragmentary, but new and interesting facts are being accumulated at an extraordinarily rapid rate. The first important fact that must eventually be explained is the remarkable selectivity of the release of anterior pituitary hormones. There are at least six substances which can be extracted from the adenohypophysis and which are generally acknowledged to be physiologically important hormones: the three gonadotrophins—follicle-stimulating hormone (FSH), luteinizing hormone or interstitial cell-stimulating hormone (LH or ICSH), and prolactin (LTH in some species); two other trophic hormones—adrenocorticotrophic hormone (ACTH) and thyroid-stimulating hormone (TSH); and somatotrophin or growth hormone (STH or GH). When a stimulus arrives at the anterior pituitary gland cells there is no sudden, massive indiscriminate discharge of all of these substances. On the contrary, there appear to be remarkably subtle and precise controls which permit the secretion of certain of these hormones specifically and selectively. In the case of the trophic hormones elaborate feedback arrangements exist in which the products of the target organs exert inhibitory effects on the brain-hypophysial trophic complex, either at the level of the central nervous system or directly on the adenohypophysis or, in some instances, at both levels.

It is now believed that neurosecretory cells in various parts of the hypothalamus secrete chemical substances into the capillary plexus at the upper terminus of the hypophysial portal system, and that these substances pass down the main channels of this system and into the sinusoids of the glandular hypophysis where they are in a position to stimulate the various hormone-producing cells of the gland to discharge their hormones. Direct microscopic inspection of the direction of blood flow in the portal system in many species has revealed that the flow is from the hypothalamus to the adenohypophysis. When the pituitary stalk is sectioned, function of the anterior lobe of the gland may not be seriously disturbed after recovery occurs. But when stalk section is accompanied by the placement of a thin mechanical barrier which prevents the revascularization of the gland by regenerating portal vessels, very striking alterations in anterior pituitary function are observed.

The chemical nature of the neurohumoral agents which arise in the hypothalamus and participate in controlling the release of adenohypophysial hormones is not known as yet. Most work has been done on substances (extracted both from hypothalamus and from crude, commercial posterior pituitary hormone preparations) which have the effect of causing the release of ACTH into the blood. Two such substances have been produced in highly purified form and are known as α and β corticotrophin-releasing factor, or CRF (see Chapter 7). They are comparatively small peptides which are slightly larger than the posterior pituitary hormone peptides. There is suggestive evidence that similar releasing factors may exist which are specific for TSH or LH release (Harris). It is possible that a separate and distinctive chemical signal mediates the release of each of the products of the anterior lobe, but a definitive solution of this problem must await the results of many new experiments. It is also possible that some mediators of neural origin may be discovered one day to have selective *inhibitory* effects on certain hormone-producing cells of the anterior lobe. The interested reader will find a fairly complete inventory of this field in the proceedings of a conference on the subject (see Nalbandov in the bibliography).

CELL SOURCES OF ADENOHYPOPHYSIAL HORMONES

All of the experimental and clinical evidence that one or another adenohypophysial cell type produces a particular hormone is circumstantial in character. Patients with pituitary gigantism, or acromegaly, show adenomata composed of acidophilic (or eosinophilic) cells at autopsy. Mice of a certain strain which have hereditary dwarfism do not have eosinophilic cells in their pituitaries. Thus it is concluded that acidophils produce growth hormone. Neither of these observations constitutes proof that some other kind of cell does not produce growth hormone. If cells of a particular type exhibit striking morphological changes when a target gland (for example, the thyroid) is removed and these changes are reversed when the hormonal product of the target gland is administered, these cells are thought to be the source of the trophic hormone for the gland in question. In a few experiments bioassays have been conducted on parts of pituitaries which show a marked preponderance of a single cell type and the hormonal activity under question has been correlated with the cell count of its suspected cell of origin. It is not surprising that there is still some disagreement among experts concerning the cytologic source of the known anterior pituitary hormones. Agreement is general that there is some specialization among the recognizable cell types and that all of the hormones are not produced by a single one, although the chromophobe cell is widely conceded to be a kind of totipotential precursor for the other two major kinds of cells, the acidophils and basophils. With the advent of the use of special staining techniques for glycoproteins and, more recently, with the application of the electron microscope to this problem, acidophils and basophils have been further subdivided. Electron-micrographs of these cells reveal small "packages," or secretory granules, believed to contain the PAS staining material which is thought to be the storage form of the hormones. One kind of acidophil may be the major source of growth hormone; the other may be a source of prolactin. The basophilic types have been separated into gonadotrophs and thyrotrophs on the basis of changes found after castration and thyroidectomy, respectively. There is even a suggestion that there are two kinds of gonadotrophs—an FSH-producing one and an LH-producing one. In Cushing's disease, a basophil adenoma presumably secretes the excess of ACTH which is responsible for the hyperadrenocorticism observed. Therefore, the basophil has been generally regarded as the cell source of ACTH, but even this view, which was taught as an incontrovertible fact a short time ago, has recently been brought into question.

Just as interesting as the differentiation of glandular cells into types which specialize in producing different hormonal end products is the possibility that the differentiation may be partly under the direction of humoral messages which are brought to the gland from the hypothalamus by way of the hypophysial portal system of vessels. Anterior pituitary cells in tissue culture quickly lose their distinctive staining characteristics, but if hypothalamic tissue (but not other brain tissue) is added to such cultures the cells apparently redifferentiate and regain acidophilia and basophilia.

HYPOPHYSECTOMY

Much information about the crucial participation of the hypophysis in the metabolic affairs of the body has accumulated as a result of observations on hypophysectomized animals of many species. The first successful experimental hypophysectomies were performed in the dog by Aschner (see chronology, p. 27), who made many pioneer discoveries in this field. But the perfection of the transpharyngeal hypophysec-

tomy in the rat by P. E. Smith excited the imagination of endocrinologists all over the world and has proved to be an extraordinarily important landmark in the history of physiology. In the 1920s, the concurrent use of the Smith operation in the rat, Houssay's studies on the toad, and experiments with crude saline extracts of pituitary glands were prominent among the events that resulted in our modern concepts of the hypophysis and its hormones. The hypophysectomized rat is now an article of commerce; it is produced on an assembly line and it can be supplied, together with appropriate intact controls, to any enthusiastic but manually inept investigator who happens to have research grant support. In man, many different kinds of hypopituitarism have been observed. Two types of panhypopituitarism, or a complex deficit which resembles that seen in completely hypophysectomized animals, have been recorded. In one of these, the condition manifests itself in early childhood and can be considered either a genetic or a developmental defect (Simmonds' disease). In the other, infarction and necrosis of the gland may occur and this has sometimes been seen following parturition (Sheehan's syndrome). In either case, the resemblances between hypopituitary patients and hypophysectomized animals as far down the phylogenetic scale as the toad are arresting. In recent years, the introduction of hypophysectomy for the treatment of breast cancer (discussed in Chapter 5) has afforded new opportunities to confirm many observations that had previously been made in experimental animals.

The hypophysis is not essential to life, and hypophysectomized animals given no substitution hormone therapy have been kept alive for months and years. They require considerable pampering, however; the room must be air-conditioned and warm, they appear to do better on paste diets which require a minimum of effort to eat, and they are very susceptible to infections and must therefore be given antibiotics, particularly when they begin to show signs of respiratory tract disease.

The most striking effect of the operation when it is performed in young animals is *slowing of growth.* It should be emphasized that growth does not stop altogether, for hypophysectomized animals do in fact grow extremely slowly over a long period of time even if they eat ad libitum. If they are force-fed by stomach tube, they can gain considerable amounts of body weight, including protein. The growth failure in the hypophysectomized animal is commonly attributed simply to lack of growth hormone, but its mechanism is no doubt far more complex. Thyroid insufficiency also produces growth failure, which can be corrected by thyroxin administration in the presence of growth hormone. Thyroxin excess does not produce excessive growth as growth hormone excess does, but rather results in protein catabolism.

The lack of ACTH not only produces *atrophy of the adrenal cortices* but also a failure of these structures to respond to many stimuli by increasing their output of glucocorticoid (see Chapter 7). The hypophysectomized animal, in addition to its other problems, suffers from secondary adrenal insufficiency. This is a rather selective kind of insufficiency, for the functional derangement is primarily in the sphere of the so-called

glucocorticoids and not so much in the province of the adrenal hormone which functions to conserve salt in the body, aldosterone. It is sufficient to say only that the comparative independence from ACTH of the aldosterone-producing cells is the reason for the fact that hypophysectomy is not a fatal operation, while adrenalectomy is fatal. The life-maintaining properties of the adrenal cortex are associated with its water and electrolyte conserving function. These subjects will be discussed more completely in Chapter 7.

Hypophysectomy removes the TSH stimulus from the thyroid and results in the condition of *secondary hypothyroidism*. Anatomically, the thyroid becomes small and on histological examination the epithelial cells are short and cuboidal rather than columnar; the general impression one gets is that of a sluggish, hypoactive gland. This impression is confirmed by dynamic studies, for the B.M.R. falls to hypo-

Fig. 3-1.—Upper, effects of hypophysectomy, low-iodine diet and propylthiouracil treatment on iodine concentration by the rat thyroid (8 rats per group). **Lower,** persistence of iodine-concentrating ability of the thyroid in the hypophysectomized rat's thyroid. (Data collected by students of the Class of 1964, State University of New York College of Medicine at Syracuse, during the course of a laboratory exercise. All values shown differ from control values at P < 0.01.)

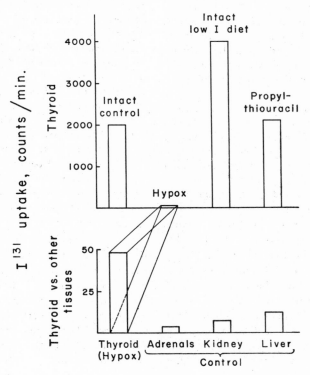

thyroid levels (-40%) and the I^{131} uptake is strikingly depressed. If, however, one compares the thyroid I^{131} uptake with that of other tissues in the hypophysectomized animal, the thyroid can still be seen to have considerable iodine-concentrating ability. Again, the distinctive machinery of the tissue continues to function in the absence of its trophic hormone, but only at a comparatively low level (Fig. 3-1). (See Chapter 6.)

The absence of growth hormone, TSH, and ACTH results in serious metabolic deficiencies in the hypophysectomized animal or man, and the capacity to adapt to many environmental or nutritional challenges is markedly impaired. The absence of the three gonadotrophins, FSH, LH, and prolactin, results in absolute reproductive failure in both males and females. For neither ovaries nor testes can function in the untreated hypophysectomized individual and in consequence there is a failure of development and/or maintenance of those tissues which are sustained by the steroid hormonal products of the gonads (Chapters 4 and 5).

In certain amphibia and fishes, apparent depigmentation of deeply pigmented skin cells occurs as a result of hypophysectomy. These cells fail to darken when the animal is placed in the dark and become pale when the animal is exposed to bright light. A pituitary hormone called melanophore-stimulating hormone (MSH, or intermedin) is responsible for the darkening of these cells (see p. 37).

It is practically impossible to discuss the adenohypophysis and its hormones as an isolated functional unit because it is so centrally involved in the physiology of so many other endocrine glands. I have therefore elected to save a detailed discussion of ACTH, TSH, and the gonadotrophins for subsequent chapters in which these substances can be considered as information-carrying molecules in separate, but related, communications and control systems. In the discussion of the anterior hypophysis here it is necessary only to give a brief general introduction to the subject of hypothalamic control of adenohypophysial function; a discussion of the growth hormone, with particular reference to the complexity of some of the metabolic effects of both hypophysectomy and crude pituitary extract administration; and an account of recent studies on intermedin.

INFORMATION TRANSFER FROM THE HYPOTHALAMUS TO THE ADENOHYPOPHYSIS

Many complementary lines of evidence indicate that the central nervous system exerts a subtle trophic influence over the adenohypophysis. According to Harris, Marshall was the first to emphasize the fact that the sex cycles of birds are set by changing light exposure patterns, and to deduce from this observation the inescapable conclusion that pituitary gonadotrophin output must be determined to some extent by information reaching the brain by way of the eyes.

The importance of this concept for the clinician cannot be overemphasized because, at about the time Marshall was observing his birds, physicians were beginning to be resensitized to the concept of psychosomatic medicine. The idea that an emotional disturbance can cause a more or less serious somatic illness is practically as old as the healing art, but the mechanisms by which disordered function can result from psychological difficulties are not well understood. Cannon, in his famous book, *Bodily Changes in Hunger, Pain, Fear and Rage,* described very well how fright initiates a complex series of physiological responses which are mediated to a large extent by the sympathetic or adrenergic component of the central nervous system. It is easy to imagine how the perception of danger can be translated into fear and how this information could be processed in the hypothalamic headquarters of the autonomic nervous system. Here, a response pattern is set and appropriate directions flow out over proper autonomic efferent pathways with the result that the sympathetic nerves to the heart are stimulated, vasoconstriction occurs in some vessels, epinephrine is discharged, glycogenolysis occurs in the liver, free fatty acids are released into the blood, and the animal or man is poised for fight or flight.

Many observations had been made in man which suggested that emotional disturbances may trigger similar alterations in function of the adenohypophysis. There is little doubt that anxiety can produce menstrual irregularities, or that the date of onset of hyperthyroidism often coincides with a period of extreme emotional strain. Infertility in the female may be the result of a psychological disturbance, and so also may the rare phenomenon of pseudocyesis, or false pregnancy.

Recent explorations of hypothalamo-hypophysial relationships are of more than academic interest, for they help to explain the route of information transfer from the brain to the endocrine system. In analogy with Cannon's fight-flight reaction, in which the mobilization signals are carried via autonomic neural efferents, the messages which arrive in the hypothalamus cause certain neurohumoral substances to be released into the capillary plexus in the region of the median eminence. These substances (as we have seen) are delivered to the cells of the adenohypophysis by way of the portal blood vessels. There they stimulate (or inhibit?) the release of hypophysial hormones. These responses can be characterized as neuro-endocrine reflexes, for the incoming information arrives in the central nervous system by way of nerves, but it leaves by way of a complex blood-borne relay which, in the case of ACTH, can be

described in this way: hypothalamus → releasing factor → hypophysis → ACTH → adrenal cortex → cortisol → target tissue response.

From this account the reader may have gained the unfortunate impression that the hypothalamo-adenohypophysial relay system was designed, in a manner of speaking, for the purpose of mediating psychosomatic disturbances. It should be emphasized that we are discussing *physiological mechanisms* which are essential for normal function and that these mechanisms represent an informational relay system which can carry either physiologically appropriate or disrupting messages.

Among the general approaches to the study of brain-pituitary relationships have been the following:

1. Studies of hypophysectomized animals bear-

Fig. 3-2.—Composite diagram of certain hypothalamic regions which have been implicated in adenohypophysial function. The regions indicated are to be regarded as tentative and are by no means as clearly demarcated as they appear to be in this diagram. Note that hypothalamic organization with respect to gonadotrophin control and sex behavior shows interspecies variations. Major sources: Sawyer, C. H., and Kawa-kami, M., in Villee, C. A. (ed.): *Control of Ovulation* (New York: Pergamon Press, 1961); Ganong, W. F., in Gorbman, A. (ed.): *Comparative Endocrinology* (New York: John Wiley & Sons, Inc., 1959); Harris, G. W., *ibid.*; and personal communication from C. H. Sawyer, to whom the author is indebted for valuable suggestions, and to Seymour Reichlin for suggesting revisions of the diagram based, in part, on his recent work.

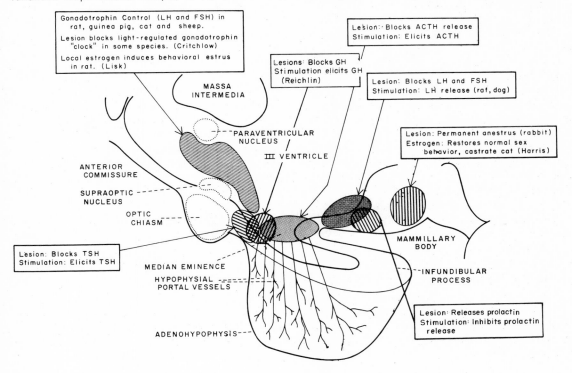

ing pituitary grafts in sites remote from the median eminence.

2. The eliciting of adenohypophysial hormone discharge by stimulating certain regions in the hypothalamus by means of stereotactically placed electrodes.

3. The blocking of certain anterior pituitary responses (for example, ACTH release, ovulation or thyroid hypertrophy in response to thiouracil treatment) by the stereotactic placement of electrolytic lesions in more or less sharply localized regions of the hypothalamus.

4. The inhibition of the release of certain anterior pituitary hormones by the placement in the hypothalamus either of very small bits of their target organ or of minute pellets of a hormone produced by their target organ.

5. Pituitary stalk section experiments, with or without a mechanical barrier to the regeneration of the hypophysial portal vessels from above.

6. Studies of the pituitary hormone *content* after placement of hypothalamic lesions.

7. The extraction and purification of hypothalamic substances which selectively stimulate the release of specific adenohypophysial hormones, preferably in the stalk-sectioned animal or in an in vitro system. In a few ingenious experiments (Harris) some of these have even been infused directly into the anterior pituitary glands of conscious animals.

The rigid proof of the physiological importance of a releasing factor would demand that it be demonstrated in hypophysial portal blood in higher concentration than it is found in systemic blood. So far this has not been accomplished for any postulated releasing factor. If the material to be tested is effective in much smaller doses when it is introduced into the pituitary than are required by the intravenous route, it is regarded as indirect evidence in favor of its probable releasing-factor role.

Many examples of experiments in which these approaches were used in the study of the thyroid, the adrenals, and the gonads will be given in the discussions to follow. Although the hypothalamus cannot be neatly mapped in the manner of the motor cortex, the tentative locations of some of the hypothalamic regions which have been implicated in anterior pituitary function are shown in Figure 3-2.

During the period 1961-1967, many investigators (notably McCann, Guillemin, Saffran, Schally, Meites, and others) have worked with individual releasing factors. Although none of them has been precisely characterized chemically, all are small polypeptides of about the size of the posterior lobe hormones. Purified preparations of CRF, LRF, FSHRF, TRF, GRF and PIF (prolactin-inhibiting factor) have been prepared without significant releasing factor or inhibiting factor activity for more than a single pituitary hormone.

GROWTH HORMONE (SOMATOTROPHIN)

The disease acromegaly is characterized by overgrowth of the ends of long bones and of the jaw and enlargement of the viscera. It is caused by an eosinophilic adenoma of the pituitary, and when it occurs before epiphysial closure it takes the form of gigantism. Hypophysectomy performed in young animals results in virtually arrested growth. Thus, the integrity of the pituitary is necessary for normal growth, and hyperfunction of the pituitary can result in abnormally rapid growth.

Gain in body weight cannot always be regarded as growth, for water retention or fat deposition may result in weight gain. Growth involves protein synthesis and an increase in the active metabolic mass of the body. It does not necessarily include lengthening of the long bones, although it often does. Thus, the growth problem eventually must be resolved in terms of some of the most elemental functions of cells: protein synthesis, and cell division. There can be no doubt that the pituitary plays an important part in these processes both by way of growth hormone and through other hormones as well.

Cushing, and Long and Evans produced syndromes in experimental animals that resembled human acromegaly by injecting crude pituitary extracts over a period of many weeks. With the development of reasonably satisfactory but not exquisite methods of bio-assay it was possible eventually to prepare growth hormone from bovine pituitaries in extremely pure form. The assay methods used most frequently are: weight increase in the hypophysectomized rat, and epiphysial widening in a long bone of a hypophysectomized rat. The latter method may be made more specific if it is performed in hypophysectomized animals which are also gonadectomized and thyroid-deprived in one way or another.

Bovine growth hormone is a globulin with a MW of about 45,000 and, for a number of years following its purification, many unsuccessful attempts were made to induce growth in human hypopituitary dwarfs or in monkeys by injecting this substance. This was rather puzzling, for the material was clearly active in the rat, mouse, dog, cat and other species. When the large scale preparation of Salk vaccine began, the pituitaries of thousands of monkeys were harvested and their constituent hormone was found to have growth-promoting effects in the monkey and pronounced nitrogen-retaining effects in the human. Subsequently it was found that growth hormone prepared from human pituitary glands collected at autopsy was growth-promoting in both monkey and man. It was also discovered that both the simian somatotrophin and its human counterpart had a much lower MW than did bovine, porcine or ovine growth hormone. Although the latter materials are ineffective in primates, the primate-derived hormones are effective in other species, such as the rat. In 1966, a team headed by C. H. Li reported an amino acid sequence analysis for human growth hormone (HGH). Having previously discovered that HGH has a molecular weight of 21,500, the Berkeley group used techniques previously used by Sanger in the description of the amino acid sequence of insulin and concluded that growth hormone is a protein with 188 amino acid residues. Although the size of the molecule discourages hope for a wholly synthetic preparation, there are indications that full biologic activity may reside in only a fragment of the intact protein which may be synthesizable. The elucidation of the structure of HGH opens the possibility for exploring structure-activity relationships of the molecule.

Of all of the known anterior pituitary hormones, growth hormone is the only one that does not require the mediation of a target gland in order to produce its widespread effects. Furthermore, typical effects of growth hormone on many tissues can be demonstrated in the hypophysectomized animal with uncorrected deficits in adrenal, thyroid, and gonadal function. In the intact animal, however, many observers have suggested that growth hormone works in collaboration with one or more of the other hormones. For example, it has been stated that the presence of growth hormone improves the growth response of androgen-sensitive tissues to androgen, and of the adrenal cortical cells to ACTH.

If whole animals are studied, positive nitrogen balance can be demonstrated to occur during growth hormone treatment, even when the food intake of the treated animals is restricted to that of their saline-injected controls. In metabolic studies of this sort, a certain amount of confusion has been engendered by the fact that hypophysectomy causes a decreased spontaneous food intake, while treatment with growth hormone (or, more strikingly, with crude saline pituitary extracts) causes overeating. Since alterations in food intake can modify metabolic responses significantly, it is necessary to look for hormonal effects with an experimental design that eliminates differences that might be attributed to variations in caloric intake. Sometimes this is done by the technique of pair-feeding, in which one animal's intake is limited to the amount eaten by his control on the day before, or by tube-feeding carefully measured amounts of diet to both experimental animals and controls.

Striking effects of growth hormone can be observed at the tissue level, particularly in bone, muscle, kidney, liver, and adipose tissue. In *bone,* the effect appears to consist mainly of a stimulation of growth of the cartilaginous component of bone. This can be seen histologically in the epiphysial widening method of bio-assay for the hormone. It is also possible to demonstrate an increased rate of incorporation of sulfur-containing amino acids labeled with (radioactive) S^{35} into the protein of the organic bone matrix of rats treated with growth hormone. Mitotic activity is greatly stimulated at the epiphysial line of growing bones, and marked osteoblastic activity is seen in such bone. If treatment with an excess of the hormone is given to an adult animal whose epiphyses are closed, there is a general thickening of bone with increased deposition of calcium throughout.

The most striking effect in *muscle* is that of growth. The muscle mass increases, and the creatinine excretion rises in consequence. Even highly purified growth preparations act as physiological antagonists to insulin in muscle and adipose tissue. This is not to say that growth hormone and insulin necessarily exert opposite effects at precisely the same biochemical locus in the cell. It simply means that a muscle cell or an adipose tissue cell under the influence of growth hormone shows marked resistance to the effects of insulin.

The *kidneys* of the hypophysectomized animal are not merely small; they also show various functional defects, including a decreased glomerular filtration rate, diminished blood flow and diminished tubular secretion of para-aminohippurate and other similar substances which are secreted by way of tubular cells. All of these defects can be corrected by the administration of growth hormone and a very small amount of thyroid hormone, and we must therefore conclude that these substances play an important role in the maintenance of normal renal function. The compensatory hypertrophy of a kidney following unilateral nephrectomy cannot occur without growth hormone, which suggests that growth hormone is essential for adaptive changes in that organ.

In *adipose tissue,* growth hormone treatment results in the liberation of free fatty acids and an interference with the ability of insulin to promote fatty acid synthesis from glucose. Associated with the fat-mobilizing effect is the liver fat-increasing effect, for GH-injected animals characteristically show a fatty infiltration of the liver. Similarly, the hormone also produces a substantial increase in the concentration of ketone bodies in the blood. There is good evidence that permissive amounts of adrenal cortical hormone are required for these effects of GH on fat metabolism.

A discussion of the mechanism of growth hormone's action on protein synthesis will be found in Chapter 12.

THE "DIABETOGENIC" EFFECT OF PITUITARY EXTRACTS

Shortly after the discovery of insulin, Houssay demonstrated that the diabetes of a depancreatized toad apparently could be improved—i.e., glycosuria was diminished and hyperglycemia disappeared—if its pituitary gland were removed. He also showed that hypophysectomized animals are extremely susceptible to the blood glucose-lowering effect of insulin. These observations, together with older ones which suggested that there was more than a chance relationship between the diseases acromegaly and diabetes mellitus, indicated that the pituitary was deeply involved in the regulation of metabolic processes. The amelioration of pancreatic diabetes by hypophysec-

tomy has been seen in many species, including man. These important studies led to a continuing search for the diabetogenic "factor" of pituitary extracts.

Another important landmark in the history of experimental diabetes was the demonstration by Young that permanent diabetes mellitus could be produced in adult dogs and cats by the chronic administration of crude anterior pituitary extracts. While the extracts are given, hyperglycemia, glycosuria, ketonemia, polyuria and polydipsia are seen, but the condition differs from pancreatectomy diabetes, in that insulin resistance is present. If the disease persists on withdrawal of pituitary extract, it is a true insulin deficiency diabetes, and hydropic degeneration of the islets of Langerhans can be seen. If insulin is given concurrently with diabetogenic doses of pituitary extract, persistent or permanent diabetes cannot be induced.

Even purified growth hormone preparations have many of the "diabetogenic" properties of earlier crude pituitary extracts. Permanent diabetes has, in fact, been produced by chronic administration of highly purified somatotrophin. But the "diabetogenic" effect of crude extracts and the contra-insulin function of the intact functioning pituitary gland probably involve other factors in addition to the growth hormone. The first hint that this may be true occurred when Long and Lukens demonstrated that adrenalectomy, like hypophysectomy, had an ameliorating effect on the diabetes of pancreatectomized animals. Subsequent studies on the metabolic activities of adrenal cortical hormones demonstrated that they are of great importance in the process of gluconeogenesis, or the formation of glycogen and glucose from amino acid precursors (see Chapters 7, 9 and 12), and that they also act permissively in certain tissues which are influenced by growth hormone. Moreover, Engel has shown that ACTH can mobilize fat from adipose tissue and increase the level of blood ketones even in the absence of the adrenals, and could therefore have contributed substantially to some of the effects on lipid mobilization that had been seen earlier with crude pituitary extracts.

The word "diabetogenic" often suggests that the pituitary gland has the function of producing the disease diabetes mellitus. This is an unforgivable distortion of the kind of teleological thinking that biologists now permit themselves to do in a restrained way. It is legitimate to ask why "growth" hormone is found in the pituitaries of animals which have long since stopped growing. Many of the so-called "diabetogenic" effects of the hormone and of crude pituitary extracts are very similar to the effects of starvation: a decrease in peripheral glucose oxidation, insulin insensitivity, fat mobilization, ketonemia, an increase in liver fat, and a tendency for the glycogen stores of the body to be maintained, after an initial depletion of liver glycogen. In the absence of the pituitary, the animal cannot withstand a fast precisely because he apparently cannot make these very sensible adjustments to it. Teleologically, then, the hypophysis can be seen to play an important role in what must have been a very crucial adaptation as the species evolved over the aeons, for the supermarket is a comparatively recent development, and the metabolic capacity to adapt to food deprivation must have had great survival value. The basic pattern of starvation adaptation is a shift from a carbohydrate to a fat metabolic mixture which tends to conserve carbohydrate. This, of course, is particularly fortunate for the obligatory carbohydrate-burning tissues, such as the brain.

The availability of an accurate method for the immunoassay of growth hormone in serum (Glick, Roth, Berson and Yalow) has revealed the fact that remarkable changes in the serum concentration of this hormone occur very quickly in response to a variety of stimuli, even in adult, non-growing animals. The minute-to-minute regulation of serum concentration of somatotrophin represents an important component of the total metabolic control machinery of the organism. Induction of hypoglycemia by insulin injection is followed by a sudden and dramatic increase in serum GH (Fig. 3-3). The levels attained are often in the range formerly thought to be characteristic of acromegaly. Similarly, starvation results in a slow rise in serum GH, and when the fast is broken by carbohydrate administration, serum GH concentration quickly returns to a normal "fed" level. Stresses, such as cold exposure or surgical trauma, also cause elevation of serum GH.

There is now little doubt that the hypothalamus participates in these acute regulations of serum GH level, for Reichlin has shown a blocking of the serum GH response to insulin hypoglycemia in monkeys with hypothalamic lesions. The

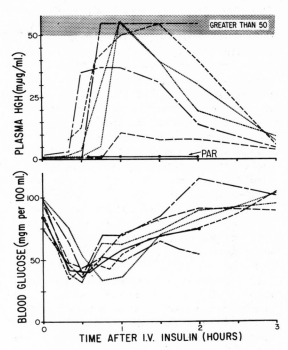

Fig. 3-3.—Plasma growth hormone and blood glucose following intravenous insulin. (Courtesy of S. Glick.)

part of the hypothalamus believed to be associated with GRF is shown diagrammatically in Figure 3-2.

The question of the existence of a separate fat-mobilizing principle of pituitary origin which is not growth hormone or ACTH has been raised from time to time and now appears to be approaching resolution. Powerfully fat-mobilizing materials have been found in human urine (but not in that of hypophysectomized humans) and they have proved to be neither GH nor ACTH. Very recently Astwood has reported on the preparation of exceedingly active fat-mobilizing peptides from pituitary glands. Whether or not these are related to the urinary secretion materials described previously has yet to be determined. (See also Chapter 10.)

Melanocyte-Stimulating Hormone (MSH, Intermedin)

Melanocyte-stimulating hormone (MSH, intermedin), secreted by the *pars intermedia* of the hypophysis, is centrally involved in the control of pigmentation in the melanocytes of fish and amphibian skin. It is also produced by the human pituitary, and the evidence is now accumulating that it plays a prominent role in the control of cutaneous pigmentation in man.

In amphibia and certain fishes, the melanocytes contain many fine pigment granules called melanosomes. When the animal is exposed to light the melanocytes appear very pale, and when they are in this condition the melanosomes can be seen to be concentrated near the cell nuclei. On exposure to dark, norepinephrine secretion is inhibited and the pituitary is stimulated to release MSH, which is properly described as a melanosome-dispersing principle, for the pituitary hormone has the effect of scattering the melanosomes through the cell and thus making it appear dark. On light exposure, pituitary release of MSH is inhibited and, concurrently, norepinephrine secretion (and possibly the secretion of other lightening, or melanosome-concentrating, materials) is elicited. These changes in amphibia have been used as the basis for a method of bio-assay which was helpful in the successful purification of MSH and in its synthesis from its constituent individual amino acids.

Several different MSH preparations have been made from the pituitaries of a number of species, including man. The most potent darkening agent known is αMSH which is a linear peptide 13 amino acids long and acetylated at the N-terminal serine. ACTH (see Chapter 7) is a 39 amino acid linear peptide and its first 13 amino acids

have precisely the same sequence as do those of αMSH. ACTH has a definite MSH type of activity in the frog skin but it is only one-thirtieth as active as αMSH. Simply acetylating the N-terminal serine of ACTH increases its activity sixfold. The structural relationships of bovine αMSH and ACTH from the same species are shown on page 123, Chapter 7. The complete *de novo* synthesis of αMSH by Hofmann and his colleagues was a landmark in peptide chemistry.

Man's relationship with his small cousin, the frog, is illustrated by the fact that MSH has been implicated as a contributing factor in certain instances of hyperpigmentation in the human. In primary adrenal insufficiency—that is, adrenal insufficiency which is not secondary to hypophysial failure—a characteristic hyperpigmentation occurs in exposed areas, body folds, mucous membranes and sites of recent trauma. This condition is associated with a very marked increase in blood ACTH, and an increased urinary excretion of MSH. On treatment with adrenal cortical hormone, the blood ACTH is lowered to imperceptible levels and there is a fall in urinary MSH excretion. Thus, since both ACTH and MSH have darkening properties, the hyperpigmentation of human adrenal insufficiency is caused to some extent by overproduction of the two because of failure of cortical hormone inhibition.

MSH-producing pituitary adenomata have been described in a small number of patients. Some of these have occurred after bilateral adrenalectomy

---

SOME LANDMARKS IN NEUROHYPOPHYSIAL CHRONOLOGY

DATE		INVESTIGATOR
1794	Diabetes insipidus distinguished from diabetes mellitus	Frank
1894	Pressor effects of pituitary extracts	Oliver and Schaffer
1897	Pressor substance localized in posterior lobe	Howell
1901	Discovery of antidiuretic action of posterior lobe extract	Magnus and Schaffer
1906	Action of posterior pituitary extracts on uterus	H. H. Dale
1910	Action of posterior pituitary extracts on mammary gland	Ott and Scott
1913	Control of diabetes insipidus by injections of posterior pituitary extracts	Von den Velden; Farini
1928	Separation of vasopressin and oxytocin	Kamm
1949	Isolation of pure oxytocin	Livermore and DuVigneaud
1953	Synthesis of posterior lobe hormones	DuVigneaud *et al.*

for adrenal cortical hyperplasia, and in a few the hyperpigmentation was very striking. While this is an extremely rare disease, its "incidence" will no doubt increase when more physicians begin to look for it.

The Neurohypophysis

The neurohypophysis, an outgrowth of the primitive brain, made its phyletic debut when our remote ancestors first ventured timidly out of the sea and assumed a terrestrial habitat. Living on land presented compelling problems in water conservation for the pioneer amphibia, and forms were selected for survival which could meet these problems. One way of meeting the challenge of water deprivation is to secrete a substance (on appropriate signal) which has the effect of diminishing water excretion. Such a substance is antidiuretic hormone (ADH, vasopessin) which is secreted by the neurohypophysis. Another posterior lobe hormone is oxytocin, whose main function in mammals is concerned with the mechanics of the process of lactation. Oxytocin is also a powerful stimulant of uterine smooth muscle.

The disease diabetes insipidus is caused by an inadequate supply of neurohypophysial ADH. It is characterized by the production of large volumes of urine due to a defect in the ability of the renal tubules to reabsorb filtered water. In severe cases, the urinary volume may reach 20 liters per day and the fluid intake is correspondingly high because of the thirst which is secondary to the polyuria. One of the chief complaints of patients with diabetes insipidus is lack of sleep caused by the polyuria and polydipsia. The symptoms of the disease can be ameliorated by the administration of a preparation containing antidiuretic hormone, either by injection or as a powder given intranasally in the form of a snuff.

CHEMISTRY OF THE POSTERIOR LOBE PEPTIDES

The elucidation of the structure of the peptides oxytocin and vasopressin and their subsequent synthesis by DuVigneaud and his collab-

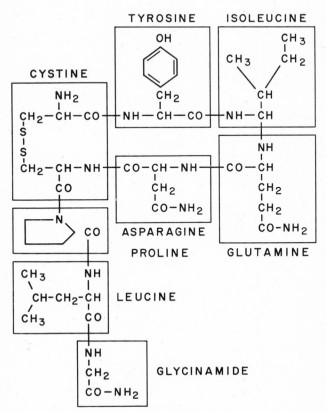

Fig. 3-4.—Structure of oxytocin.

orators was one of the most important events in modern biochemistry. The substances are very similar octapeptides in which an amino acid ring structure is formed by the closure of an S–S bond between No. 1 and No. 6 cysteine molecules to form cystine (Fig. 3-4). Oxytocin is found in practically all bony vertebrates. The comparative activities of these compounds in several assays is shown in Table 3-1.

Arginine vasopressin has been found in man, horse, sheep and other species, but lysine vasopressin (position 8) is characteristic of the pig and hippopotamus. Now that the amino acid sequence is known in specific proteins of different species it may be possible to identify relationships or differences on the basis of protein structures.

An intriguing example of the discovery of a biochemically important compound *before* it was isolated from its natural source is the story of arginine vasotocin. During a study of structure activity relationships by Katsoyannis and DuVigneaud, the side chain of arginine vasopressin was attached to the ring structure of oxytocin as shown in Figure 3-5. The resulting compound, arginine vasotocin, had about equal oxytocic and vasopressin or ADH activities in mammals, unlike the starting materials. But when it was tested in nonmammalian vertebrate systems (frog bladder and isolated frog skin) it was many times more powerful than mammalian ADH. Meanwhile other investigators had postulated the existence of a specific "amphibian water balance principle" or "natriferin." The experience with the synthetic hybrid hormone stimulated a search for the material in amphibia with the result that

TABLE 3-1.—COMPARATIVE POTENCIES OF NEUROHYPOPHYSIAL HORMONES IN DIFFERENT ASSAYS*

HORMONE	UTERINE STIMULATION (rat, in vitro)	MILK EJECTION (rabbit)	PRESSOR (rat)	ANTIDIURETIC (dog)
Oxytocin	500	500	7	3
Vasopressin	30	100	600	600

*Data of VanDyke et al.: Recent Prog. Hormone Res. 11:1, 1955.

arginine vasotocin is now known to be the naturally occurring water balance principle of those forms.

Many synthetic variants of the posterior lobe peptides have been prepared and studied. The interested reader is referred to the review by Sawyer for a detailed account of the results.

The molecular weight of arginine vasopressin is about 1100. A perceptible antidiuretic effect can be produced in man with only 2 millimicrograms (0.000002 mg) of pure material; less than 0.1 microgram (0.0001 mg) produces a maximal antidiuresis.

THE FUNCTIONAL UNITY OF THE POSTERIOR LOBE AND ITS HYPOTHALAMIC NUCLEI

The supraoptic and paraventricular nuclei are connected by a bundle of nonmyelinated nerve fibers with endings in the neural lobe of the hypophysis. The nerve endings are in close approximation to capillaries and a venous effluent drains from the gland. The functional unity of

Fig. 3-5.—Arginine vasotocin, showing its relationship with oxytocin and vasopressin.

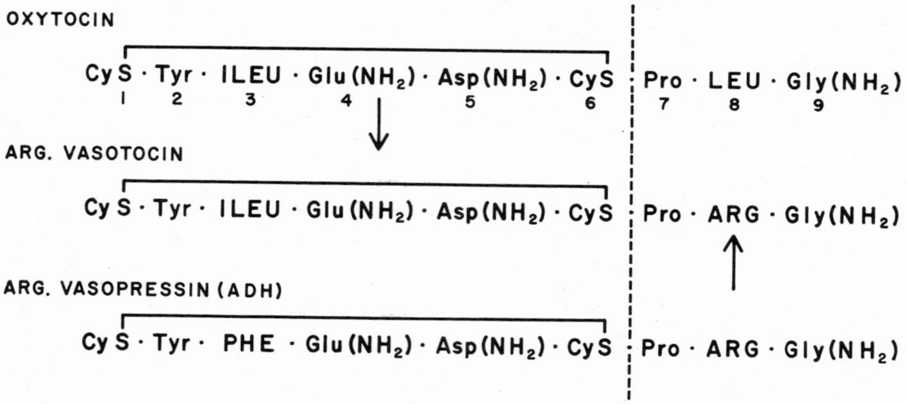

the supraoptico-hypophysial system was put on a strong experimental basis by the work of Fisher, Ingram and Ranson, who produced diabetes insipidus in the monkey by interrupting the tract just behind and below the optic chiasm by means of electrolytic lesions placed with a stereotaxic instrument. When such lesions are made, the fibers which lead from the site of the lesion into the posterior lobe are seen to degenerate.

There is now no reason to doubt that the posterior lobe hormones are synthesized in the supraoptic and paraventricular nuclei. They are "packaged" in small secretory granules in association with a carrier protein (MW about 30,000), and the granules migrate down the nerve fibers and accumulate at the nerve endings in the posterior lobe. The migration of the granules has been observed in the living animal, and they have been timed at the rate of about 3 mm/day. The granules can be studied either with special stains which stain the carrier protein or by means of the electron microscope. When a stimulus which elicits a discharge of ADH is given, a sharp decrease in the number of granules can be seen in the posterior lobe. If the pituitary stalk is cut, no granules can be seen distal to the cut, but a piling up of granules occurs immediately above the cut and resembles granule aggregation in the "rest-

Fig. 3-6.—Diagrammatic sketch of migration of neurosecretory granules down the hypothalamo-hypophysial tract, and of the effect of stalk section. Suggested by studies of Bargmann and Scharrer. (See Sawyer, W. H.: Pharmacol. Rev. 13:225-277, 1961, for many references.)

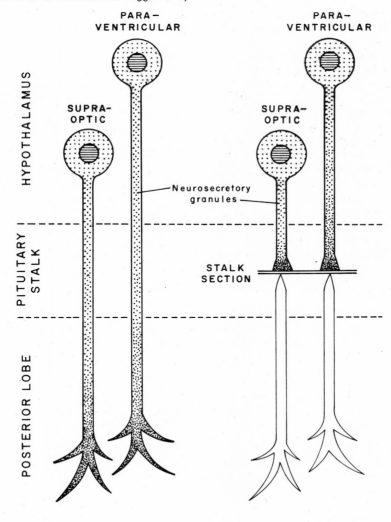

ing" posterior lobe (Fig. 3-6). In fact, there can be a vascular reorganization above such a cut with the development in time of a reconstituted release system for the hormones. If S[35]-labeled (radioactive) cysteine is injected into the subarachnoid space, the supraoptic nuclei of rats incorporate the label very actively, and several hours later labeled protein is detectable in the posterior lobe. Labeled methionine (not present in the peptides) is not so incorporated. The release of the active peptides into the blood stream is accomplished by the transmission of a message down the nerve fiber over which the secretory granules migrated to the posterior lobe. Presumably, the peptides are split from their carrier protein and enter the capillary circulation. Very small vesicles resembling acetyl choline vesicles have been seen at the nerve terminals in electron-micrographs, and these may contain a release mediator. It is not likely that the mediator is acetyl choline, for there is no choline acetylase activity in the posterior lobe and, therefore, no obvious mechanism for quick acetyl choline synthesis. The biological problem here is very much like that in the thyroid where a substance of small molecular weight is split from a protein storage substance and secreted into the blood. It is tempting to imagine that the nerve impulse somehow liberates a peptidase enzyme (from lysosomes?) and thus frees it to split the hormones from their protein carrier.

There is some discussion of the problem of the selective release of vasopressin and oxytocin. Some stimuli, notably hemorrhage, elicit a predominantly vasopressin discharge, while others (anesthetics, nicotine) stimulate the release of both vasopressin and oxytocin, the latter in larger amounts. Assays of the supraoptic and paraventricular nuclei reveal that the latter has more oxytocic activity and the former more vasopressin. This suggests that different types of signals arising in the nervous system may evoke a hormone mixture rich in one or the other hormone.

PHYSIOLOGICAL AND OTHER STIMULI FOR THE RELEASE OF VASOPRESSIN

If hypertonic saline is injected directly into the carotid artery, evidence of ADH release (antidiuresis) and oxytocin release (milk ejection and uterine contraction) may be seen. Conversely, if an animal or a man is water loaded,

one of the mechanisms involved in the establishment of water diuresis is the inhibition of ADH release. While several possible signals for these responses have been described, it is presently impossible to assess the quantitative importance of each.

According to one hypothesis (Verney), there are specific osmoreceptors in the brain, which are capable of responding to fluctuations in the osmotic pressure of plasma by signaling either for a discharge of posterior pituitary hormones or for an inhibition of their release. Dehydration is presumed to evoke ADH release by this mechanism, and water diuresis could also set up an inhibition signal via osmoreceptor activity. The precise location of the osmoreceptor cells is not now known; neither is it known whether or not the supraoptic and paraventricular nuclei cells are themselves equipped to detect small fluctuations in serum osmotic pressure. A dehydrated animal excretes large amounts of a substance with ADH activity in the urine.

Hemorrhage is one of the most powerful known stimuli of ADH release. It would be difficult to see how the osmoreceptors could participate in this response, since hemorrhage results in hemodilution rather than hemoconcentration. It is considered more likely that a different mechanism is responsible for eliciting a secretion of the hormone, particularly after massive hemorrhage. Certain baroreceptor cells associated with blood vessels appear to be able to monitor continuously a signal which reflects the blood volume. When there is a critical fall in this volume, afferent nerves from these "volume receptors" carry an alert to the central nervous system. There, the neuroendocrine reflex arc is completed when the message is received by the cells of the supraoptic and paraventricular nuclei, which then "call" promptly for ADH. The likeliest location for these baroreceptors is in association with the vessels of the neck, and it is worth noting that a similar mechanism is believed by some investigators to be operative in the case of the salt-retaining hormone of the adrenal cortex, aldosterone (see Chapter 7). It is interesting that many of the clinical conditions associated with secondary aldosteronism (edema, ascites) are also associated with the appearance of large amounts of ADH activity in the urine. From a teleological point of view, both ADH and aldosterone would offer a great survival advantage following hemorrhage in an animal or a man whose fluid intake had been interrupted, for one hormone would conserve water and the other one sodium chloride for the critically depleted body fluids. The ADH response to hemorrhage is quantitatively much larger than that to other stimuli; in fact, this is the only known circumstance in which sufficient ADH is secreted to act as a vasoconstrictor agent. In most other situations, it is unlikely that the vasoconstrictor effect of ADH plays a significant physiological or adaptive role, but in the case of hemorrhage the large discharge of the posterior lobe hormone may conceivably assist in the maintenance of an effective circulating blood volume.

There is another whole group of neurogenic stimuli which elicit ADH release. In Chapter 7, the participation of the ACTH-adrenal axis is the nonspecific response to a very wide variety of insults, and stresses will be considered in some detail (Alarm Reaction). Trauma, pain, even the anxiety incident to taking an examination, can cause ADH release from the posterior pituitary just as they cause ACTH release and adrenal cortical excitation. In cold exposure, on the other hand, ACTH is elicited but *inhibition* of ADH has been described, so that two materials apparently are not invariably released together. Presumably, nerve impulses either arising in the periphery (pain), or by way of special sense organs (frightening sight or sound), or recalled stored information within the brain (anticipation of a difficult experience), can trigger the release of these substances and often of aldosterone as well. The significance of the increased availability of these hormonal materials for adaptation or survival is not now understood. They may be extremely important or the secretory response patterns we have described may represent a physiological vestige of the time when the animal's adaptive response to injury began to take place in anticipation of the injury proper. The endocrine responses of a man who fears that he will lose a large sum of money on a horse race are qualitatively similar to those of a jungle animal who fears an attack by a predatory enemy. In the former case, the statistical probability of a severe hemorrhage is not high; in the latter case, it is not low. In computer idiom, a variety of "alarm reactions" may have been "programmed" into the brain a long time ago.

Many drugs cause release of ADH; among them are morphine, nicotine, acetyl choline, lobeline, certain tranquilizers and certain general anesthetics. Probably all do not operate in precisely the same fashion, but whether they are stimulatory, or whether they release certain suprahypothalamic cells from an inhibited state the final common pathway—the supraopticohypophysial system—is excited and release of hormone occurs in the posterior lobe. Ethyl alcohol has the interesting property of inhibiting the release of ADH in response to an osmotic stimulus.

TRANSPORT AND FATE OF THE HORMONES

Although the peptides appear to be released into the capillaries of the posterior lobe without their associated granular protein, they are probably transported in the blood stream in loose association with a plasma globulin. The extent of protein binding is variable in different species.

If vasopressin is injected into rats or dogs it disappears very quickly (half-life in man, 8 minutes), but if either the liver or the kidneys or both are excluded from the circulation, its half-life in blood is markedly prolonged. In the kidney, only about one fourth of the peptide that passes into the glomerular filtrate appears in the urine; the rest probably is destroyed or fixed in the kidney, possibly as a consequence of its antidiuretic action. Both oxytocin and vasopressin are inactivated by homogenates of liver or kidney *in vitro*, and the destruction is enzymatic in nature. Other tissues (skeletal muscle, uterus) also exhibit vasopressinase and oxytocinase activity, but there is no suggestion that the systems which destroy these substances have very precise specificity for them.

In pregnant women (but not in nonpregnant women or in men), there are large amounts of circulating oxytocinase and vasopressinase activities. The suggestion has been made that this material protects the gravid uterus from stimulation by oxytocin and thus prolongs pregnancy to term. This would be somewhat difficult to prove.

TISSUE EFFECTS

The most important effect of *vasopressin* or ADH is on the kidneys where it accelerates the rate of water reabsorption, probably from the loop of Henle, the distal convoluted tubule, and even from the collecting ducts. The counter-current concentrating apparatus of the kidney functions especially in the loop of Henle and associated structures, but it evidently requires some ADH in order to operate, for in the absence of the hormone, only urine with a specific gravity of 1.002–1.006 can be produced. The fraction of the total volume of filtered water involved in concentrating the urine is extremely small, and it is within this small fraction that adaptive adjustments can occur to either water deprivation or excess. In general, ADH secretion is elicited by stimuli set up by water deprivation or fluid loss and its secretion is inhibited by the ingestion of an excess of water (water diuresis).

ADH and the kidney illustrate the concept that as hormones evolved the capacity of target cells to respond to them evolved in parallel, for there is an extremely rare form of diabetes insipidus which is due not to a lack of ADH but to an inability of the kidney tubular structure to respond to ADH. The disease is an inborn error of metabolism and represents one of the few striking examples we have of a hormone communications system failure at the site of the reception of the hormonal message.

Completely hypophysectomized animals may not show diabetes insipidus even when the supraoptic nuclei are destroyed. We have already seen that growth hormone, thyroid hormone, and the adrenal hormones all have important effects on metabolism generally, on hemodynamics and on the kidneys specifically. If they are returned to the hypophysectomized animal in various combinations they may "permit" (in Ingle's phrase) the diabetes insipidus to become apparent.

The vasoconstrictor effect of ADH which is implicit in its other name, vasopressin, probably is not physiologically important to mammals, except possibly in the case of massive hemorrhage already mentioned. For in all but this one circumstance the amounts of ADH secreted do not have readily perceptible effects on vessels. In doses far above those effective in the kidney, the material is a powerful vasoconstrictor and acts directly on the smooth muscle of the vessel wall. It also stimulates smooth muscle of other structures, including the intestine and (weakly) the uterus.

The most important physiological effect of *oxytocin* in mammals is that of milk ejection. The release of oxytocin in response to afferent neural signals which arise in the nipple stimulated by suckling represents the humoral afferent phase of a neuroendocrine reflex. After milk is secreted, it is expressed from the lumina of the alveoli and fine-bore ducts into the large ducts and collecting cisterns by the contraction of highly specialized cells called myoepithelial cells. Many contractile cells of the body are stimulated to contract by neural impulses, but the myoepithelial cells of the breast are stimulated by oxytocin, which is carried to them via the blood. The effect of oxytocin in the mammary gland is seen most dramatically in the cow, for the pressure in the udder cistern can be raised 10–15 mm Hg by a single injection of the hormone.

The effects of oxytocin on the uterus are confusing, and the physiological role of the substance in the initiation of labor is still uncertain. If a uterine strip were mounted in a water bath and oxytocin were added to the fluid medium, the intensity of the contractile response (if one occurred) would depend on: (1) the species of animal, (2) whether or not the animal had been pregnant, and the stage of pregnancy, (3) the phase of the estrus or menstrual cycle at the time the sample was removed, and (4) unknown factors. The human uterus becomes progressively more sensitive to oxytocin as pregnancy proceeds and is most sensitive at term. The contractions induced by oxytocin show a rhythmic, peristaltic wavelike activity similar to those seen in spontaneous contractions. In some species, like the rabbit, sensitivity to oxytocin is diminished by progesterone injected systemically, but this is not the case in the human.

In experimental animals a neuroendocrine reflex has been described in which excitation of the afferent neural component is stimulated by dilation of the uterine cervix. This reflex, first described by Ferguson, was originally observed in animals *postpartum* and has recently been seen during labor, but not in nonpregnant animals. On the face of it this would appear to be circumstantial evidence in favor of a physiological role for oxytocin in labor and the puerperium. Skeptics argue, however, that the oxytocin level of blood does not rise during labor and that labor can proceed satisfactorily even in some (but not all) animals with hypothalamic lesions that cause diabetes insipidus. While no didactic statement can be made, it seems fair to suggest that oxytocin not only participates in the process of normal parturition but that it may serve a useful function during the very early involutional changes that occur in the uterus in the postpartum period and during the puerperium.

Another possible role of oxytocin in integrative physiology is even more uncertain. On the grounds that spermatozoa in the female generative tract reach the site of fertilization far faster than they would if they had to travel under their own power, it has been argued that they get a kind of escalator ride up the tract because of stimulation of movements of the muscle of the uterus and associated structures. There is some evidence that the act of mating produces a reflex discharge of oxytocin and that this in turn influences the mobility of these organs in such a way that seminal fluid transport is accelerated. This is an interesting possibility, but it cannot now be regarded as an established fact.

THE MECHANISM OF ACTION OF THE PEPTIDES

Very little is known about the manner in which oxytocin influences the contractility of mammary gland myoepithelial cells or uterine smooth muscle cells. In contrast, there is a large and growing literature on the general subject of the effect of neurohypophysial peptides on water movement through membranes.

Striking effects of these peptides, particularly arginine vasotocin, can be seen in intact frogs and toads kept in water, The administration of substances with ADH activity markedly increase water uptake through the skin in these animals; moreover, a similar effect can be demonstrated on isolated bags of skin or fragments of skin to which hormone is added in vitro. Most students of the subject agree that the effect of the hormone is to *accelerate the passive osmotic movement of water across the skin*. The water has a tendency to move in the direction of the osmotic gradient; the peptides simply make it go faster. This water movement is not merely independent of sodium movement; it has actually been observed to occur when the net sodium flux was in the opposite direction. Ussing and others have supported the hypothesis that normally osmotic flow occurs through tiny pores, and that these pores can be widened under the influence of the antidiuretic hormone. The net effect would be the transformation of the membrane from a fine sieve to a coarse one, and osmotic flow would be enhanced. (These hypothetical pores have not been seen, but then, neither has the handle of a sodium pump.) This response apparently does not require an expenditure of oxidative or glycolytic energy, for increased water movement is not accompanied by an increase in oxygen consumption and it is not inhibited by various poisons that disorganize the cell's metabolic machinery. This is in contrast to the transport of sodium, which can be shown to be linked with metabolic processes.

In order to exert its effect the peptide hormone, which is equipped with an S–S group, attaches firmly to the tissue. There is some evidence to support the view that the attachment takes place between the S–S "handle" of the hormone molecule and SH or SS groups in the target cell. This is of interest beyond the ADH problem, for the insulin molecule also contains S–S groups and it has been suggested that this hormone, too, is bound to tissue by S–S linkages formed as the result of the interaction between an S–S group of the hormone and S–S or SH groups at the surface of the receptor cell.

In the toad bladder, ADH, unlike aldosterone, causes accelerated transcellular transport of sodium from the mucosal to the serosal, side even in the presence of inhibitors of protein synthesis. (See Chapter 12 for a detailed discussion of this type of analysis.) We can infer from this observation that all of the machinery necessary for the expression of the response already exists in the cell when it is stimulated by the hormone. Largely due to the work of Orloff and Handler, it is now generally accepted that ADH interacts with its receptor cell, either in toad bladder or mammalian kidney, in such a way as to cause the production of 3′, 5′ cyclic adenylic acid. In fact, the effect of the hormone can be duplicated to a certain extent either by a xanthine inhibitor of phosphodiesterase (the enzyme which destroys 3′, 5′ cyclic AMP) or by the cyclophosphate itself. (A more complete discussion of the role of cyclic adenylic acid in the action of several hormones will be found in Chapter 8). How the cyclic nucleotide accomplishes its effects on water and solute movement in hormone sensitive tissues is quite unknown.

These observations and suggestions have been made by investigators who worked with amphibian skin, and it is therefore legitimate to inquire

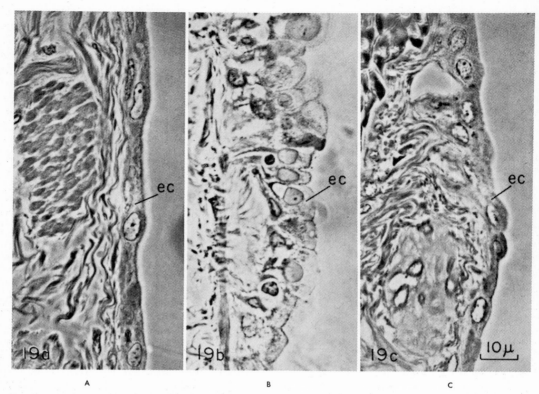

Fig. 3-7.—Phase micrographs of toad bladders. **A,** control; **B,** fixed while exposed to antidiuretic hormone; **C,** fixed after effect of hormone had disappeared. (ec = epithelial cell.) (Reprinted with permission from Peachey, L. D., and Rasmussen, H.: J. Biophys. & Biochem. Cytol. 10:529-553, 1961.)

what all of this has to do with the effects of the hormone in the kidney. The similarities between the effects of ADH on water transport in toad skin or bladder and on renal tubular reabsorption of water are, in fact, quite striking. The observations on frog skin may very well help to clarify the problem of the mechanism of action in the mammal for the reason that the increased permeability to water of the ascending limb of the loop of Henle and of tubular structures distal to the loop also involves free water flow in the direction of an osmotic gradient.

At one time, I was attracted by Ginetzinky's idea that ADH worked primarily by permitting water to pass more freely *between* cells. On the basis of work by Peachey and Rasmussen, I am now persuaded that, in the case of the toad bladder, there is little doubt that water traverses the cells on which ADH exerts its effect. These investigators have demonstrated marked swelling of toad bladder epithelial cells under the influence of arginine vasopressin by light microscopy (Fig. 3-7). Electron micrographs of "resting" cells and hormone-stimulated cells reveal striking differences: in the former, mitochondria, endoplasmic reticulum and other structures are closely packed, while in the latter, which were fixed when the rate of passage of water through the bladder was very high, one can see only an occasional stray mitochondrion or fragment of reticulum.

Neurohypophysial Hormones and Adenohypophysial Function

We have seen how certain adenohypophysial hormones, particularly growth hormone, TSH, and ACTH, may be necessary for the full expression of ADH lack in the kidney. In addition, it was suggested that together ADH and aldosterone are partners in the enterprise of water and electrolyte conservation, and that many of the physiological circumstances which require an adaptive response to water or salt loss are characterized by an increased secretion of both of these substances.

There is another postulated link between the neurohypophysis and anterior lobe physiology; namely, the possibility that the posterior lobe peptides may function as releasing factors for anterior lobe hormones. Some investigators have been inclined to the view that vasopressin may be a physiological corticotrophin-releasing factor (CRF), but others argue that the releasing factors isolated from hypothalamic tissue and commercial (crude) posterior lobe extracts are different compounds. The most potent known CRF is β CRF (Guillemin *et al.*), a compound that contains all of the amino acids present in arginine vasopressin plus alanine, serine and histidine. In the dog, the injection of arginine vasopressin into the third ventricle in extremely small doses causes an increase in adrenal glucocorticoid secretion, while equimolar amounts of related peptides fail to do this. I have not seen a report on the comparative efficacy of β CRF and arginine vasopressin in this test, but in other tests the CRFs are said to be more potent corticotrophin releasers than is vasopressin. The fact that the dog's hypothalamus contains a much higher concentration of arginine vasopressin than that of other species tested may constitute circumstantial evidence for a special role of this material as a neurohumoral mediator in the canine species.

Even if vasopressin itself does not prove to be a physiological releasing factor for anterior lobe hormones, its molecular size and amino acid composition in comparison with known CRFs suggest that it may turn out to be a precursor of one or more releasing factors. Different neurosecretory cells in the hypothalamus may play synthetic variations on some basic peptide structure (possibly vasopressin or oxytocin) in much the way steroid hormone-producing cells differentiate to produce different steroid end products. We must leave open the possibility for the differential synthesis and delivery into the portal hypophysial vascular system of many releasing factors, each with a high degree of specificity for some secretory cell type in the adenohypophysis.

The Pineal Gland

The pineal gland, long a skeleton in the closet of endocrinology, has recently become an honorable object of study. For many years, there were vague and sometimes conflicting reports about the effects of tumors in the region of the pineal on gonadal function. In a critical review of the untidy literature in 1954, Kitay concluded that the presence of true pineal tumors was associated with depressed gonadal function, whereas pineal-destroying lesions were more likely to be present in patients with increased gonadal function. This suggested that the pineal may produce something that has an inhibitory effect on the gonads. As early as 1941, Fiske had demonstrated that female rats exposed to constant light for several weeks exhibited vaginal smears which were characteristic of estrus more of the time than did similar animals exposed to normally cycling photoperiods of light and dark. An extraordinarily interesting conceptual bridge has now been built between Fiske's studies and Kitay's conclusions, largely through the efforts of A. B. Lerner and of Wurtman, Axelrod and their colleagues.

Wurtman discovered that pinealectomy reproduced Fiske's results in the female rat; i.e., estrus was stimulated and ovarian hypertrophy occurred following the operation. Pineal extracts had been found by Jochle (1956) to inhibit light-induced ovarian growth. These findings suggested that the effects of light on the gonads might be mediated by way of the pineal gland.

In a parallel study of the effect lightening agents had on the melanocytes of frog skin, Lerner discovered the compound called *melatonin* (5 methoxy N-acetyl tryptamine), which is produced only in the pineal gland and was found to be the most potent lightening agent for frog melanocytes that had ever been seen. Wurtman, Axelrod and their colleagues subsequently demonstrated that the synthesis of melatonin in the pineal proceeds as follows:

1. Serotonin $\longrightarrow$ N-acetyl serotonin
2. N-acetyl serotonin $\longrightarrow$ melatonin
$$\text{(HIOMT)}$$

Reaction (2) is catalyzed by an enzyme uniquely found in the pineal, hydroxyindole-O-methyl transferase (HIOMT).

There are now many lines of circumstantial evidence which link the pineal and melatonin to light-induced changes in the ovaries. Melatonin treatment of rats resulted in an inhibition of ovarian growth and of the incidence of estrus.

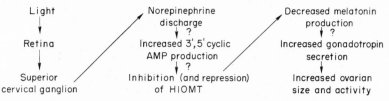

Fig. 3-8.—A composite hypothesis concerning the participation of the pineal in the regulation of gonadal activity. (See text for details.)

As little as 1 microgram per day gave a significant decrease in ovarian weight, whereas 2 micrograms per day halved the total time spent in estrus. Small doses of melatonin were able to prevent light-induced estrus.

The effects on the pineal gland of exposure to light or dark are quite consistent with the hypothesis that melatonin is the agent by which photoeffects are exerted on the gonads. Light exposure is associated with a decrease in pineal weight, decreased serotonin content and decreased RNA synthesis. Moreover, the shift to a dark environment results in a 3- to 10-fold increase in the activity of the enzyme HIOMT, which catalyzes the formation of melatonin. Thus, melatonin formation is stimulated in the dark and inhibited in the light. Since melatonin inhibits the ovary, the ovarian hypertrophy and hyperfunction seen in light-exposed animals can be interpreted as the response to the removal of an inhibitory influence.

The effects of light on the pineal require an intact pathway from the retina via the superior cervical ganglia to the pineal. Ultrastructure studies of sympathetic nerve endings by Pellegrino de Iraldi *et al.* (1965) have suggested that these endings are probably both 5-hydroxytryptamine- and norepinephrine-producing structures. Thus, we can infer that there is an adrenergic link in the chain of communication from the retina to the pineal. If one contemplates the information that has accumulated on this subject, it is possible to construct an hypothesis (Fig. 3-8) which contains only a small amount of fantasy.

All of the steps in this hypothesis but those marked ? have been well validated by experiment. Whether or not this theory turns out to be true in detail, it is a fascinating discovery that deep in a tiny organ, which was formerly thought to be the seat of the soul, there exists a rate-limiting enzyme which functions as a light meter and probably participates in the modulation of gonadal activity, at least in some species. Incidentally, this modulation may not be restricted to the female animal, for gonadal atrophy has been described in the light-exposed male hamster and pinealectomy prevents atrophy under these conditions (Hoffman and Reiter, 1965).

The precise mechanism by which melatonin exerts its inhibitory effect on the gonads is not known with certainty, but there is suggestive evidence that it prevents gonadotrophin release, probably by decreasing the rate of discharge of hypothalamic gonadotrophin-releasing factors (Ortavant, 1964; Donovan and van der Werff ten Bosch, 1956).

REFERENCES

Acher, R.: Biochemistry of the protein hormones, Ann. Rev. Biochem. 29:547–576, 1960.

Berde, B.: *Recent Progress in Oxytocin Research* (Springfield, Ill.; Charles C Thomas, Publisher, 1961).

Caldeyro-Barcia, R., and Heller, H.: *Oxytocin* (New York: Pergamon Press, 1961).

Friesen, H., and Astwood, E. B.: Hormones of the anterior pituitary body, New England J. Med. 272:1216–1223; 1272–1277; and 1328–1335, 1965.

Harris, G. W.: *Neural Control of the Pituitary Gland* (London: Edward Arnold & Co., 1955).

Harris, G. W., and Donovan, B. T. (eds.): *The Pituitary Gland,* 3 vols. (London: Butterworth & Co., Ltd., 1966).

Harris, G. W., Reed, M., and Fawcett, C. P.: Hypothalamic releasing factors, Brit. M. Bull. 22:266–272, 1966.

Heller, H.: *The Neurohypophysis* (New York: Academic Press, Inc., 1957).

Knobil, E., and Greep, R. O.: The physiology of growth hormone with particular reference to its action in the rhesus monkey and the "species specificity" problem, Recent Prog. Hormone Res. 15:1–69, 1959.

Leaf, A., and Hays, R. M.: The effects of neurohypophysial hormone on permeability and transport in a living membrane, Recent Prog. Hormone Res. 17:467–492, 1961.

Lerner, A. B.: Hormonal control of pigmentation, Ann. Rev. Med. 11:187–194, 1960.

Martini, L., and Ganong, W. F.: *Neuroendocrinology*, vols. I and II (New York: Academic Press, Inc., 1966).

Nalbandov, A. V.: *Advances in Neuroendocrinology*. Proceedings of the Symposium on Neuroendocrinology sponsored by the National Institutes of Health (Urbana, Ill.: University of Illinois Press, 1963).

Raben, M. S.: Growth hormone, New England J. Med. 266:31–35, 1962.

Reichlin, S.: Functions of the median-eminence gland, New England J. Med. 275:600–607, 1966.

Relkin, R.: The pineal gland, New England J. Med. 274:944–950, 1966.

Sawyer, W. H.: Neurohypophysial hormones, Pharmacol. Rev. 13:225–277, 1961.

Smith, R. W., Jr., Graebler, O., and Long, C. N. H.: *The Hypophysial Growth Hormone, Nature and Actions* (New York: McGraw-Hill Book Co., Inc., 1955).

Thorn, N. A.: Mammalian anti-diuretic hormone, Physiol. Rev. 38:169–195, 1958.

4

Reproductive Endocrinology in the Male

SOME LANDMARKS IN TESTIS CHRONOLOGY

DATE		INVESTIGATOR
Remote antiquity	First observation of castrate men	Anon.
300 B.C.	Effects of castration in birds and men compared	Aristotle
1849	Effects of castration on cock's comb; prevented by testis transplant	Berthold
1889	Claim of increased vigor after self-treatment with testicular extracts	Brown-Sequard
1903	Lipid seen in Leydig cells; lipid nature of testis internal secretion suggested	Loisel
1911	Comb growth in capons by injection of saline extracts of testis	Pézard
1927	Highly potent extracts of bull testis	McGee
1931	25 mg of androsterone isolated from 15,000 liters of human urine	Butenandt
1935	Crystalline testosterone from bull testis	Laqueur
1935	Synthesis of androgens from cholesterol	Butenandt, Ruzicka

ENDOCRINOLOGY began with androgen deprivation just as surely as pharmacology began with ethanol intoxication (see chronology above). The 1849 experiment of Berthold was the first in which the effects of hormone replacement were clearly shown. The 1889 experiment of Brown-Sequard was one of many that contributed to endocrinology's early lack of respectability.

The testis is a compound organ with two distinct and specialized groups of cells which have quite different but related functions. The male sex hormone testosterone is synthesized in and secreted by the interstitial cells of Leydig, which are interspersed between and among the seminiferous tubules. It is in the latter structures that spermatogenesis occurs and thus the germinal epithelium functions as a sort of DNA bank for the perpetuation of the species. The Leydig cells are under the direct control of the hypophysial interstitial cell-stimulating hormone (ICSH) which is indistinguishable from luteinizing hormone (LH). They are also responsive to chorionic gonadotrophin (CG).

The germinal epithelium is maintained and stimulated directly by hypophysial follicle-stimulating hormone (FSH) and indirectly by ICSH by way of the Leydig cell androgen. Many observers believe that the anatomical juxtaposition of Leydig cells and the base of the seminiferous tubules indicates that androgen produced in the former can influence the latter by local diffusion.

The two functions of the testis can proceed independently of each other in animals and men. There can be persistence of androgen production with failure of the germinal epithelium and, in certain experimental circumstances especially, there can be stimulation of spermatogenesis in the absence of Leydig cell function, but not without androgen. Testicular failure in either sphere may be secondary to a failure of hypophysial stimulation or primary as the result of a local disease of the organ. Primary testicular insufficiency of varying types may be seen following surgery, trauma, infection, radiation, chemical intoxication, or a developmental defect of the organ.

Embryogenesis of the Gonads

Up to a certain critical stage in its development the embryo is sexually nonspecific. Both testes and ovaries and the complicated duct systems associated with sexual function arise from the same primitive embryological structures; in fact, there are vestiges of each sex in the other. Sex is determined by two quite distinct processes: sex determination and sex differentiation.

Sex determination is a genetic phenomenon and the thing that is determined is the *sex genotype,* or *genetic sex.* In most cases, genetic sex and the final outcome of development are appropriate to one another, but there are certain circumstances in which genetic sex and apparent sex may have little to do with one another.

Both oogonia and spermatogonia contain 46 chromosomes: the former's complement can be designated as $44 + X + X$, while that of the latter can be represented as $44 + X + Y$. At the stage of oogenesis between the primary and secondary oocyte, halving of the chromosome numbers occurs, so that each secondary oocyte (and therefore each ovum) receives $22 + X$. At the analogous stage in the development of the sperm, two kinds of secondary spermatocytes are formed, $22 + X$ and $22 + Y$. Genetic maleness or femaleness is therefore determined by the chance that an ovum is fertilized by an X- or Y-bearing sperm; XX = female and XY = male.

In 1949, Barr and Bertram discovered that the somatic tissues of females carry a visible chromatin mass which is believed to be derived from the apposition of certain regions of the XX chromosome pair. The XY pair does not form a readily detectable mass. Therefore, it is now possible to determine sex genotype simply by examining smears of the buccal mucous membrane or vagina, or of leukocytes. As a result of the enthusiastic application of this method, individual people may now be observed whose genetic sex and anatomical sex are not in harmony. Such observations have been particularly helpful in the study of patients with the complaint of sterility, for paradoxical genetic and anatomical sex is an adequate explanation for a history of sterility. The growth of human cells in tissue culture has led to further understanding of chromosome abnormalities in man.

Several diseases have been shown to be associated with chromosomal abnormalities. Mongolism in both males and females is characterized by the presence of an extra autosomal chromosome, and therefore a total chromosome number of 47 instead of 46. Klinefelter's syndrome (apparent male with feminine stigmata and small testes) is often, but not invariably, accompanied by an XXY chromosome pattern and a positive Barr chromatin test (Fig. 4-1). Patients with Turner's syndrome (small stature, amenorrhea, absence of secondary sex characteristics) are often, but not always, found to have only one X chromosome and a total chromosome number 45 (Fig. 4-1). Rare individuals called "superfemales," but disappointingly less than normally feminine, have been found to carry an extra X chromosome, and are therefore designated as XXX. Table 4-1 summarizes some of the chromosomal abnormalities that have been described to date.

Sex differentiation is the process that occurs in the embryo, most commonly in harmony with

NORMAL FEMALE   NORMAL MALE

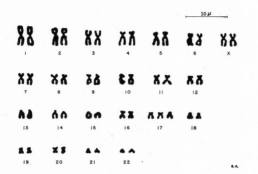

TURNER'S SYNDROME   KLINEFELTER'S SYNDROME

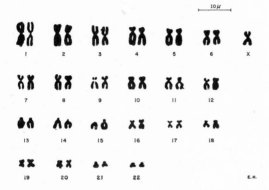

Fig. 4-1.—Human chromosomes of the normal female and normal male, and in Turner's syndrome and Kline-felter's syndrome. Photograph courtesy of Mary Voorhess and Lytt Gardner. (See Tjio, J. H., Puck, T. T., and Robinson, A.: Proc. Nat. Acad. Sc. 45:1008, 1959.)

TABLE 4-1.—SUMMARY OF CHROMOSOMAL ABNORMALITIES IN MAN*

Clinical State	Barr Chromatin Body	Sex Chromosomes	No. of Autosomal Chromosomes	Total No. of Chromosomes
Normal female	+	XX	44	46
Normal male	−	XY	44	46
Superfemale	+	XXX	44	47
Klinefelter's †	+	XXY	44	47
Turner's †	−	X	44	45
Female, mongolism	+	XX	45	47
Male, mongolism	−	XY	45	47

*Barr, M. L.: Science 130:679–685, 1959.
†See text for qualification.

previously determined genetic sex. It consists of differentiation of the gonads themselves, the genital ducts, the urogenital sinus and the external genitalia. The details of this, as of other embryonic differentiations, are not known, but it is a fact that sex specificity appears in the seventh week of embryonic life, and the differentiation of the testis occurs before that of the ovary. According to one hypothesis, the primordial testis secretes a substance that inhibits the differentiation of the ovary. In the absence of this hypothetical substance, ovarian development occurs. The genetic code for the manufacture of such a substance could travel on the Y chromosome.

The anlagen of both male and female duct systems occur in the undifferentiated fetus. In the male the müllerian tract degenerates, and in the female the wolffian duct degenerates. Vestigial

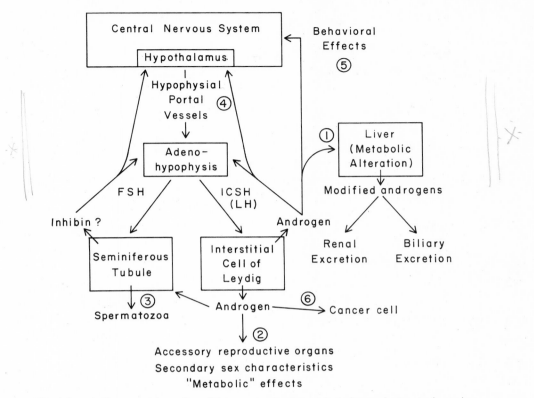

Fig. 4-2.—A diagrammatic outline of the neuroendocrine control of reproduction in the male.

remnants of each persist in the adult of the opposite sex.

Evidently, the character of the internal and external genitalia is positively determined by the secretion or secretions of the testis, for if the gonads are removed from a fetus of either sex, only female internal and external genital organs develop. It is also true that the administration of certain androgenic or progesterone-like drugs during pregnancy may cause virilization of the female fetus. Discrepancies between genetic sex and anatomical sex represent failures in sex differentiation. These few discrepancies are not nearly as astonishing as the fact that the developmental process proceeds to a reasonably successful conclusion in so large a sample of the total population.

Figure 4-2 represents a diagrammatic outline of the discussion to follow. It illustrates the dual function of the testis and the central role of androgen in both the maintenance of primary and secondary sex characteristics and in the gametogenic activity of the tubules. The following organization of the discussion will be used. The circled numbers correspond to those in Figure 4-2.

① Chemistry and metabolism of androgens, and the trophic control of Leydig cell function.

② Effects of androgen deprivation and replacement.

③ The germinal epithelium.

④ CNS control of gonadotrophins.

⑤ Behavioral effects of androgens (see Chapter 5).

⑥ Androgen and prostatic cancer.

① Chemistry and Metabolism of Androgens

The main hormonal product of the Leydig cell is testosterone (Fig. 4-3). Although estrogens have been extracted from bull testis and have been isolated from the urine of other male species, the physiological function of female sex hormone in the male, if any, is as yet undetermined. Studies with C^{14}-labeled acetate or cholesterol

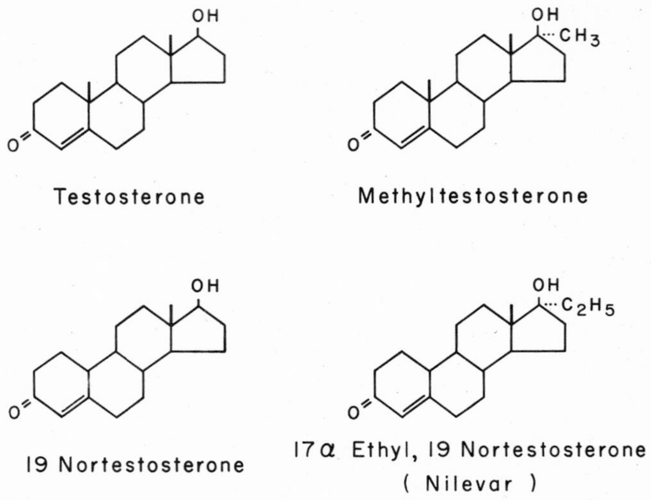

Fig. 4-3.—Testosterone and synthetic analogues.

Testosterone

Methyltestosterone

19 Nortestosterone

17α Ethyl, 19 Nortestosterone (Nilevar)

show that testosterone can be made from either starting material. Cholesterol ester is present in Leydig cells and is presumed to be the main precursor of the male hormone.

The precise details of steroid interconversions in the Leydig cell that lead to the production and secretion of testosterone have not been worked out in minute detail. For the present, we can regard the Leydig cell as entirely analogous to the adrenal cortical cell which also has the problem of making a steroid hormone out of cholesterol as a stored precursor. During biochemical differentiation there was a "deletion" or "masking" of the enzymatic machinery for 11- and 21-hydroxylation and the development of an enzyme profile which characteristically results in the production of testosterone (see Fig. 5-5, p. 67). How this kind of enzymatic differentiation occurs is one of the great mysteries of biology.

In the hypophysectomized animal or man, there is marked gonadal atrophy of both interstitial cells and tubular structures. ICSH specifically stimulates the Leydig cells to a high level of androgen output in either the hypophysectomized or sexually immature individual. The effect is analogous with that of ACTH on the adrenal cell, but the mechanism of the effect is by no means as well understood as is that of ACTH. Treatment of immature rats with ICSH for 7 days caused a striking increase in the cholesterol ester content of the interstitial cells, an effect that was apparent on both chemical and histochemical analysis. It was associated with evidence of increased androgen output.

Androgen assay usually is carried out by noting the magnitude of the effect of androgen on some androgen-sensitive or androgen-dependent tissue. Thus, in the experiments just cited on the effect of ICSH in the immature male rat, increased androgen output was indicated in the ICSH-treated animals by increases in the weight of the seminal vesicles and ventral prostate. A bio-assay of this sort is capable of detecting and quantifying small amounts of androgen. Another bio-assay for androgen (Munson) involves the growth of the comb of the baby chick, and is one of the most discriminating bio-assays known. As little as *0.05 microgram* of androsterone applied directly to the comb daily for 7 days produced a definite growth-promoting effect. In recent years, with the development of chromatographic methods for isolating steroids, androgens have been estimated chemically. It is still necessary to use bio-assay methods for the characterization of unknown steroids.

As Figure 4-2 indicates, the ICSH-testosterone system operates in the familiar feedback manner, for androgen, whether endogenous or exogenous, exerts an inhibitory effect on the system of tissues in the brain and adenohypophysis which are responsible for the production and release of ICSH. Such inhibition may occur in the pituitary or in some structure in the hypothalamus or other part of the central nervous system. Unilateral orchiectomy results in compensatory hypertrophy of the contralateral testis, and this effect is mediated by way of the hypophysis.

The liver figures prominently in the metabolism of androgens as it does in that of many steroids. Androgens are metabolically modified in that organ in a number of ways: alteration of the hormone, conjugation with glucuronic or sulfuric acids, and even (to the extent of 5%) complete oxidation of the steroid structure with the appearance of ring carbons in respiratory CO_2. The effect of the liver can be seen in experiments in which androgen pellets are implanted in the spleen and must therefore traverse the liver before entering the systemic circulation. In such experiments, doses can be found which are systemically ineffective when given intraportally but extremely effective when given directly into the general circulation.

Hepatic inactivation is believed to be the major reason for the comparative ineffectiveness of native androgens when given by mouth. Certain synthetic androgens, such as methyltestosterone, owe their effectiveness by the oral route to the fact that they resist inactivation in the liver.

In addition to chemically modifying the androgens, the liver may secrete them and their transformation products into the bile. This has some toxicologic importance in the case of methyltestosterone, for this substance may cause a curious kind of jaundice which is due to the plugging of bile canaliculi with a highly insoluble material which is either the steroid or a biliary excretion product of it.

While it is rendering androgens biologically inactive in various ways, the liver unaccountably transforms other nonandrogenic steroids into active androgens. These are known as *proandrogens* and are mainly of adrenal cortical origin. They include: cortisone, cortisol, 17-alpha hydroxy-11 desoxycorticosterone, and 17-hydroxy progesterone. This fact is of some clinical importance, for female patients treated with pharmacological doses of cortisol often exhibit menstrual disturbances, hirsutism, and occasionally acne, all of which are associated with the appearance of increased 17-ketosteroids in the urine. This syndrome has been explained on the basis of transformation of cortisol to androgens and suppression of endogenous gonadotrophins.

The excretion of 17-ketosteroids (17-KS) has been used as an index of endogenous androgen production. The rationale of its use is based on the fact that the 4 principal urinary excretion products of testosterone are androsterone, dehydroepiandrosterone, epiandrosterone, and etiocholanolone. As one can see in Figure 4-4, each of these compounds has a keto group at the seventeenth carbon which is detectable by the formation of a yellow color on treatment with m-dinitrobenzene in alkaline solution. The 17-KS compounds may be derived from either the testis

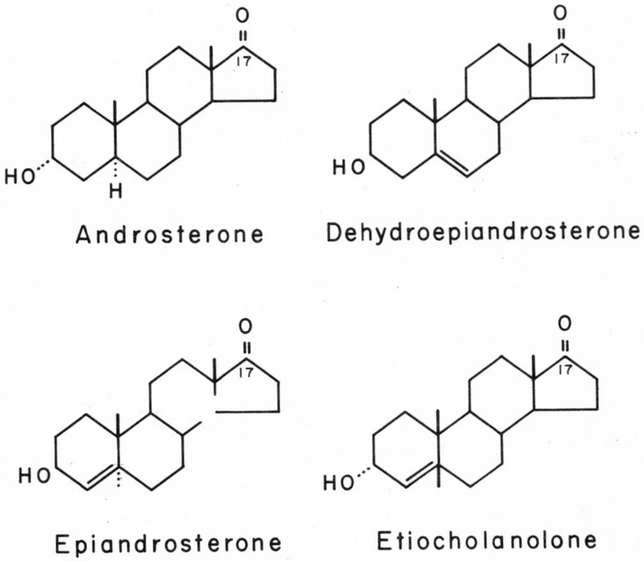

Fig. 4-4.—17-Ketosteroid excretion products of androgens.

Androsterone

Dehydroepiandrosterone

Epiandrosterone

Etiocholanolone

or the adrenal cortex, for the normal woman excretes approximately two-thirds the amount excreted by the normal man. There is great variability in both sexes, however, since the ranges given are 4–17 mg KS per day for females and 6–28 mg/day for males. It· has been suggested that androgen of testicular origin is less likely to appear in the urine as 17-KS than is androgen of adrenal origin. Very recently certain women with the chief complaint of excessive body hair were found to have elevated blood levels of testosterone but normal amounts of 17-KS in their urine.

The urinary excretion products of the androgens are conjugated with glucuronic and sulfuric acid and are biologically inactive unless they are hydrolyzed. In addition to those derived from the adrenals and testes, androgen metabolites may appear in the urine of certain rare females who bear androgen-secreting tumors of the ovary.

② Effects of Androgen Deprivation and Replacement

The physiological function of androgen can be seen best by examining the effects of androgen deprivation. Such effects are apparent in the *primary* and *secondary sex characteristics,* in *general metabolic* effects on skeleton, skeletal muscle, and water balance, and in the sphere of *behavior.* In all cases a distinction should be made between prepuberal and postpuberal results of castration, for in general prepuberal testicular androgen deprivation results in a failure of development of both the morphological and behavioral marks of maleness. Postpuberal castration, on the other hand, does not necessarily cause complete regression of androgen-dependent tissues, and it is not incompatible with a certain amount of sexual activity. It is possible that testicular androgen is necessary for the development of the male primary and accessory sex structures, but once these have been developed they may be partially maintained by androgen from another source, possibly the adrenals.

The *primary sex structures* are the ducts associated with the transport of spermatozoa, the seminal vesicles and prostate, the bulbourethral glands, and the external genitalia. All of these structures are absolutely dependent upon androgen both for their morphological and functional integrity. This dependence can be seen best in the bio-assays for androgen in which the weight of the empty seminal vesicles or ventral prostate can be used as a very precise indication of the amount of androgenic stimulus the structure has received. On histological examination the columnar epithelial cell of the lining of the androgen-deprived seminal vesicle shows a marked shrinking in height and a loss of the normal basophilic granules in the cytoplasm. On androgen replacement, the cell organelles reappear and the height of the cells is proportional to the intensity of the androgen stimulus just as the height of the thyroid cell is a measure of the TSH stimulus. The penis and scrotum are similarly androgen-dependent and, in the case of prepuberal castration they fail to develop. Following postpuberal castration they regress in size, but may remain within normal limits.

The *secondary sex characteristics* are a group of marks that distinguish the male from the female of the species. In some species, such as birds, deer, monkeys, and others, these marks may be of great importance in courting and mating behavior, as Charles Darwin noted a century ago. The head dressings of roosters, the antlers of deer, and the glands which produce the male odor of goats are of some importance in the perpetuation of their respective species. While there are analogous differentiating marks in the human species, the complexity of human society and behavior has resulted in the development of an elaborate set of prosthetic secondary sex characteristics typified by the sports car and the etching collection.

Androgen deficiency produces marked changes in the texture and distribution of body hair. The prepuberal castrate fails to develop a beard, axillary, or pubic hair, and the head hair may remain soft and silky. Postpuberal castration causes slowed growth of the beard and regression and thinning of body hair. Hair distribution is not entirely dependent on androgen, for the pattern, quantity, and texture of body hair is partly determined by inheritance. Certain races of men of undoubted virility and proved procreative capacity have no beards and minimal body hair. In these cases, since there is obviously no lack of androgen, we must assume that there is a genetically determined failure of hair follicles to respond to available androgen.

Common baldness is a genetically determined condition, but, curiously, it does not develop in eunuchoid individuals. A number of such individuals who have been hereditarily predisposed to baldness begin to manifest it only after treatment with replacement doses of androgen. This is an instance of the requirement of androgen for hair loss. Since the mechanism of the development of baldness is unknown, the role of androgen in its facilitation is a complete mystery.

Androgens have a stimulating effect on sebaceous glands which is evident from the fact that oiliness of the skin appears at puberty and on treatment with androgen. The disease acne vulgaris, multiple infections of sebaceous glands, is not seen in castrate males or in prepuberal children. It is extremely common in adolescents of both sexes, and it may appear in patients who are treated either with androgens or with proandrogens, such as cortisol. The acne of girls and women is believed to be dependent on the action of androgens of adrenocortical origin.

Other skin characteristics are associated with androgen deprivation. The skin of castrates and eunuchoids is soft, pale yellow and very finely wrinkled. It does not tan on exposure to sunlight, but the ability to tan appears on treatment with androgen.

The timbre of the voice is a well-recognized secondary sex characteristic. In some cultures, in fact, men were castrated to insure a continuing supply of high-pitched voices for individual and group singing. Androgen administration to the eunuchoid male or to the female results in a lowering of the pitch of the voice and some degree of hoarseness.

The *general metabolic effects* of androgen lack and replacement are difficult to separate from those on the secondary sex characteristics. For example, the eunuchoid male often shows a typically feminine distribution of subcutaneous fat, particularly in the region of the hips and lower abdomen. Conversely, the virilized female who suffers from diffuse adrenal hyperplasia fails to show this typically feminine distribution of subcutaneous fat. While there is some doubt among authorities about whether the feminine fat distribution of the eunuchoid is regularly influenced by androgen, there is no doubt whatever that typically feminine fat padding appears in patients whose adrenal virilism is successfully treated with replacement doses of cortisol.

The effects of prepuberal castration on skeletal growth suggest that there is a failure of epiphysial closure in the growing androgen-deficient indi-vidual with consequent overgrowth of the long bones. Paradoxically some hypogonadal boys whose growth appears to have been stunted, grow more rapidly when they are given androgen. Such observations as these are extraordinarily difficult to interpret because of the many nutritional, genetic, and hormonal determinants of both growth rate and growth pattern.

The aggregate skeletal muscle mass of castrate and eunuchoid men is smaller than that of normal men, and an increase in muscle strength has been observed to occur on treatment with androgen. As the sculptors of antiquity noted, the muscle markings of the male figure are very prominent, whereas those of the feminine figure tend to be obscured by subcutaneous fat. Treatment with androgen accentuates visible muscle markings.

A common denominator of the skin, skeletal, and muscle effects of androgens may be a general protein anabolic effect of these compounds. In many balance experiments, it has been found that androgens cause nitrogen, potassium, and phosphorus retention, and an increase in the total amount of skeletal muscle. The magnitude of the nitrogen retention is much greater in castrates than it is in normal men. That the active metabolic mass of the body increases under androgen treatment is indicated by the fact that there is a small but consistent increase in the basal metabolic rate.

The discovery of the anabolic effects of androgen has stimulated a search for steroid compounds structurally related to androgens which would have a maximum amount of anabolic activity and a minimum androgenicity. A number of promising compounds have been developed in which the anabolic-androgenic ratio has been markedly altered. For example, certain steroids in the 19-nor series (i.e., lacking the methyl group in the 19 position) have a ratio of 20:1 as compared with 1:1 for testosterone. But the skeletal muscle whose growth was used as an index of skeletal muscle growth generally is the *levator ani* muscle of the male rat, a structure which is practically vestigial in the female, and which doubtless participates in the ejaculatory reflex of the male. The sexual nonspecificity of such a muscle is certainly open to question, and therefore there is dubious justification for using it as an index of responsiveness of skeletal muscle generally. While the 19-nor compounds are less androgenic than testosterone none of them has so far failed to exhibit androgenic activity in clinical trials. Such trials have occurred most commonly in patients who require "building up" in order to endure contemplated surgery, in some postoperative patients, and in premature infants. Some favorable reports on the use of the anabolic agents in these circumstances have appeared, but it is sometimes difficult to decide whether the encouraging results are due to increased protein anabolism or to improved nutrition secondary to a feeling of well-being that is often produced by a number of hormonally active steroids, including androgens and their congeners. The formulas of two anabolic steroids are shown in Figure 4-3. The biochemical mechanism of action of androgens will be discussed in Chapter 12.

③ Spermatogenesis

By far the largest volume of the testis is filled with an intricately coiled system of seminiferous tubules, the so-called germinal epithelium. It is here that the undifferentiated germ cell, the spermatogonium, differentiates into the mature spermatozoon. This is a very rapidly proliferating cell population; in some species, such as the ram, billions of spermatozoa may be produced in a day. In addition to germ cells in various stages of development—from the most primitive stages at the periphery of the tubule to mature spermatozoa in the lumen—another cell type, the Sertoli cell, can be seen. The Sertoli cell has been described, pondered over and written about by many observers, but its precise function is not known. On the basis of the fact that certain Sertoli cell tumors of dogs produce estrogen, an estrogen-producing function has been attributed to it. Most authorities, however, now believe the major source of testicular estrogen to be the Leydig cell which produces androgen. Some authors attribute a nutritive role to the Sertoli cells for the developing germ cell, but this appears to be entirely speculative.

Whatever the relationship between the germ cells and the Sertoli cells they are certainly differentially susceptible to injury of various kinds. For example, in either naturally occurring or experimentally produced *cryptorchidism,* in which a testis is kept within the abdominal cavity and not permitted to descend into the scrotum, the germ cells disappear, but the Sertoli cells persist (Fig. 4-5). Normally, the temperature of the contents of the scrotal sac is slightly lower than that of the abdomen, and the lower temperature apparently is necessary for the process of spermatogenesis to occur. The reason for the inhibition of the process at intra-abdominal temperatures is not known. The interstitial cells of Leydig function well at intra-abdominal temperatures, for there is no obvious evidence of androgen deficiency in a bilaterally cryptorchid man or animal unless the condition is allowed to persist for a very long time, and the Leydig cells of the latter have been shown to respond to stimulation by ICSH with the secretion of androgen.

The germinal epithelium (again excepting the Sertoli cells) can be destroyed by certain doses of radiation that spare the endocrine cells of the testis. Presumably, this is due to the fact that rapidly proliferating tissues, such as intestinal mucosa, bone marrow, and the testicular tubules are most vulnerable to the lethal effects of radiation. This is also true for certain so-called radiomimetic drugs, such as the nitrogen mustards, and for a class of chemical compounds known as furfurans. Certain developmental defects of the testis are characterized by hyalinization of the seminiferous tubules and the absence of spermatogenesis, although androgen production in the Leydig cells may proceed normally.

The process of spermatogenesis fails in the hypophysectomized animal or man. In such animals, spermatogenesis is blocked at the stage of the primary spermatocyte, just before the halving of chromosome number occurs. Essentially, full spermatogenesis can be restored by combined treatment with hypophysial FSH and ICSH. The former is believed to exert its effect directly on the process of germ cell maturation and, on the basis of the point of arrest of the process in the hypophysectomized animal, we can guess that an important primary or secondary effect of FSH occurs at the stage of the formation of the secondary spermatocyte. ICSH is said to influence spermatogenesis by way of Leydig cell androgen production. That androgen may act by local diffusion within the testis is suggested by experiments in which pellets of the hormone were implanted in the testes of hypophysectomized rats. Spermatogenesis was stimulated, the tubules increased in diameter in the region of the pellet, and there was a progressive decrease in this effect on tubules more and more distant from the implant. It is also true that very large doses of

NORMAL TESTIS   CRYPTORCHID TESTIS

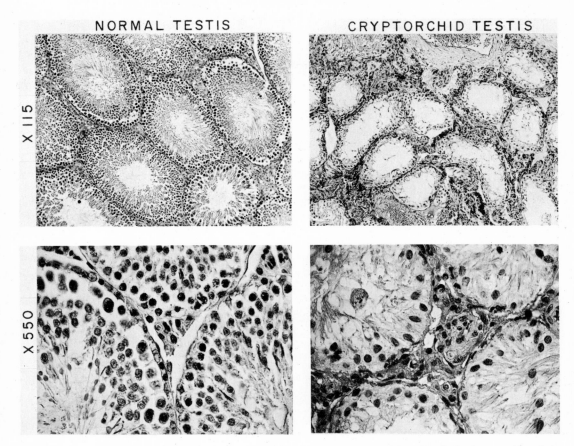

Fig. 4-5.—Histological appearance of normal and experimentally cryptorchid rat testis. The cryptorchid gland was attached to the posterior abdominal wall with a silk ligature and remained in the abdomen for 1 month. Note persistence of Sertoli cells in the atrophic tubules on the right. (See Tepperman, J., Tepperman, H. M., and Dick, H.: Endocrinology 45:491-503, 1949.)

testosterone will cause maturation of the germinal epithelium in the hypophysectomized rat. In the human, however, androgen administration usually suppresses hypophysial gonadotrophin output *and* gametogenesis because the amounts given do not begin to approximate the doses used in the rat experiments cited here. In certain individuals with low sperm counts, suppression of hypophysial gonadotrophin with testosterone and withdrawal of the androgen may be followed by a rebound increase in sperm count above the initial level. It has been claimed that some infertile males may have been rendered temporarily fertile by this procedure, but evaluation of the results of this complicated type of clinical investigation is extraordinarily difficult.

Studies of barren marriages are made on both partners, and the realization has dawned that the difficulty is just as likely to occur in the male as in the female. Fertilization of the ovum requires that the ejaculum contain enough viable and motile spermatozoa to accomplish the mission. The volume of the ejaculum is normally between 2 and 4 ml, and the sperm count per milliliter is of the order of 80–100 millions. No categorical statement can be made about the "minimal effective dose" of spermatozoa, although 50 million per ml is often given as a dangerously low count. On the other hand, sperm counts of 20 million per ml have been found in men of proved fertility. Not only are absolute numbers significant, but the quality control of the individual sperm factory is equally so. A large percentage of abnormal forms (i.e., two-headed, or poorly motile) is associated with infertility even when the total count is respectably high.

Nor can we ignore the fact that the mature spermatozoon is little more than an elaborately gift-wrapped package of DNA. Its cytoplasm is nearly invisible and certainly incapable of sustaining viability for any length of time. The sperm cell is therefore obliged to depend for its nourishment on the secretions of the secondary sex glands. Since the semen has a higher concentration of fructose than the blood does of glucose, the sperm cells may be peculiarly dependent upon fructose as their metabolic fuel. Thus, it is possible to conceive of male failure in the fertilization process as a failure, (1) of spermatogenesis, or (2) of the accessory tissues to provide a proper supporting medium in which the ejaculated sperm can thrive and reach the ovum. Fructose, contributed by the seminal vesicles, is only one of many constituents of the semen that may have important sperm-maintaining functions. The prostate contributes acid phosphatase, citric acid, calcium and fibrinolysin, but little is known about the function of any of these. The production of acid phosphatase by the prostate is of considerable clinical importance because prostatic cancer cells retain the capacity to synthesize large amounts of this enzyme, and patients with this type of cancer have elevated amounts of acid phosphatase in their blood. Blood levels of acid phosphatase, in fact, are often used as an index of the effectiveness of certain kinds of treatment in this condition.

In both castration and cryptorchidism, the pituitary production of FSH is increased and typical "castration cells" appear in the adenohypophysis. Thus, FSH appears to be overproduced when spermatogenesis fails. This suggests that some event associated with active spermatogenesis causes an inhibition of hypophysial FSH production and/or release. A hypothetical hormone has been postulated as the tubular FSH inhibitor and has been variously referred to as "inhibin" or "X hormone." Indeed, the claim has been made that certain aqueous (and therefore presumably nonsteroidal) extracts of testis reverse the cytologic changes in the pituitary which occur in the castrate, but "inhibin" has never been characterized more precisely than this, and many investigators remain unconvinced of the existence of such a substance.

④ Hypothalamo-Hypophysial Relationships in the Male

The male child produces little androgen, for the excretion of 17-KS in the urine is very small. At puberty, a complicated process of differentiation occurs and the child is transformed into a sexually mature adult. The nature and source of the messages involved in the initiation of puberty are not known, but certain general statements can be made about the process.

In the first place, the gonads of the immature animal are capable of responding to gonadotrophic stimulation, and the androgen-sensitive cells of the prostate and seminal vesicles are capable of responding to the androgen secreted by the stimulated Leydig cells. Thus, it is unlikely that puberty is initiated by a change in the testis itself. That the pituitary itself is not the locus of the change that occurs at puberty is suggested by work on female rats in which the pituitaries of immature animals transplanted to the sella turcica of mature animals were capable of maintaining mature sexual function. In the reverse experiment, i.e., the transplantation of a pituitary of an adult animal to the sella of a sexually immature animal, no sexual differentiation occurred. This suggests that influences which play upon the adenohypophysis from the brain by way of the hypophysial portal system of blood vessels trigger the rise in gonadotrophin secretion that occurs at puberty. It is of some interest to note that precocious puberty has been described in both young boys and young girls who have tumors in the hypothalamus. The mechanisms by which such destructive lesions modify the production of gonadotrophins by the pituitary are not now understood.

In addition to the central nervous system changes that occur at puberty, changes in the sensitivity of androgen-sensitive tissues to the hormone occur at the same time. Hooker found that rats castrated at birth showed an increase in weight of the seminal vesicles during the expected sexual maturation period in response to doses of testosterone only one-fifth as great as those which produced a similar effect either earlier or later. The mechanism of this increased sensitivity of the seminal vesicles is not known, but it is certainly possible that some substance of hypophysial origin other than gonadotrophins may have been secreted at about the age when puberty would be expected to occur and that this material sensitized the seminal vesicles to the action of androgens. It is at least possible to conceive of the apparently local change in sensitivity of the seminal vesicles as a derivative effect of a change in the brain.

We can provide a tentative answer to the question of the site of initiation of the process of puberty by saying that a change occurs in the brain which causes increased output of gonadotrophic hormones by the adenohypophysis (see also Chapter 5). The nature of the change in the brain—whether it involves stimulation, release of inhibition, or complicated combinations of both—is quite unknown, as is the reason the change occurs at a particular time of life. This is an example of the action of what has been termed a "biological clock"—in this case, one that measures a long segment of time.

Another line of investigation supports the view that the central nervous system strongly influences the gonadotrophic activity of the anterior hypophysis, and at the same time illustrates the operation of a "biological clock" over shorter periods of time. In man, once spermatogenesis is instituted it proceeds at a constant high rate over many years before it declines in late middle life. There are no seasonal fluctuations in gametogenesis and there are no demarcated "rutting seasons" through the year. In certain animals (sheep, deer, birds), in which the sexual interest of the male is seasonal, the rate of spermatogenesis coincides with sex drive and with periods of maximal receptivity in the female. That the failure in spermatogenesis during the off-season is not locally determined in the gonad is illustrated by the responsiveness of the quiescent gonad to stimulation by exogenous gonadotrophin. The mechanism of the operation of the "clock" is suggested by the fact that increased spermatogenesis can be induced by changing the illumination pattern of the animal's environment. Thus, light enters by way of the eyes, is metered somewhere in the brain, and the results of the light measurement are somehow made available to those structures in the brain that are responsible for setting the level of hypophysial gonadotrophin secretion. There is nothing to prevent our admiring this accomplishment even if we do not understand it very well.

Although spermatogenesis in the adult remains at very high levels, and there are well-authenti-cated instances of persistence of fertility into the ninth decade of life and later, there is gradual diminution in sperm count and 17-KS excretion that may begin as early as the fourth decade but usually occurs in the sixth or seventh. We have seen that the initiation of puberty occurred as a result of the awakening of the gonads by increased gonadotrophin secretion. The gradual decrease in gonadal activity that occurs in the later decades of life in the male is not due to a failure of gonadotrophin secretion but to an increasing refractoriness of the gonad to gonadotrophic stimulation. This may be due to a gradually diminishing blood flow through the gonads which, in turn, may be related to the atherosclerosis and other cardiovascular-pulmonary changes that occur with advancing age.

An account of the effect of androgen treatment of newborn female animals and a discussion of sex behavior will be found in Chapter 5.

⑥ Androgen-Deprivation and Prostatic Cancer

When certain cells undergo mutation to become cancer cells, they often retain many of the biochemical characteristics of the cells of origin. Thus, in spite of the removal from them of influences that normally prevent wildly proliferative, invasive, and metastatic behavior, cancer cells, while killing their host, may implausibly go about the day-to-day business of the cells from which they were derived. Thus, we find metastatic hepatoma cells in the lung producing bile, metastatic cells from primary tumors in the gastrointestinal tract producing mucus, and metastatic thyroid cancer cells trapping iodine and making thyroid hormone.

Among the biochemical functions retained by cancer cells is responsiveness to, and (in the case of still well-differentiated cells) actual dependence upon, certain hormones. The prostatic cancer cell may be nearly as dependent on a continuing supply of androgen as is the prostate cell from which it was derived. This biological fact has been the basis for the recent reintroduction of an old concept into the management of many patients with cancer: The idea of attempting to slow the growth of the cancer and delay death by modifying the hormonal environment of the tumor to its disadvantage. In the case of prostatic cancer, this amounts to treatment by androgen-deprivation. A knowledge of endocrine physiology is just as essential for the physician who manages patients by depriving them of hormones which stimulate and support the growth of a malignant tumor as it is for one who uses hormones for substitution therapy or for their pharmacological effects.

These ideas were given powerful support by the work of Huggins who showed immediate and, in many cases, dramatic improvement in the clinical condition of patients with metastatic prostatic cancer following castration. This was a case of using an iatrogenic disease compatible with life—sterility and androgen deficiency—as a weapon against a naturally occurring disease that would be certainly and quickly lethal. The administration of estrogens which, in the male, represents a pharmacological castration because the gonadotrophins are inhibited, produced similar results, though the response was more gradual. In one series, the 3-year survival rate of patients with metastatic cancer was tripled by the combination of orchiectomy and estrogen treatment. The lengthened time of survival tells only part of the story, for the clinical condition and comfort of these patients was markedly improved as a result of this treatment. Recently, Huggins was awarded the Nobel prize for his work in this field.

Relapses occur, and the cancer tissue begins to escape from its androgen requirement. There is no proved reason for this, but the following suggestion is offered: In the cell population of the tumor, the nature of mutation may have been uneven, so that there was a whole spectrum of relative androgen-dependence and independence. Androgen deprivation "selects" the relatively independent cells for reproduction in the same way that an antibiotic gives the reproductive advantage to bacterial cells which happen to be resistant to it. Eventually, the hormone-independent clones overrun the field and take over. With an increased rate of cell division, the statistical probability of the appearance of other, more malignant, secondary mutants becomes greater and greater, and hormone deprivation is no longer effective in preventing the fatal outcome.

When the prostatic cancer begins to escape from the effects of the initial procedures, castration and estrogen treatment, further temporary benefit may be obtained by cutting off its supply of adrenal androgens, either surgically or (as has been done more recently) by pharmacologically inhibiting ACTH with hormones of the cortisol type. Recently acquired knowledge of hormonal substitution therapy has made such therapeutic maneuvers feasible.

Large doses of estrogen are required to inhibit the growth of metastatic prostatic cancer. It is possible that the estrogens may competitively inhibit the effects of any adrenal or other androgens that happen to persist after inhibition of gonadotrophins. In a similar way, androgens are used in the management of estrogen-dependent breast cancer. It should be emphasized that treatment by modifying the hormonal environment of prostatic cancer is not to be regarded as a substitute for surgery but rather as an adjunct to it.

REFERENCES

Barr, M. L.: Sex chromatin and phenotype in man, Science 130:679–685, 1959.

Dorfman, R. I., and Shipley, R. A.: *The Androgens: Biochemistry, Physiology, and Clinical Significance* (New York: John Wiley & Sons, Inc., 1956).

Drill, V. A., and Riegel, B.: Structural and hormonal activity of some new steroids, Recent Prog. Hormone Res. 14:29–76, 1958.

Huggins, C.: Control of cancers of man by endocrinologic methods: A review, Cancer Res. 16:825–830, 1956.

Lipsett, M. B., and Korenman, S. G.: Androgen metabolism, J.A.M.A. 190:757–62, 1964.

Mann, T.: Male sex hormone and its role in reproduction, Recent Prog. Hormone Res. 12:353–376, 1956.

Munson, P. L.: Endocrine pharmacology: Selected topics, Ann. Rev. Pharm. 1:315–350, 1961.

Nalbandov, A. V.: *Reproductive Physiology: Comparative Reproductive Physiology of Domestic Animals, Laboratory Animals, and Man* (San Francisco: W. H. Freeman & Co., 1958).

Velardo, J. T.: *Endocrinology of Reproduction* (New York: Oxford University Press, 1958).

5

Reproductive Endocrinology in the Female

LIKE THE TESTIS, the ovary is a compound organ with a dual function: The production and release of ova and the production of certain hormones, estrogens and progesterone, which have important regulatory roles in the growth, development, and maintenance of the structures necessary for the continuation of the species. Among these are the reproductive organs themselves, including both the gravid and nongravid uterus, the secondary sex characteristics, and the mammary glands. Figure 5-1 is intended to convey some idea of the complexity of the interrelationships of the neural, endocrine and end-organ tissues which are concerned with reproductive function in the female. The author does not expect this diagram to be more meaningful to the beginning student at this time than the design of an especially complex interchange on the Los Angeles Freeway would be. It is suggested that the reader examine the diagram mainly to get a panoramic view of the structures and substances that will be discussed in this chapter; read the chapter; and return to the diagram to see how the individual components in this communications system fit the larger pattern.

The following subjects will be discussed (the circled numbers correspond to those in Fig 5-1):

① Chemistry, biosynthesis, and metabolism of estrogens and progestins.

② Chemistry and cell source of gonadotrophins.

③ Effects of estrogens and progestins on tissues.

④ Role of the central nervous system in the hypophysial-ovarian relationship.

⑤ Hormonal control of ovulation and the estrus cycle.

⑥ Hormonal regulations in pregnancy and lactation.

⑦ Cellular mechanism of action of hormones which affect reproduction in the female.

⑧ "Nonreproductive" effects of ovarian steroids.

⑨ Hormones and breast cancer.

⑩ Relaxin.

⑪ Behavior.

① Chemistry, Biosynthesis, and Metabolism of Estrogens and Progestins

The hormone produced and secreted by the ovary of many species, including the human, is estradiol 17β. This compound is in equilibrium with estrone, which can be converted by the liver and placenta to estriol, an estrogen believed to be the principal one secreted by the placenta. The structural relationships of these compounds are shown in Figure 5-2. All of them have estrogenic effects, estradiol 17β being the most active. While the ovaries of some species make female sex hormones which are not precisely the same as these, all naturally occurring estrogens have an

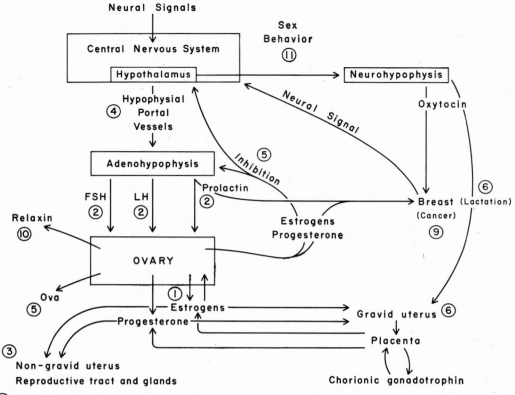

Neural Signals

Central Nervous System

Hypothalamus

Sex Behavior ⑪

Neurohypophysis

Hypophysial ④ Portal Vessels

Neural Signal

Oxytocin

Adenohypophysis

Inhibition ⑤

FSH ②   LH ②   Prolactin ②

Relaxin ⑩

OVARY

Estrogens Progesterone

Breast (Lactation) ⑥

(Cancer) ⑨

Ova ⑤

① Estrogens

Progesterone

Gravid uterus ⑥

Placenta

③

Non-gravid uterus
Reproductive tract and glands

Chorionic gonadotrophin

⑦ (Biochemical mechanisms)

⑧ Non-reproductive effects

Fig. 5-1.—A diagrammatic outline of the neuroendocrine control of reproduction in the female.

Fig. 5-2.—Estrogen interrelationships.

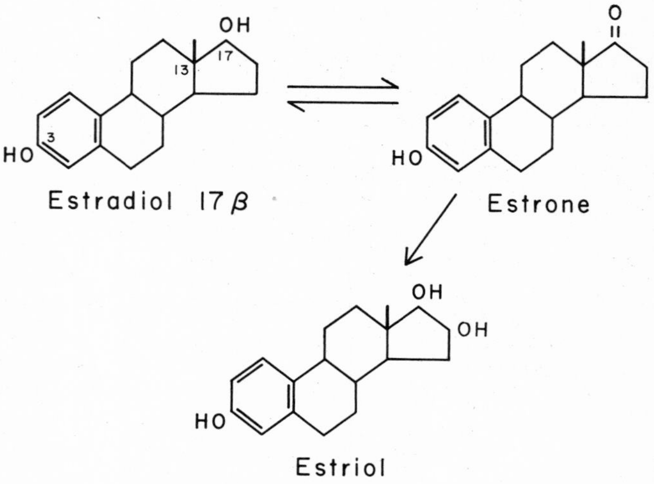

Estradiol 17β

Estrone

Estriol

64

SOME LANDMARKS IN CHRONOLOGY OF REPRODUCTIVE ENDOCRINOLOGY IN THE FEMALE

DATE		INVESTIGATOR
1896	First experimental demonstration of ovarian activity	Knauer
1896	Origin of corpus luteum described	Sobotta
1897	Relationship between corpus luteum and pregnancy suggested	Beard
1900	Prevention of uterine atrophy and loss of sex function by ovarian grafts in castrate animals	Knauer
1903	Interruption of early pregnancy by corpus luteum removal in rabbits	Fraenkel
1905	Concept of endocrine function of placenta introduced	Halban
1910	First demonstration of endocrine activity of corpus luteum	Ancel and Bouin
1912	Gonadal atrophy posthypophysectomy	Aschner
1927	Chorionic gonadotrophin in urine of pregnant women	Ascheim, Zondek
1928	Prolactin discovered	Stricker and Grüter
1919–1930	Isolation of crystalline estrogen by 3 independent groups	Doisy; Butenandt; Marrian
1918–1930	Purification and bio-assay of luteal extracts; prevention of abortion after ovariectomy in early pregnancy in rabbits	Corner and Allen
1932	Structure of estrone and estriol Structure of progesterone	Marrian; Butenandt Butenandt
1932	Feedback control of pituitary gonadotrophin output suggested	Moore and Price
1932	Participation of CNS in feedback control of gonadotrophins suggested	Hohlweg, Junkmann
1935	Isolation of estradiol 17β	Doisy *et al.*
1936	Discovery of synthetic estrogens (stilbenes)	Dodds
1939	Luteotrophin distinct from LH suggested	Astwood, Fevold
1941	Identity of prolactin and luteotrophin in rat suggested	Evans, Simpson, Lyons

unsaturated A ring, a phenolic hydroxy group at position 3 and a methyl group at 13. Synthetic congeners of the naturally occurring estrogens have been prepared, and one of these will be discussed in the section on nonreproductive functions of estrogens.

Estrogens are comparatively inactive when taken by mouth, mainly because they are inactivated in the liver where they are conjugated with glucuronic or sulfuric acids or otherwise modified. The discovery that certain nonsteroidal compounds, especially stilbene derivatives, were able to produce all of the physiological effects of naturally occurring estrogens, even when given by the oral route, proved to be of great therapeutic importance. Two of the most widely used synthetic estrogens are diethylstilbestrol and hexestrol, shown in Figure 5-3.

The naturally occurring hormone of the corpus luteum is progesterone, shown in Figure 5-4 with its excretion product, pregnanediol. Progesterone is important not only because of its role in

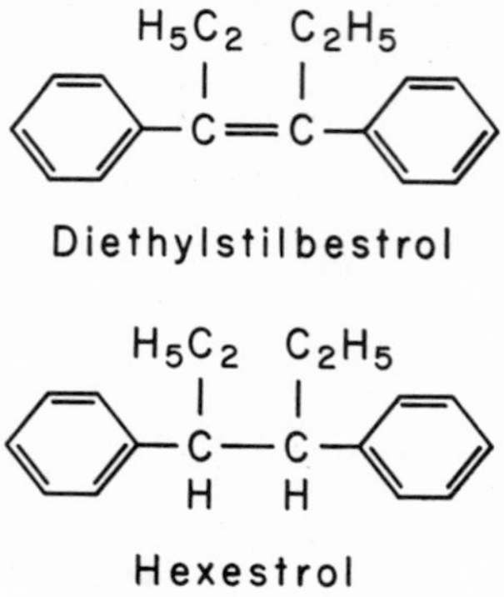

H_5C_2 C_2H_5

Diethylstilbestrol

H_5C_2 C_2H_5

Hexestrol

Fig. 5-3.—Synthetic estrogens.

the maintenance of pregnancy but also because it is an intermediate in the biosynthesis of adrenal, testicular and gonadal steroids from cholesterol. In Figure 5-5 a schematic representation of some of the intermediates in the synthesis of cortisol, testosterone, estradiol 17β, and progesterone is given. It is designed to suggest that the enzymatic machinery which enables the cell to perform the many reactions distal to progesterone is specialized in each kind of steroid-producing cell; that is, in the testis and ovary the 21-hydroxylation and 11-hydroxylation equipment necessary for cortisol synthesis is either absent or in such short supply that only very small amounts of steroid can be carried beyond the indicated block. Similarly, the capacity for demethylation which is necessary for the formation of 19-nortestosterone may be variably feeble in the testicular Leydig cell. Although we are not sure that the synthetic route from testosterone to estradiol 17β is the main route of estrogen formation in the ovary, we do know that ovarian slices incubated with C^{14}-labeled testosterone make labeled estradiol 17β. The corpus luteum cell evidently differentiates further by producing progesterone as a secretory product while retaining the ability to produce

estrogen. It is emphasized that the various steroid-producing cells may retain some capacity to make hormonal products in addition to the main ones. For example, estrogen is made by Leydig cells and estrogens and androgens are produced in adrenal cortical cells. In this connection, it is interesting to recall that mutants of ovarian or testicular cells which undergo metaplasia and form tumors may specialize in making estrogens or androgens, whether they developed in a testis or an ovary.

The differentiation of steroid-producing cells was demonstrated dramatically by Dorothy Villee, who has succeeded in persuading an endocrine gland (A) grown in organ culture to produce steroid patterns characteristic of another steroid-producing gland (B) by incubating gland (A) in the presence of RNA extracted from (B). Thus, ovaries could be induced to increase their production of adrenal cortical hormones by incubating them with RNA extracted from adrenals! (Federation Proceedings, 1967).

The naturally occurring steroids are rendered water-soluble when they are conjugated in the liver with glucuronic or sulfuric acid. The conjugated steroids are excreted in the urine and are themselves biologically inactive. Estrogen conjugates, such as glucuronides, can be rendered biologically active because the body has the capacity to hydrolyze them and release the active material. In the case of pregnanediol glucuronide, the steroid is biologically inactive even after hydrolysis.

② The Chemistry of Gonadotrophins

Five gonadotrophins have been studied extensively: the 3 hypophysial hormones, follicle-stimulating hormone (FSH), luteinizing hormone (LH, or ICSH), and luteotrophic hormone or prolactin (LTH); human chorionic gonadotro-

Fig. 5-4.—Progesterone and pregnanediol.

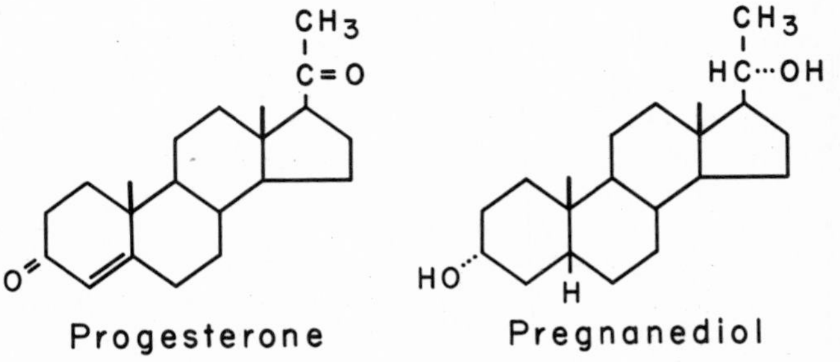

CH_3

$C=O$

Progesterone

CH_3

$HC\cdots OH$

Pregnanediol

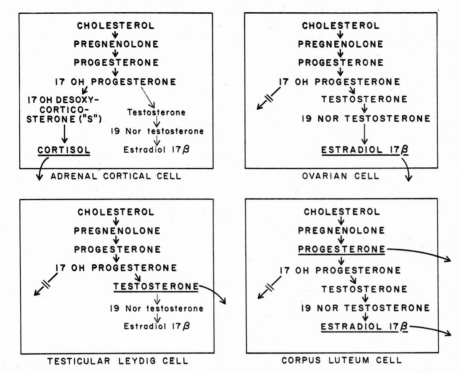

Fig. 5-5.—Biochemical differentiation of steroid-producing cells. The synthesis of estrogen via nortestosterone is only one of several suggested possibilities. This diagram is designed to suggest that a common enzymatic pattern underlies the capability of all of these cells and that biochemical differentiation involves "deletion" or "de-emphasis" of certain pathways, with the result that one or another steroid becomes the predominant secretory product.

phin (CG or HCG) and the gonadotrophin of pregnant mare's serum (PMS). All of these are proteins and at least 4 (FSH, LH, CG, PMS) are glycoproteins, although in the case of CG the carbohydrate moiety is not essential for biological activity. LH, a protein with a MW of about 30,000, has been prepared in a highly purified form: 6000 times the effective dose of the material shows no signs of contamination with FSH. Although FSH (MW6700) has been highly purified and, in some preparations, appears to be electrophoretically homogeneous, it has never been prepared free of traces of LH as indicated by responses of the interstitial cells of hypophysectomized rats of both sexes. It is possible that the trace of LH activity may not represent contamination but an actual shared amino acid sequence with LH. This, of course, is speculative, for amino acid location analyses are not yet available for these compounds, aside from a few end group analyses.

Once it was suggested that there was only one hypophysial gonadotrophin and that the distinction between FSH and LH was the result of a chemical artifact. This is no longer believed to be true, for it has been shown by very refined assay methods that the proportion of FSH to LH activity in the urine of normal, nonpregnant women varies at different parts of the menstrual cycle.

Luteotrophic hormone or prolactin has been prepared in highly purified form and, indeed, was the first hypophysial hormone to be crystallized. It is a single peptide chain with a MW of 24,200 and, like insulin and the neurohypophysial hormones, it contains disulfide bridges. When the three —S–S— bonds are reduced, the biological activity is lost.

Human chorionic gonadotrophin is a glycoprotein and has been very highly purified. Its biological activity mimics that of hypophysial LH, but there are certain minor differences between the two.

Pregnant mare's serum gonadotrophin (PMS) has been' highly purified, and is known to be a glycoprotein which is composed of 60% carbohydrates, glucosamine and galactosamine, and sialic acid and only 40% protein. Its biological activity is that of a mixture of purified LH and FSH.

In the case of the gonadotrophins, the differences between hormones prepared from the tissues of different species do not appear to be as striking as they are in the case of growth hormone, for primates respond readily to gonadotrophins of nonprimate origin.

Recent studies suggest some overlapping in function between prolactin and purified growth hormone. Activities characteristic of the 2 hormones appear to travel with each other during extraction and isolation procedures. Whether this is a problem in purification or another example of a shared amino acid sequence remains to be determined.

③ Effects of Estrogens and Progestins on Tissues

ESTROGENS

EMBRYONIC.—Although the differentiation of the female reproductive tract and organs seems to be determined largely by the absence of androgen, estrogen (either from the fetus or the mother) appears to be essential for the full development of the uterus and vagina in some species. If androgens, progesterone, or synthetic progestins are given to the mother at the critical time at which sex differentiation is occurring, masculinization of the external genitalia of the female fetus may occur.

PREPUBERAL.—Throughout childhood estrogen is secreted at levels which are too low to cause development of the reproductive tissues. Like the immature testis, the immature ovary can be stimulated to a high level of activity by exogenous gonadotrophin; therefore, the persistence of the prepuberal state does not signify any lack of competence of the ovaries to respond to gonadotrophic stimulation, but rather a lack of such stimulation. The pituitary of the prepuberal animal, male or female, can readily assume adult responsibility if it is transplanted to the *sella turcica* of the hypophysectomized adult.

This suggests that lack of maturation or its presence is determined not by the ovary or pituitary, but by the state of suprahypophysial tissues, that is, the brain. According to one theory of the initiation of puberty (Harris), the small amount of estrogen secreted by the ovaries of the prepuberal female is still sufficient to inhibit the output of gonadotrophins at the level of the central nervous system. At the time of puberty, there is a crucial change in sensitivity of these tissues, so that they require very much larger amounts of estrogen to signal inhibition of gonadotrophins. Gonadotrophin is called for up to the new "set" of the "gonadotrophostat" and sexual maturation occurs. It would be pleasant to know something about the operation of the biological clock that brings about this kind of change in the central nervous system. As physiologists, we are obliged just as much to provide some sort of mechanistic description of the effect of estrogen on the brain as we are to describe its effect on the uterus.

PUBERTY.—Puberty, then, is initiated by an increased output of gonadotrophins by the pituitary acting on instructions from the hypothalamus. In response to the gonadotrophins, increasing amounts of estrogens are secreted by the ovary, producing accelerated growth of the uterus, vagina, accessory sex glands, external genitalia, pelvis, breasts, and pubic and axillary hair. This growth is specific, that is, it occurs at rates far more rapid than those at which somatic growth is occurring at the same time. The process begins at the age of 9 or 10 and the first menstrual period may appear at age 12 or may be delayed until age 16. Some of the wide variation in time of onset may be genetically determined. Whenever the menarche occurs it may take several years before the establishment of typical, regular, adult ovulatory menstrual cycles.

NONPREGNANT ADULT.—During the (approximately) 35-year period of fertility in the adult woman, estrogen production fluctuates in a cyclic way which will be described in greater detail in a later section. In general, estrogen functions as a growth hormone for those tissues which are either immediately or secondarily related to the reproductive process.

There are some observations which suggest that estrogen may have local effects in the *ovary* which are quite analogous to those described for testosterone in the testis, and that they may be similarly exerted by local diffusion. In both immature and hypophysectomized rats, priming with rather high doses of estrogen enhanced the ovarian response to gonadotrophin. The synergistic effect of FSH and LH on the ovary may be visualized as a synergism between FSH- and LH-stimulated estrogen produced in the gland. Just as spermatogenesis can be stimulated in the hypophysectomized male rat by large doses of testosterone, estrogen can stimulate follicular growth and oogenesis in the hypophysectomized female. Estrogen pellets implanted into rabbit maintain the corpora lutea beyond their normal span in both intact and hypophysectomized animals.

In the *uterus,* estrogen stimulates growth of the glandular epithelium of the endometrium. The earliest detectable effect is hyperemia and transudation of water and salt into the tissues of the uterus. Estrogen is also a growth hormone for the smooth muscle of the uterus, and (possibly indirectly) for the uterine vascular system.

The epithelium of the *vagina* is so sensitive to the action of estrogen that examination of vaginal smears is used as a bio-assay of the effect of the hormone. The vaginal epithelium of the castrate or immature female consists of only 2 or 3 layers of low cuboidal cells. At the height of estrus there are approximately 10 layers of cells and those near the surface are squamous and cornified. These large flat cells with small nuclei appear in the vaginal smears of women under estrogen stimulation, and examination of such smears is important in analyzing a menstrual cycle or in gauging the effect of estrogen replacement therapy.

Estrogen effects on the *mammary gland* are seen best during pregnancy since the glandular elements of this structure are under the combined influence of estrogen and progesterone. Growth of the ductile components is stimulated by the former, while that of the glands themselves is stimulated by the latter. Growth of the mammary glands and duct development are seen in the nonpregnant animal given large doses of estrogen.

MENOPAUSE.—The end of the active reproductive life in the female is marked by diminished production of estrogen by the ovaries in spite of continued and increasing gonadotrophic stimulation. Again, as in the case of the testis, the ovarian failure is believed to be a local one, possibly on the basis of a failure of vascularization. It seems unlikely that it is related to atherosclerosis generally, for many women have been seen to experience the menopause at a time when the rest of their blood vessels show only minimal atherosclerosis. Although there may be some atrophy of some of the estrogen-supported structures enumerated above, there is by no means a cessation of interest in sexual activity in many women. That some estrogen may continue to be secreted by the ovary following the menopause is indicated by the fact that the urinary excretion levels for estrogens are higher in menopausal women than in surgically ovariectomized women.

PROGESTERONE

In the mature, nonpregnant individual progesterone is secreted by the corpus luteum during the second half of the menstrual cycle. There is some evidence in favor of the view that it begins to be secreted before ovulation. It changes the estrogen-primed endometrium to the secretory type.

Progesterone probably has effects on the mammary gland of the nonpregnant individual, but these are not prominent or clearly described. There is little doubt that the compound plays a part in the development of the secretory apparatus of the mammary gland during pregnancy. In the rabbit it diminishes the sensitivity of the uterus to oxytocin, but this effect has not been seen in the human.

④ Role of the Central Nervous System in Hypophysial-Ovarian Relationship

Many observations of patients suggest that the central nervous system is a link in the communications network between the adenohypophysis and the ovary. Either ovarian hyperfunction or hypofunction may be seen in patients with destructive lesions of the central nervous system, particularly those at the base of the brain. The facts that emotional disturbances can cause profound irregularities of the menstrual cycle and that they can impair fertility in women are commonplace knowledge. During the past decade, the realization that the hypophysial-portal system of blood vessels represents a route of information transfer from the hypothalamus to the adenohypophysis, and the increasingly wide application of stereotactic exploration of the brain by neuroendocrinologists have begun to suggest a physiological basis for some of the older studies.

Many kinds of evidence in addition to that

obtained in the clinic suggest that gonadotrophin output is controlled by messages which reach it from the brain, and the locus of the feedback action of estrogens may well be in the central nervous system. In ferrets, for example, exposure to light induces a condition known as "constant estrus," which is believed to be due to an increased output of FSH induced by photic stimulation. This, of course, is very similar to the induction of off-season gametogenesis in seasonally breeding males by exposing them to light. There now seem to be excellent data in support of the view that in some species certain special odors, by their presence or absence, can have a dramatic effect on gonadotrophin output. In these cases, sensory afferents send information to the central nervous system, which then sends a humoral message to the pituitary by way of the portal system of blood vessels. The light effect, at least, has been prevented by stalk section and the placement of a mechanical barrier to the regeneration of the portal vessels across the section. FSH-RF and LRF, virtually free from other releasing factor activity, have been prepared.

Ovulation, as we have seen, does not occur in the hypophysectomized animal and is brought about by the release of pituitary LH (and FSH?) in the intact animal. The event can be triggered in the hypophysectomized animal by the administration of hypophysial gonadotrophins in proper proportion in a suitably prepared pituitary-deprived animal. Ovulation is therefore used in many experiments as an indicator of LH release.

In animals which normally ovulate only in response to coitus or to mechanical stimulation of the vagina (rabbit, cat), ovulation can be produced in the animal in estrus by electrical stimulation of very precisely demarcated regions of the hypothalamus (Fig. 5-6). Ovulation does not occur in such species if the hypophysis is removed immediately following vaginal stimulation, but it does if the operation is delayed for as short a time as 1 hr after stimulation. The compound neuroendocrine reflex in rabbits is blocked by certain drugs (i.e., atropine, morphine, pentobarbital) which act in the central nervous system. In drug-blockaded animals, electrical stimulation of the hypothalamus near the pituitary still produces ovulation (Fig. 5-6). Similar experiments on electrically induced ovulation may be performed in drug-blockaded animals which normally ovulate spontaneously. Electrolytic lesions

Fig. 5-6.—Hypothalamic structures associated with LH release and sex behavior. (After Sawyer, C. H., in Lloyd, C. W. [ed.]: *Endocrinology of Reproduction* [New York: Academic Press, Inc., 1959].)

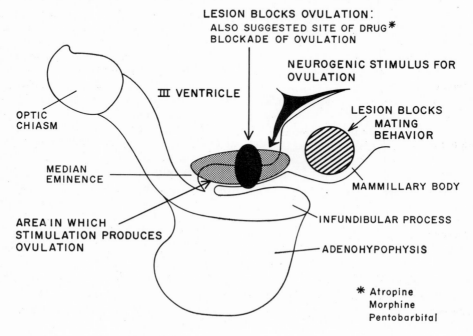

of the same regions in which stimulation is effective produce a block in ovulation in reflex ovulators.

There have been many experiments in which pituitary glands have been grafted into a hypophysectomized animal at a site remote from the brain, i.e., the anterior chamber of the eye or beneath the renal capsule. The tissue becomes revascularized in its new site and recovers a certain amount of its original capacity to secrete trophic hormones, but the gonadotrophins are not secreted in sufficient amounts to support normal gonadal function, at least for many weeks postoperatively. If such a transplanted gland is retransplanted back to the sella turcica where it can be shown to be revascularized by the hypophysial vessels, perfectly normal gonadal function is observed to occur in animals in which portal revascularization is most successful.

There is some evidence that the brain is involved in the feedback- inhibition of gonadotrophin secretion by estrogens and androgens. Flerko and his colleagues have discovered that lesions in the hypothalamic paraventricular nuclei prevent gonadal atrophy which occurs on steroid hormone administration. When they autotransplanted tiny pieces of ovarian tissue to this region of the brain, they demonstrated suppression of gonadotrophin secretion, presumably by the estrogen secreted by the graft.

The suggestion has been made that the sex steroids may alter the threshold of response to stimulation of brain centers which regulate gonadotrophin secretion. We have already met this idea in the discussion of the mechanism of onset of puberty. For example, an estrogen-treated rabbit will ovulate in response to vaginal stimulation alone if it has been progesterone-primed, but not otherwise. Estrogen treatment of intact rabbits increased the sensitivity of the brain to the sort of stimulation that causes ovulation, but very high doses of estrogen *decreased* the sensitivity, that is, *raised* the threshold of stimulation. Certainly, these experiments are consistent with the effects of high and low doses of estrogen on gonadotrophin output.

All the experiments mentioned above were concerned with FSH and/or LH release. The data for prolactin or luteotrophin (in the rat) are more meager. When the hypophysis is transplanted to a site remote from the sella all evidence suggests an *increase* in prolactin output

rather than a decrease. This could be explained if signals of hypothalamic origin constantly inhibit prolactin output, and transplantation constitutes a form of release from this inhibition. There appears to be some sort of reciprocal relationship between FSH and LH on the one hand and prolactin on the other, for those physiological conditions in which the latter increases are the ones in which FSH and LH decline. Since it is still not clear that prolactin and luteotrophin are identical in primates, the significance for man of much of the animal work on prolactin is far from obvious.

⑤ Hormonal Control of Ovulation and the Estrus Cycle

In no area of endocrinology are interspecies differences more obvious than in the comparative physiology of the sex cycle in the female. Some species have 1 or 2 estrus cycles per year, at which time ovulation and receptivity to the male neatly coincide with the male's sexual interest in the female. As we have seen, in some species (rabbit, ferret, cat), ovulation is the result of a compound neuroendocrine reflex which is initiated by intravaginal tactile stimulation and involves the secretion of LH by the pituitary. In the rabbit and ferret this may be followed, even in the absence of fertilization, by elaborate changes in the uterus and mammary glands, which resemble those of pregnancy and, in fact, are called "pseudopregnancy." Only primates have menstrual periods or cycles; others have estrus cycles. In some species, like the baboon, a structure called the sexual skin provides an interesting and colorful exterior indication of the waxing and waning of the sex cycle. The average duration of the cycle in various species is as follows: rat and mouse, 4–6 days; guinea pig, 14 days; sheep, 16 days; cow, 20 days; sow, 21 days; macacus monkey, 27 days; woman, 28 days; chimpanzee, 36 days. The bitch has 2 cycles per year; the bat and marmot, 1 cycle per year.

From his studies of the histology of the endometrium the reader is familiar with the striking structural alterations that occur in that tissue during the menstrual cycle, which is conventionally dated from the first day of bleeding. First, there is a gradual thickening of the lining of the uterus and the proliferation of straight glands; then, in the postovulatory half of the cycle, the glands become complicated and tortuous and the submucosal layer of tissue becomes very vascular and edematous and is infiltrated with leukocytes. The formation of this secretory or progestational type of endometrium is essential for the reception, nourishment and encouragement of the fertilized ovum.

Ovulation occurs at midcycle, but it should be emphasized that this is a statistical fact and there is wide variation from one individual to another. Most commonly, ova are found on the fifteenth day after the first day of menstruation, but many are found from the twelfth to the twenty-first, for cycles are of variable length. Moreover, there is no guarantee that the day of ovulation will remain constant for the same individual from cycle to cycle. The so-called "rhythm method" of birth control is based on sound statistical observations, but such statistics have little meaning for individuals who deviate significantly from the large group. Fertilization has even been reported to occur as a result of insemination during or immediately after the menstrual period in a few individuals. Fertility is at its peak during the 2 days following ovulation, and this fact is used clinically in the management of patients with the chief complaint of infertility.

There were several objective ways of inferring that ovulation has occurred in any given cycle. This is especially important information to have in the assessment of a problem in infertility, for anovulatory cycles occur frequently not only in adolescent girls but also in mature women. Basal body temperature taken in the morning immediately on awakening varies between 36.3° C and 36.8° C during the preovulatory half of the cycle and increases by 0.3–0.5° C at the time of ovulation. It continues at the higher level throughout the latter half of the cycle, falling to the initial level at the time of menstruation. This simple technique not only reveals whether a cycle is ovulatory or anovulatory; it also reveals the approximate time of ovulation, which is a useful datum for couples with a history of infertility. The rise in basal body temperature does not occur in anovulatory cycles.

Other changes that occur at about the time of ovulation are, (1) an increase in the urinary gonadotrophins, (2) an increase in the number of large acidophilic squamous cells with small nuclei in the vaginal smear, (3) a peak in estrogen output just before ovulation, (4) a rise in pregnanediol excretion (a reflection of increasing progesterone secretion) 3–4 days after ovulation. None of these events occurs in anovulatory cycles.

If fertilization has not taken place, degeneration and sloughing of the endometrium occur. The details of this process have been observed directly in endometrial transplants placed in the anterior chamber of the eye of experimental animals and inspected through the transparent cornea. At the time of sloughing there is a marked vasoconstriction of arterioles and a slowing of circulation with extravasation and pooling of blood in the stroma layer. The submucosal blood pools coalesce, and the superficial layers of endometrium, leukocytes and mucus are shed as the menstrual discharge. The blood of this discharge does not ordinarily clot, and it may vary in amount from 20 to 200 ml in volume for a single period. The flow lasts 3 to 7 days in 95% of women. In 30–40 years of active reproductive life a woman menstruates 300–500 times. At 100 ml per period, 400 periods could account for the cumulative loss of 40 L of blood, a figure which helps to explain why some women tend to have a mild to moderate degree of chronic hypochromic anemia.

In about 3–4 days, the premenstrual endometrium loses about half its thickness and the reparative process begins to be apparent. It is now appropriate to re-examine the cycle from the point of view of the pattern of hormonal substances which are involved both in mediating the changes observed and in controlling and timing the events of the cycle.

A complicated reciprocal relationship exists between the two main ovarian hormones, estrogen and progesterone, and the hypophysis, which produces three gonadotrophins: FSH, LH, and LTH or luteotrophin. It is extraordinarily difficult to assess the role of these hormones in the control of ovulation and in the preparation of the endometrium for the nidation and nourishment of the fertilized ovum. In many cases, the data are conflicting: species differences make extrapolation from one to another hazardous; the estimation of gonadotrophins has not often been very precise, and it has not always been possible to assay for LH and FSH differentially; the steroids, particularly estrogen, appear to have different effects at low doses and high doses; and many of the effects seen appear to be the result of the collaborative action of 2 or more hormones which seem to be required not only in "correct" amounts but also in proper ratios. Most of the following account was reconstructed from observations on ovariectomized women and animals, from the effects of estrogen and progesterone administration separately and in combination to ovariectomized individuals, and from studies in intact women of the urinary excretion of gonadotrophins and steroid hormone excretion products correlated with the major events of the cycle, ovulation, and menstruation. Studies on hypophysectomized animals were particularly important in evaluating the relative roles of FSH and LH in ovulation. A few studies on the concentration of steroids in the blood have revealed very small cyclical changes. The recent development of radioimmunoassay methods for the gonadotrophins promises important new insights into this perplexing problem.

There is probably a low level of continuing estrogen production in the unstimulated ovary, and it is now generally accepted that both the ovarian interstitial cells and the thecal cells of the developing follicle can make estrogen. Experimental evidence supports the view that estrogens have important local effects in the ovary, and that they may indeed prepare the ovary for stimulation by the hypophysial gonadotrophins. This, of course, is very similar to the state of affairs in the testis, where development of the germinal epithelium is the result of a collaboration between FSH and androgen. Small doses of estrogen produce atrophy of the interstitial cells in both intact and hypophysectomized rats, presumably by directly inhibiting them. Larger doses in the intact animal stimulate these same cells by increasing the output of hypophysial LH.

At the very earliest stage of the cycle several follicles can be seen to be undergoing beginning differentiation and growth, but when, in a very short time, the hypophysial gonadotrophic stimulation begins with FSH, a single follicle is selected for maturation and ovulation (or, more rarely, 2) and the others undergo regression or atresia. The mechanism of the survival advantage of 1 follicle and the failure of all the others to develop is not known, but it is not improbable that the very early development of many follicles may play a physiologically meaningful role in sending signals to the hypophysis, for small amounts of estrogen elicit the release of increasing amounts of gonadotrophin from the pituitary. The fractionation of this gonadotrophin into its FSH and LH components is too imprecise to give more than a semiquantitative estimate of the ratio, but it is safe to state that a mixture of the 2 hormones is secreted by the hypophysis. The early part of the preovulatory phase of the cycle is characterized by a gonadotrophin mixture which is predominantly FSH.

As this mixture stimulates the ovaries to produce more and more estrogen, information about the state of affairs in the ovaries is fed back to the hypothalamic centers which regulate the composition of the gonadotrophin recipe. At the critical state (this may be either a critical concentration of estrogen, or a critical rate of increase of estrogen) there is a sharp shift in the gonadotrophin mixture in the direction of LH. Now the predominantly LH gonadotrophin secretion participates in causing ovulation, and the ovum is extruded from the ruptured follicle to make its devious way to the site of fertilization—the fallopian tube in the human.

Under the strongly LH stimulus, the cells of the ruptured follicle change their characteristics to those of typical, lightly staining lutein cells and, astonishingly, change their enzyme profile at the same time. This is an extraordinary example of a sort of physiological and cyclically recurring form of biochemical differentiation, for in the act of making the quick change from follicular cells to lutein cells, these miniature steroid factories change the character of their major end product. They produce progesterone, for its excretion product, pregnanediol, can be detected in the urine within 3–4 days after ovulation. Very recently small amounts of pregnanediol have been found in the urine during the preovulatory phase of the cycle, but this may be due simply to the fact that progesterone is such a prominent intermediate in steroid biosynthesis that some of it may diffuse out of cells. But corpora lutea also produce estrogens; in fact, a secondary estrogen excretion peak can often be detected during the second half of the postovulatory phase of the cycle.

The role of the third hypophysial gonadotrophin is still uncertain. In the rat, it appears to be firmly established that luteotrophin and prolactin are the same substance, and that this material has much the same kind of effect on the functioning corpus luteum as ACTH has on the adrenal cor-

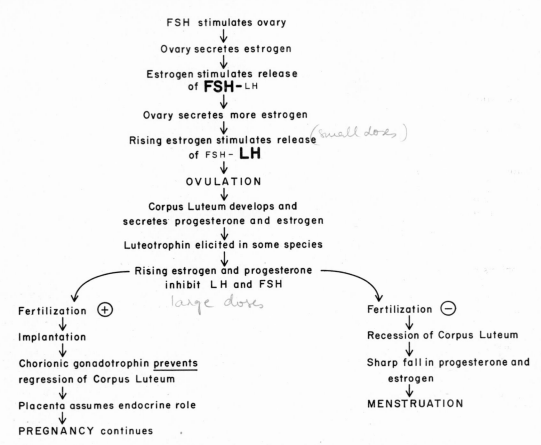

Fig. 5-7.—Summary of hormonal control of ovulation, menstruation and pregnancy.

tex. The growth and development of the lutein cells seems to be promoted by LH, but the stimulation of the cells to secrete progesterone is accomplished in this species by LTH. Unfortunately these results cannot now be extrapolated to the primates generally and to the human in particular. In monkeys, the luteal phase of the menstrual cycle cannot be prolonged by injections of prolactin, although the life of the functioning corpus luteum can be extended by the administration of human chorionic gonadotrophin.

If fertilization does not occur, the large amounts of estrogen and progesterone constitute instructions to the pituitary by way of the hypothalamus to cut down the production and release of gonadotrophins, which amounts to a form of suicide for the corpus luteum. Deprived of its gonadotrophic stimulus, the corpus withers and dies, and as it does so there is abrupt withdrawal of progesterone and then of estrogen. In its turn,

the endometrium, which has grown accustomed to lavish amounts of estrogen and progesterone, suddenly finds itself with an inadequate hormonal stimulus to sustain it, and it promptly deteriorates. Sloughing and bleeding occur and the cycle is begun 3–4 days later.

If fertilization does occur, the chorionic gonadotrophin that appears quickly prevents the degeneration of the corpus luteum and sustains it until the placenta can assume the burden of producing the large quantities of steroid hormones required during pregnancy.

This account of the hypophysial-ovarian relationship is summarized in Figure 5-7.

It is improper to dismiss the subject of steroid-gonadotrophin relationships with the too pat account of the menstrual cycle presented here. The literature on this subject is vast and confusing, and the results of observations in animals and women do not always fall into neat patterns.

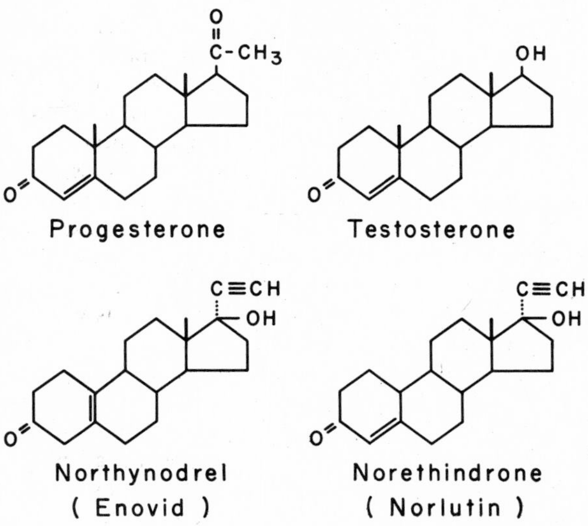

Progesterone

Testosterone

Northynodrel
(Enovid)

Norethindrone
(Norlutin)

Fig. 5-8.—Progesterone and synthetic ovulation inhibitors.

The menopause and surgical or radiological castration are followed by a marked rise in urinary gonadotrophins, predominantly FSH (although FSH and LH are not differentiated in most assays). Estrogen injection under these circumstances causes a fall in gonadotrophin excretion. The same result can be obtained with progesterone, but only if huge doses are injected intravenously. Since progesterone may be a biosynthetic precursor of estrogen, it seems fair to guess that this inhibition may be accomplished by estrogen derived from the injected progesterone.

On the other hand, several lines of evidence suggest that small doses of estrogen stimulate the release of LH. This has been claimed in the clinic following the administration of stilbestrol, and small doses of estrogen injected into ovariectomized rats decreased the pituitary *content* of both FSH and LH. It is often difficult to interpret experiments in which hormone content of a gland is measured, but in these the inference was that the gland content of gonadotrophins was low because they were being secreted at a rapid rate. Estrogen administration to immature rats led to corpus luteum formation. Since this did not occur in hypophysectomized animals, the result was attributed to the stimulation of hypophysial LH release. In general, these results are consistent with the view that estrogen stimulates FSH output in small doses, inhibits FSH output in large doses and stimulates LH release in moderate doses. These effects conform reasonably well to the pattern of hormonal interplay described in Figure 5-7.

One effect of a series of steroids on gonadotrophins is of more than passing interest to the clinician and public health officer—the use of certain artificial progestins, the 19-norsteroids, for the inhibition of ovulation in women. Ovulation can be inhibited by both progesterone and testosterone, but certain newer synthetic compounds related to these are extremely effective and produce fewer undesirable side effects. Among these are: norethindrone (Norlutin), which is also classified as a 19-nortestosterone, and norethinodrel (Enovid), which is more closely related to the estrogens (Fig. 5-8). According to recent estimates, more than 6,000,000 women are now taking some form of oral contraceptive agent in the United States alone. Drugs in this series may well prove to be among the most important ever developed in the history of man.

On the other side of the coin, other substances have been used successfully in the management of infertility due to ovulation failure. Gemzell has used gonadotrophin mixtures for this purpose, occasionally with almost too much success, for, early, there was a striking tendency for superovu-

Fig. 5-9.—Clomiphene.

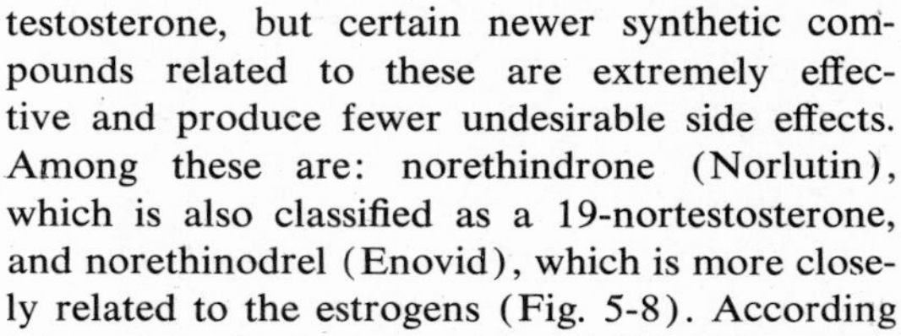

lation to occur, and infertile women began to be embarrassingly fertile—some delivered quite large litters of babies. As more is learned about dosage and treatment schedules, this tendency to multiple births may be better controlled. Meanwhile, a drug called *clomiphene* (Fig. 5-9) has also proved to be effective in inducing ovulation in women with a history of infertility. This drug apparently works by canceling out inhibitory influences which play upon the gonadotrophin-releasing-factor complex in the hypothalamus.

⑥ Hormonal Regulations in Pregnancy and Lactation

The participation of the hormones in pregnancy begins before fertilization and the implantation of the fertilized ovum, for all of the uterine changes of the postovulatory phase of the menstrual cycle can be regarded as preparation for these events. If fertilization does not occur and there is a decrease in the production of estrogen and progesterone by the corpus luteum, endometrial shedding and bleeding appear, as we have seen. If fertilization and endometrial implantation of the fertilized ovum do occur there is no drop in production of sex steroids by the corpus luteum and both estrogen and progesterone continue to exert their effects on the pregnant uterus.

In some species, estrogen and progesterone are produced by the corpus luteum, which remains critically functional throughout pregnancy. In other species, including the human, the corpus luteum provides these steroids during early pregnancy, but later the placenta takes over the job of producing them. Though the corpus luteum persists because it is stimulated by a gonadotrophin which is made by the placenta (chorionic gonadotrophin, CG, or HCG), it is not essential for the successful continuation of the pregnancy after about the third month of gestation.

The persistence of the functioning corpus luteum in very early pregnancy, and hence the prevention of menstrual bleeding, is due to the fact that the chorionic tissue begins to produce CG at least as early as 2 weeks after ovulation. Thus, the corpus luteum is sustained although the pituitary trophic influences that normally stop stimulating it at this time are removed. The appearance of chorionic gonadotrophin in the urine is the basis of many tests for pregnancy, the first of which was the famous Aschheim-Zondek, or

A-Z test. All of these tests are based on the fact that CG has essentially the same biological effect as pituitary LH, and therefore is capable of stimulating the ovaries or the testicular Leydig cells to produce their respective steroid hormones in sexually immature animals of many species.

As the placenta grows and differentiates, it begins to make more and more estrogen and progesterone, and as the output of these steroids mounts, that of CG diminishes. The most obvious changes that occur in pregnancy are the great growth of the uterus to accommodate its growing contents, and the growth of the mammary glands, as if in anticipation of their use following parturition. Both estrogen and progesterone participate in the continuing growth of both of these structures. Estrogen, which functions as a specific growth hormone for uterine smooth muscle cells, stimulates the growth of the uterine muscle mass, and thus contributes to the contractile force that will ultimately be needed to expel the fetus at the time of delivery. Progesterone, by its inhibiting effect on uterine smooth muscle, prevents the establishment of effective, coordinated uterine muscle contractions and insures that feeble, ineffectual, fibrillatory contractions persist until the appropriate signals for the expulsion of the fetus are given.

Progesterone, in partnership with estrogen, helps to prepare the mammary glands for lactation by stimulating the formation of new glandular elements. Lactation does not occur during pregnancy, but the mechanism of its suppression is unknown. Prolactin may be inhibited at its source or its effect may be blocked at the tissue level.

The *placenta* is a fascinating organ because it is practically a whole endocrine system in one tissue package. From the rich variety of its hormonal products, it appears to combine the biochemical capability of the pituitary, the ovaries, the corpus luteum, the adrenal cortex and other structures. There appears to be no reason to doubt that the placenta produces CG, estrogens (particularly estriol in the human), and smaller amounts of progesterone. Adrenal cortical steroids may be produced in small amounts, so that we must assume that placental cells have at least vestigial enzyme systems for 11-hydroxylation and 21-hydroxylation. Various investigators have extracted from human placental tissue trace amounts of the following: ACTH, growth hormone, lactogenic hormone, androgens, vasopressin, and relaxin. The androgens, of course, could simply be metabolic intermediates in estrogen synthesis. The others are all protein or peptide in nature, and at least some of them could be artifacts of preparation. There is also the possibility that traces of hormones found in the placenta might simply represent substances present in maternal blood. In any case, the presence in the same tissue of a trophic hormone (CG) and steroid hormones suggests that the former may act locally to stimulate the production of the latter. The suggestion has been made by Velardo that chorionic gonadotrophin is produced by one cell type in the placenta (cytotrophoblast) while the steroids are made by an adjacent cell type (syncytial trophoblast) and that these adjacent cells have a relationship similar to that of a gonadotrophin-producing anterior pituitary cell and a corpus luteum cell. This is an interesting speculation, but there is no proof for it.

There is some indirect evidence that steroids produced by the placenta act locally within the uterus. The birth of twins at different times from the 2 horns of a bicornuate uterus suggests the possibility of a local action of progesterone. Also, Csapo has measured the membrane potential of the endometrium and has found that it is higher at the placental implantation sites than between such sites. The potential of the interplacental sites can be raised to the level of that of the placental sites by local application of progesterone.

The mechanisms involved in *parturition* are not clearly understood, and the stimulus which initiates the train of events that we call labor has not been identified. Just before the onset of labor both progesterone and estrogen levels fall, the progesterone fall occurring before that of estrogens. Some authors suggest that an "aging process" occurs in the placenta and that its impaired vascularization is the cause of its diminished steroid hormone output at term. The decrease in availability of progesterone has 2 important consequences: (1) the withdrawal of its inhibitory effect on uterine muscle makes possible the development of coordinated squeezing movements of the uterus which assist in the expulsion of the fetus and placenta, and (2) the withdrawal of its depressing effect on prolactin release by the pituitary is essential for the initiation of the process of lactation in mammary glands which have previously been prepared for this event by the complementary actions of estrogen and progesterone.

Other hormones, notably thyroxin and cortisol, are produced in greater than normal amounts during pregnancy and their concentration in the blood progressively increases up to the time of parturition. In both cases, the specific hormone-carrying globulins appear to be synthesized rapidly in the pregnant woman and they accumulate in the blood. In neither case is there evidence of overstimulation of the tissues by the hormone in question, and the increased blood levels appear to be set by the fact that more carrier protein accumulates in the blood. In the case of the thyroid hormone, we know that the level of activity of the thyroid gland itself is high because the uptake of tracer doses of I^{131} by the gland is elevated. The production of cortisol is also increased in the pregnant woman because the rate of excretion of 17-hydroxycorticoids in the urine goes up. Whether or not these events are physiologically important in the maintenance and completion of pregnancy is not known. They may simply be sequelae of some modification that occurs in the rate of globulin production by the liver which is inundated with large amounts of estrogen and progesterone for disposal in one way or another.

In the latter part of pregnancy, the urinary excretion of aldosterone is markedly elevated (Venning). It is possible that intra-abdominal pressure and the consequent inferior vena caval compression may set up a volume receptor "call" for aldosterone. This would be comparable to the secondary aldosteronism described in Chapter 7. A summary of the hormonal excretion pattern in pregnancy is given in Figure 5-10.

As we have seen, many of the events that are associated with the onset of parturition may function as important signals for the initiation of *lactation*. Most prominent among these are progesterone and estrogen withdrawal, and the subsequent release of prolactin from inhibition. Prolactin participates in the growth and milk secretory activity of the mammary gland, but the initiation of milk flow, or let-down, is accomplished by way of a neuroendocrine reflex which is initiated by the tactile sensation from the nipple induced by the infant's sucking. The afferent nerves from the nipple carry the message to the central nervous system where a connection is made with the preoptic nucleus and a "request" for the posterior pituitary hormone, oxytocin, is made. This octapeptide hormone is then released

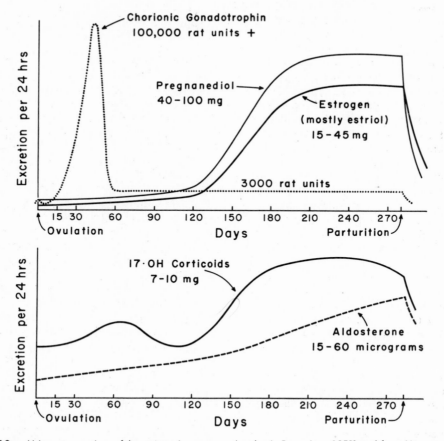

Fig. 5-10.—Urinary excretion of hormones in pregnancy. (From Venning, E. H., and Beck, J. C., in Lloyd, C. W. [ed.]: *Endocrinology of Reproduction* [New York: Academic Press, Inc., 1959] and from Houssay, B. A. [ed.]: *Human Physiology* [New York: McGraw-Hill Book Co., Inc., 1955].)

from the neurohypophysis and travels by way of the blood stream to the mammary gland where it facilitates the flow of milk by acting on the myoepithelial cells in the mammary gland.

All of this seems delightfully ingenious, but it is even more complicated. For lactation is associated with a marked increase in spontaneous food intake in both women and experimental animals. In fact, Kennedy has shown that the lactating rat eats as much spontaneously as the nonlactating animal does if its medial hypothalamic satiety "centers" are destroyed by electrolytic lesions (see Chapter 10). It is almost as if something about the process of lactation resulted in the production of a transitory functional (i.e., reversible) hypothalamic "lesion" of the type that causes obesity in the nonlactating animal. The

mechanism of the effect of lactation on spontaneous food intake is not known, but it could somehow be related to the same afferent stimuli which arise in the nipple and which trigger the release of oxytocin. We know of another circumstance in biology in which a neural signal produces transitory overeating—light-induced premigratory hyperphagia in birds. A possible alternative explanation states that the lactating mammary gland abstracts so much glucose (and other metabolites) from the body pool that the "appestat" is reset at a higher level, in much the way it must be reset as a result of exercise or cold exposure.

The importance of food and water intake in the maintenance of lactation is suggested by experiments on hypophysectomized rats, in which it was possible to prepare mammary glands for lactation by giving a combination of estrogen, progesterone, growth hormone, and prolactin. When insulin was given, however, only estrogen and progesterone were required. This suggests that the pituitary hormones may have functioned by increasing food intake. But Lyons injected prolactin into the mammary gland of a pseudo-pregnant rabbit and found local stimulation of the injected segment of gland only, and it is therefore difficult to believe that prolactin is not involved in the process of lactation under physiological conditions.

Insulin and prolactin may have very similar effects on the mammary gland, for, as we have seen, prolactin markedly accelerates the rate of glucose utilization and secondarily stimulates various synthetic processes in the mammary gland, such as lipogenesis from carbohydrate. The mammary gland cell must synthesize fat and protein for secretion in milk, and it appears to combine the metabolic characteristics of an adipose tissue cell, which synthesizes fat for storage, and (for example) an exocrine pancreatic cell, which synthesizes large amounts of protein enzyme precursors.

In addition to an adequate food and water intake, the continuation of lactation, once established, appears to require many hormones. Hypophysectomy prevents lactation, and the thyroid hormone, adrenal hormones and hypophysial growth hormone have all been implicated in the process. In the lactating woman, there is suggestive evidence of an inhibition of gonadotrophins (particularly LH?), with the result that ovulation and menstruation may be inhibited for a while. In many nursing mothers, however, the conditions for ovulation may return during lactation and pregnancy may occur even while lactation continues. A certain number of couples who had been taught that the period of lactation is a "safe" period have been rudely shocked in this way. In this circumstance, at least, a rising production rate of estrogen and progesterone are not sufficient to prevent the continuation of established lactation.

Many women have been given large doses of estrogens, sometimes combined with progestins in order to stop lactation, but there is no firm evidence that estrogens or binding the breasts or similar maneuvers stop lactation any faster than the absence of the suckling stimulus does.

⑦ Cellular Mechanism of Action of Hormones which Affect Reproduction in the Female

The biochemical mechanism of action of estrogens will be discussed in Chapter 12.

Progesterone appears to have an inhibitory effect on uterine muscle; for example, progesterone treatment renders the myometrium comparatively unresponsive to the stimulatory effect of oxytocin in the rabbit (but *not* in the human!). A similar refractoriness to oxytocin stimulation can be produced by changing the fluid bathing the uterine muscle strips to a high potassium, low sodium buffer. Progesterone treatment does, in fact, result in a decrease in potassium and an increase in sodium in the myometrium. The quieting effect of progesterone on uterine contractility may be achieved by a change in the differential permeability of the membranes of smooth muscle cells to sodium and potassium. This calming effect of progesterone on the uterus may have some importance in the initiation of labor in some species, for the progesterone influence on the uterine muscle may have to be withdrawn before powerful, rhythmic contractions can occur.

Although the mechanism of action of the *gonadotrophins* is by no means as well understood as is that of ACTH, recent work has begun to illuminate this problem. Bovine corpus luteum slices increase their production of progesterone when pituitary LH preparations or HCG are added in vitro. Moreover, hormone production is similarly stimulated by the addition of TPNH or a TPNH-generating system. This is certainly reminiscent of the work with ACTH, for it suggests that in the corpus luteum, as in the adrenal cell, hormone production requires TPNH for the crucial hydroxylation reactions that occur during the biosynthesis of steroid hormones. Another experiment that recalls work with ACTH is one in which slices of corpus luteum from pseudopregnant rats injected with pituitary LH showed increased glucose utilization rates in vitro when compared with similar slices obtained from saline injected animals. Acute effects of this sort were not observed. A third similarity between a gonadotrophin and ACTH was provided by the demonstration that injections of luteotrophin in the rat produced a fall in the ascorbic acid content of the corpus luteum coincident with an increased rate of release of progesterone. Recently 3′, 5′ cyclic adenylic acid has been implicated as a mediator of the effects of LH both in the human corpus luteum and in the interstitial cells of the testis. All of these studies suggest that there may be common denominators in the mechanisms of action of pituitary trophic hormones on their respective steroid hormone-producing target cells. A detailed account of the biochemical mechanism of action of ACTH will be found in Chapter 12. Future analysis of the mechanism of action of LH will depend on the ideas that have been generated by studies on ACTH.

An interesting in vitro effect of prolactin on slices of rat mammary gland of the pregnant rat has been described by McLean, who found that the hormone caused increased glucose utilization, especially for fat formation, and that substrate traffic via the direct oxidative pathway was markedly stimulated. There was no effect on slices of lactating mammary gland which were probably being stimulated maximally at the time it was obtained.

Work with FSH and PMS at the cellular level has not yet been sufficiently intensive to report here.

⑧ Nonreproductive Effects of Ovarian Steroids

BONE METABOLISM

Osteoporosis is commonly seen in postmenopausal women. When patients with this condition are treated with estrogens (or sometimes with a mixture of estrogens and androgens) they are reported by some observers to show symptomatic improvement. Considerable disagreement prevails among clinicians about whether or not there is any objective evidence of improved calcification of bones in x-rays. In a few studies, it has been shown that positive calcium balance can be induced in such patients who were in negative balance at the time of onset of estrogen therapy. Recent studies on rats may have some connection with this problem, for it has been shown that the bones of estrogen-treated ovariectomized animals take up Ca^{45} more rapidly than do bones of untreated castrate controls.

Estrogen deficiency which occurs prior to the completion of puberty may cause a failure of epiphysial closure. Girls with this condition may show a retarded bone age on x-ray, and may grow abnormally tall. Estrogen treatment accelerates epiphysial closure in this circumstance. But, just as in the case of androgen, severe deficiency of estrogen during the immediate prepuberal growth phase may cause stunting of growth.

SERUM CHOLESTEROL AND ATHEROSCLEROSIS

Statistically, the incidence of death and morbidity from atherosclerotic heart disease is greater among young and middle-aged men than it is among women of the same age. This difference tends to disappear in menopausal and surgically ovariectomized women. Similarly, the significantly lower serum cholesterol values in women shown statistically tend to disappear when ovarian function is diminished or eliminated.

There is a vast body of epidemiological literature which suggests a statistical relationship between serum cholesterol levels and the incidence of arteriosclerotic heart disease. In addition, the results of many experiments on animals support the view that elevation of the serum cholesterol is one of a number of contributory factors in the etiology of atherosclerosis. The apparent protective effect of estrogens against the disease has led to the administration of female sex hormones to men who have experienced an episode of coronary occlusion for the purpose of preventing or delaying further attacks. While there is no doubt that estrogen lowers the serum cholesterol significantly in men who begin treatment with comparatively high cholesterol levels, there is still some question about its effect on the natural history of the disease in such patients. Certainly, the reader appreciates the difficulties involved in evaluating results in individual patients even when trends may be suggestive in a large population of patients.

Understandably, the feminizing effect of this kind of therapy was an undesired side effect. Now it is claimed that certain synthetic steroids, which are structurally related to the estrogens, retain the cholesterol-lowering properties of estrogen but have only minimal estrogenic activity. Compounds in this series are currently being tested for their possible benefit in the prevention of heart disease. It is hopeful to note that estrogen-treated men who died of prostatic cancer showed significantly less atherosclerosis than did a control group of similar age. This, of course, does not prove that this result was brought about by the estrogen treatment, but neither can this possibility be dismissed.

The mechanism of the serum cholesterol lowering effect is not now known. It is known that the livers of female animals have quite distinctive metabolic patterns as compared with those of males (for example, a much more active direct oxidative pathway for glucose), and it is certainly possible that the capacity of the estrogen-stimulated liver to abstract cholesterol from the circulation is greater than that of the liver which lacks such stimulation. It is worth noting that a conjugated estrogen preparation is one of four drugs currently under study in a large national program designed to discover whether or not the lowering of serum cholesterol in survivors of heart attacks has a perceptible effect on the incidence and severity of recurrent attacks.

Other nonreproductive effects of estrogens include those on nitrogen retention and water and electrolyte balance. Estrogens have been reported to have some general protein anabolic effect, but less than that of androgens. Both estrogens and androgens show some activity in anti-inflammatory assays, such as the inhibition of the development of paw edema in the rat following the administration of an irritating substance. They also show a minor degree of salt-retaining activity, but less than either the adrenal steroids or androgens. In mice, local application of estrogen to the skin produces cutaneous edema, which reminds us that they are frequently dispensed as a constituent of cosmetics. This kind of self-medication with a powerful drug is not generally encouraged by physicians because some of the material may be absorbed percutaneously and may produce undesirable systemic effects.

In experimental animals large doses of estrogen may produce cancer of estrogen-sensitive tissues such as the uterus. This may be explained on the basis of the marked stimulation of mitotic activity and cell division which occurs when the hormone is given. This is readily visible in the endometrial gland cells, for example. If such stimulation is intense and prolonged and many cells divide, the statistical probability of the occurrence of a somatic mutation in the direction of the cancer cell type is greatly increased. It has not yet been established that there is a substantial risk of cancer in treating men and women with estrogen, possibly because the doses used do not approach those used in the experimental animal cancer model. Nevertheless, it cannot be too strongly emphasized that these are powerful and effective agents and they must be treated with respect. It is sad to report that estrogens, like vitamins and tranquilizers, are often prescribed by busy physicians in loco placebo for minor, self-limiting complaints.

It used to be said that progesterone has a mild aldosterone-like effect and that premenstrual edema is due to the salt- and water-retaining effects of this hormone. While it appears to be true that progesterone and related steroids do show some degree of salt- and water-retaining activity in animal assays, the situation in man appears to be quite the reverse, for the administration of progesterone to men or women results in salt loss rather than salt retention. This effect is more pronounced in treated addisonian patients deficient in adrenal cortical hormones. Therefore, the salt loss is believed to be due to an anti-aldosterone effect of progesterone, which means that (to reverse the usual designation) progesterone is a sort of naturally occurring spirolactone (see Chapter 7). There have been sporadic reports in the clinical literature of the appearance of a salt-losing steroid in the urine of patients. It is possible that the mystery substance could be progesterone or a closely related steroid.

⑨ Hormones and Breast Cancer

The rationale of androgen deprivation and estrogen treatment in prostatic cancer was reviewed in Chapter 4. Many of the same concepts have been applied with some success in the management of breast cancer in the female.

Cancer of the breast, like cancer of the prostate, often retains the hormone dependence characteristics of the tissue of origin. But the management of breast cancer is much more complicated than that of prostatic cancer for the reason that breast cancer which develops premenopausally is frequently quite different biologically from that which develops some time after the menopause.

In the premenopausal individual, the aim is to

deprive the cancer of estrogen. There is a staged progression of procedures: First, *ovariectomy,* which is said to be of benefit in 40–50% of women. Again, as in the case of prostatic cancer, the tumor may become resistant to the new hormonal environment and *adrenalectomy* or *hypophysectomy* may be performed. Approximately 30% of patients treated in one or the other of these ways experience a further remission in symptoms of the disease, and metastases can be seen to regress. This is rather remarkable since most of these patients have already been through one cycle of benefit-to-relapse after ovariectomy. There is some evidence that the adrenal glands produce estrogen in ovariectomized women and that its production is stimulated by ACTH. It is also possible that hypophysectomy may yield further benefits by depriving the cancer cells of some other hypophysial hormonal stimulant (growth hormone? prolactin?). *Androgens* may be given at any stage, even before ovariectomy, when they not only inhibit the endogenous output of gonadotrophins and thus produce a pharmacologic castration, but also may competitively inhibit the stimulatory action of traces of estrogen at the cellular level. Again, as in the case of prostatic cancer, these maneuvers (which are under active study at the present time) are adjuncts to surgery and not replacements for it. It should be recalled that women treated in the manner described have metastatic disease, and are frequently desperately ill. It is encouraging not only that the lives of such patients are being prolonged but that a considerable number of them can be changed from bed-ridden invalids to active, productive citizens by the tactic of changing the hormonal environment of their tumors.

The rationale underlying the procedures outlined above is readily understood, but the biology of postmenopausal cancer is not easy to describe, much less to comprehend. In some women androgen is effective in causing a regression of the disease, while in others estrogen may be just as effective. This makes very little sense, for one would think cancer derived from an estrogen-dependent cell would thrive with estrogen. It is almost as if the type of cancer cell that is inhibited by large doses of estrogen may respond to the hormone because it has been selected for growth on the basis of its ability to survive in an estrogen-poor environment. There is suggestive evidence that the 2 hormones work on 2 biologically different kinds of tumors. Testosterone appears to be more beneficial in patients with bone metastases while estrogen is more likely to be effective in those with soft tissue metastases.

⑩ Relaxin

In 1926, Hisaw discovered that aqueous extracts of sow ovary contain a substance that causes relaxation of the pelvic ligaments of the guinea pig and widening of the symphysis pubis. Similar activity is detectable in the blood of other pregnant mammals, particularly late in pregnancy. In humans, the concentration drops at parturition. The substance, known as relaxin, has been progressively purified with the aid of a guinea pig symphysis pubis widening test as a bio-assay and is now known to be a low molecular weight protein or polypeptide.

A variety of physiological effects has been attributed to relaxin, among them being (a) a stimulatory effect on breast growth in ovariectomized animals when it was added to estrogen and progesterone, (b) a diminution in uterine contractions, and (c) softening of the uterine cervix. It has been tried clinically in a number of circumstances including labor induction, dysmenorrhea, and on uterine contractions of premature labor. Variable results have been reported, but those experiments in which the double-blind method of testing was used gave the least indication of an effect. This method is designed to conceal the nature of the treatment from both the patient and the physician-evaluator of the results of treatment so that the possibility of bias by suggestion in either is minimized.

There is little doubt that relaxin exists or that it has some of the effects attributed to it, but there is considerable doubt that there has ever been a well-recognized human deficiency of it or that there are well-established indications for its use. Relaxin can best be described as a hormone in search of a deficiency disease.

⑪ Sex Behavior

Each species has encoded in its DNA elaborate blueprints for the construction of certain kinds of sex behavioral patterns. In many species, mating behavior may be observed in the decorticate animal, but not in the spinally transected animal. Therefore, the neural integrative circuits for sex behavior in these species lie below the cortex and above the spinal cord. These circuits must be extraordinarily complicated. One can think of them as preprogrammed computers into which information is fed in the form of visual, tactile, olfactory, and auditory stimuli which elicit a response that involves the many widely scattered muscles and nerves involved in mating behavior. There are skeletal muscle reflexes associated with posture and movement and there is a widespread involvement of the autonomic nervous system, particularly those parts of it which are concerned with cardiopulmonary reflexes and those associated with the act of copulation.

Both sexes are believed to possess the central nervous integrative circuitry which is essential for the mediation of both masculine and feminine sex behavior. It is easier to demonstrate this ambivalence in the female than in the male, for one can frequently observe male copulatory thrusting movements in an untreated spayed female dog. In many species the androgen-treated female may show typical male mounting behavior and assume dominance over females—and even over males. An androgen-treated hen quickly climbs to the top of the barnyard peck order.

The effects of castration on sex behavior vary from species to species. In man, as has been indicated, prepuberal castration abolishes sex behavior, while postpuberal orchiectomy may only diminish it. In woman, oophorectomy does not eliminate sex interest and activity, but adrenalectomy does. Full sexual activity can be restored to the prepuberally castrate male animal by androgen treatment, and the same is true of female animals treated with estrogen if they belong to a species in which sexual activity is abolished by estrogen deprivation.

In the homosexual human male, who often shows no overt evidence of androgen deficiency, treatment with androgen may increase sex drive, but it does not alter its direction. The administration of androgens to heterosexually adjusted women is said to increase libido and responsiveness to sexual stimulation.

Certain regions of the hypothalamus have been identified which are deeply involved in the central integration of sex behavior. Lesions in the posterior hypothalamus in both male and female rats abolishes such behavior, and it should be noted that these lesions are not in the same place as are those which interfere with the production and release of hypophysial gonadotrophins (Fig. 5-6). Recording electrodes in the hypothalamus of the cat reveal bursts of electrical activity on artificial stimulation of the vagina.

It had been assumed that the central structures associated with mediating and integrating sex behavior are under the influence of the sex steroids and that, while the gonadal hormones did not originate the circuitry, by their presence they permit it to operate. There was, however, no direct proof of a local effect of a sex steroid in the brain until Harris performed the ingenious experiment of inserting an ester of a synthetic estrogen (stilbestrol) into that part of a spayed cat's hypothalamus that had previously been associated with sex behavior. The stilbestrol ester's solubility characteristics were such that it could diffuse for short distances locally, but not enough of it entered the blood stream to affect the reproductive organs. By this maneuver, a cat which had greeted potential mates with hostile, vicious, spitting, back-arching behavior was transformed into one which readily assumed the female copulatory posture when confronted with a male. Implantation of similar amounts of estrogen into the cerebellum, preoptic region, caudate nucleus, thalamus or amygdaloid nucleus did not elicit normal sexual behavior in similar experiments.

HORMONES AND BRAIN ORGANIZATION IN INFANT ANIMALS

The embryologic anlagen of the male and female generative tract are the same. Presumably, very small amounts of androgen can "steer" development in the direction of the male pattern, while, in the absence of androgen, the tract develops in a characteristically feminine way. The most dramatic demonstration of this fact is the masculinization of the genetically feminine fetus when the pregnant mother is treated with androgen.

As the result of work done during the past couple of decades, it is now possible to conceive of analogous events occurring in very crucial parts of the brain, particularly those concerned with sexual behavior, gonadotrophin secretion, and thyroid and adrenal cortex modulation. The newborn animal has not yet "set" his collection of "stats" in his brain. If, during a very crucial period immediately after birth, the brain is exposed to certain kinds of hormonal influences, a powerful imprinting process occurs on cells involved in complex regulatory circuits so that both behavior and endocrine function may be profoundly modified in the adult animal. It is as if these crucial parts of the brain "remembered" having been exposed to a certain hormone during a very critical period of infancy.

In 1936, Carroll Pfeiffer transplanted the gonads of newborn male rats into newborn females and demonstrated that, when the animals matured, they were acyclic and showed persistent vaginal cornification. He concluded that all rats are physiologically female but that the male pattern of differentiation is brought about by small amounts of androgen. This was long before the flowering of the field of neuroendocrinology, and Pfeiffer was inclined to the view that androgens were capable of "masculinizing" the hypophysis.

Later, other investigators showed similar effects in female animals treated with androgens from birth. In about 1954, Barraclough and his colleagues began to study the effects of single injections of androgen on the subsequent behavior and endocrine function of neonatal female rats. He discovered that the administration of androgen any time between day 2 and day 5 resulted in the development of sterile adult rats with polyfollicular ovaries which contained no corpora lutea. It was later found that these polyfollicular ovaries were perfectly capable of making corpora lutea if they were transplanted to a normally cycling adult female, so the original effect of the steroid was not on the gonad itself. As little as 10 micrograms of testosterone at 5 days produced sterility in 70% of animals.

The androgen effect is now believed to occur not in the pituitary but in those parts of the brain which are associated with gonadotrophin release. Barraclough has suggested a dual control theory of gonadotrophin control: (1) a basic "tonic" control zone in the vicinity of the ventromedial-arcuate nucleus region of the hypothalamus and (2) a superimposed "cyclic" control zone in the pre-optic region. The latter complex is conceived to be a biologic clock which integrates cyclic release of gonadotrophins. Before the characteristic features of the clock become fixed, androgen can imprint the cyclic zone in such a way as to prevent it from responding to environmental influences that normally set it into motion. This hypothesis, though somewhat impressionistic, is a useful construct, for it suggests that other neuroendocrine centers in the brain may also undergo developmental changes during the immediate postnatal period and that their function may be modified by events that happen during this crucial time.

Levine and Mullins (1966) have collected a number of examples of "hormonostat" disturbances produced by doing various things to infant animals. The production of permanent hypothyroidism by the administration of thyroxine to the newborn rat has been described by Bakke and Lawrence (1965). Also, there is a growing body of evidence that indicates an effect of handling rats in infancy on their subsequent ACTH responses to stress (Levine and Mullins, 1966). The implication is that handling may modify the set point of the "CRF-stat."

At present, it is possible to discuss these interesting phenomena only in the most general terms. In some cases, such as the atrophy of the reproductive system in male rats given estrogen at 4 days, it is even difficult to construct a plausible theory of the CNS locus of the effect. Why does the male rat, castrated in infancy, respond to low doses of estrogen and progesterone by exhibiting characteristically female behavior, while the adult, similarly treated, does not?

It should be emphasized that practically all of these experiments have been done on rats. We do not even know whether or not they have relevance for man. But, on the chance that they do, this interesting interphase between endocrinology and psychology deserves the energetic study it is receiving.

ENVIRONMENT AND SEX BEHAVIOR

Although the neural machinery for sex behavior may be subcortical, there is abundant evidence that cortical influences play heavily upon it, especially in man, certain primates and the guinea pig. Young has demonstrated that guinea pigs reared in solitary confinement have an impairment of sexual activity as compared with those raised in litters. This immediately brings to mind the experiments of Harlow who raised baby monkeys with artificial cloth-and-wire mothers and discovered that adult males so raised, when confronted with female monkeys, were completely disinterested in them. Successfully bred female monkeys with the same history showed not just an absence of affection for their young but actual hostility toward them. These experiments vividly illustrate the role of learning and conditioning in the modulation and modification of instinctive patterns of behavior.

In man a moral, social, and cultural environmental mosaic of influences has produced a complex cortical overlay on the basic central integrative structures for sex behavior. That "problems of living" in the sphere of sex behavior can occur in the absence of any readily detectable disorder of the endocrine or nervous system is beyond doubt. It is equally true that emotional difficulties can work through either the behavioral brain mechanisms or through those brain mechanisms involved in maintaining the integrity of the endocrine system to produce functional changes in the physiological machinery concerned with reproduction. It is also true that behavioral disorders can be secondary to disease of the endocrine glands. The truly sophisticated physician will scorn none of these possibilities.

REFERENCES

Barraclough, C. A.: Modifications in the CNS regulation of reproduction after exposure of prepubertal rats to steroid hormones, Recent Prog. Hormone Res. 22:503–539, 1966.

Everett, J. W.: Central neural control of reproductive functions of the adenohypophysis, Physiol. Rev. 44:373–431, 1964.

Levine, S., and Mullins, R. F., Jr.: Hormonal influences on brain organization in infant rats, Science 152:1585–1592, 1966.

Linzell, J. L.: Physiology of the mammary glands, Physiol. Rev. 39:534–576, 1959.

Lloyd, C. W.: *Recent Progress in the Endocrinology of Reproduction* (New York: Academic Press, Inc., 1959).

Noble, R. L.: Hormonal regulation of tumor growth, Pharmacol. Rev. 9:367–426, 1957.

Parkes, A. S.: Hormones in reproduction, Brit. M. Bull. 11:83–170, 1955.

Parkes, A. S., and Bruce, H. M.: Olfactory stimuli in mammalian reproduction, Science 134:1049–1054, 1961.

Villee, C. A.: *Control of Ovulation* (New York: Pergamon Press, 1961).

Young, W. C.: *Sex and Internal Secretions* (Baltimore: Williams & Wilkins Co., 1961).

6

The Thyroid

PHYSICIANS HAVE BEEN interested in the thyroid gland from the beginning of recorded medical history. The accompanying chronology points to a long tradition of cooperation between clinician and laboratory worker in the study of thyroidology. The main reason for the modern physician's preoccupation with the thyroid is the existence of certain diseases which are grouped as hypothyroid and hyperthyroid states. With increasing knowledge of the facts of thyroid physiology and biochemistry, more and more refined diagnostic and therapeutic methods have been, and are being, applied to this group of disorders.

The purpose of this chapter is not so much to discuss diseases of the thyroid gland as to describe, insofar as this is possible, some of what is known about the iodine cycle and its relation to thyroid physiology in animals and man. Each animal is part of a continuum with its environment with respect to food and water supply, oxygen, temperature, and so on. He is also dependent on his environment for certain trace substances, such as iodide. A knowledge of the way in which iodide is used by the body for the synthesis of thyroid hormones and the role of these hormones in the vital economy of the body is the basis of the modern management of thyroid disease.

Figure 6-1 represents a diagrammatic outline of the discussion to follow. It shows the absorption of I⁻, its abstraction by the thyroid gland, the biosynthesis, storage, and release of the hormone by the gland, the trophic influences which stimulate the thyroid and are in turn inhibited by thyroid hormone, the transport of the hormone in the blood and its effect on tissues. The circled numbers in the headings and in the text refer to the numbers in this diagram. It is suggested that the student first inspect the diagram and then use it as a guide as the detailed discussion proceeds.

① Nutritional Requirement for Iodide

Although dried seaweed and sea sponge had been fed to patients with goiter by Egyptian physicians in antiquity, a clear relationship between iodine lack and goiter was only established in this century by Marine. He showed convincingly the high incidence of endemic goiter in an inland population and demonstrated that the disease could be prevented by the administration of as little as 2 Gm of potassium iodide twice yearly. The amounts of iodine involved in goiter prevention are small: only about 150 micrograms of iodide are ingested daily even in seacoast regions where there is an abundance of the halide. When the amount of iodide available to the thyroid is markedly lowered, there is a sort of "work hypertrophy" of the gland which may take the form of diffuse hypertrophy and hyperplasia. Wherever cell division is stimulated, there is the statistical possibility of an increased rate of somatic mutation; therefore, it is not surprising to see adenomatous growth in some iodine-deficient glands.

Most patients with endemic goiter compensate successfully for the lack of iodine intake and are able to maintain normal levels of thyroid

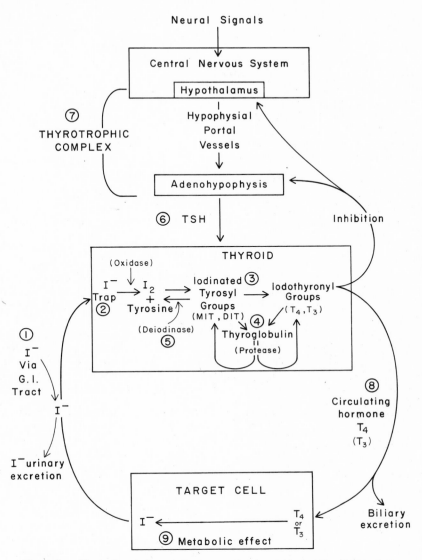

Fig. 6-1.—The iodine cycle and the neuroendocrine control of thyroid function.

SOME LANDMARKS IN THYROID CHRONOLOGY*

DATE		INVESTIGATOR
1526	Goitrous cretinism described	Paracelsus
1850	Cretinism described in patients without thyroid	Curling
1856	Thyroidectomy in dogs	Schiff
1871	Sporadic, nongoitrous cretinism	Fagge
1874	Cretinoid state in adult women	Gull
1880	Gull's disease named myxedema	Ord
1884	Thyroidectomy in monkeys with myxedema-like picture	Horsley
1882–1883	Thyroidectomy in man	Reverdin; Kocher
1888	Similarity between postthyroidectomy syndrome and myxedema	Semon
1890	Relief of myxedema symptoms in man by sheep thyroid grafts	Bettancourt and Serrano
1891	Prevention of postthyroidectomy syndrome in dogs by I.V. injection of extracts of their own thyroids	Vassale
1891–1892	Substitution therapy in human myxedema	Murray; Fox; Mackenzie
1895	Increased BMR in hyperthyroidism	Magnus-Levy
1896	Discovery of iodine in thyroid	Baumann
1911	Discovery of di-iodotyrosine in thyroid	Baumann
1915	Isolation and crystallization of thyroid hormone	Kendall
1927	Determination of structure of thyroxin and synthesis	Harington and Barger
1942 et seq.	Antithyroid drugs discovered	Richter; Astwood; Mackenzie
1952	Discovery of tri-iodothyronine	Gross and Pitt-Rivers

*Adapted from Means, J. H., in *Disease and the Advancement of Basic Science*, H. K. Beecher (ed.): (Cambridge, Mass.: Harvard University Press, 1960).

hormone output. Some, however, become hypothyroid, and in these instances the disease probably represents the result of the interplay of an unfavorable environment and an inborn predisposition. When endemic goiter was much more prevalent than it is now, it was not unusual for iodine-deficient goitrous mothers to give birth to cretinous babies. One of the most effective methods of preventing goiter in endemic areas is the addition of iodide to table salt.

Events in the Thyroid Gland

② THE IODIDE TRAP

The availability of radioactive iodine (I^{131}) has contributed greatly to our understanding not only of the iodide trapping-mechanism of the thyroid gland but also to all other aspects of thyroid physiology. When either stable or radioactive iodine is ingested or injected, the thyroid accumulates it against a concentration gradient and abstracts a high percentage of the administered dose. A knowledge of this highly specialized function is important to the physician for two main reasons. First, the general level of activity of the thyroid can often be estimated in the non-anesthetized patient by external monitoring over the gland following the administration of a tracer dose of I^{131} (as little as 40 microcuries). This is true because the rate of uptake often serves as an indicator of the rate of hormone biosynthesis and release, although there are important exceptions to this generalization.

Second, the iodide-trapping function of the thyroid is used when therapeutic doses (in the millicurie range) of I^{131} are used for the purpose of radiologically ablating hyperactive glands in patients with Graves' disease. This is possible because the gland is incapable of distinguishing between the radioactive and nonradioactive isotopes, and the I^{131} functions as a sort of ionic Trojan horse. When it enters the gland, the intense local beta radiation destroys the thyroid tissue selectively, leaving undamaged such closely neighboring structures as the parathyroid glands. It is beyond the scope of this account to give a comparative evaluation of current methods of treatment of hyperthyroidism, but it is no exaggeration to say that the technique of radiological ablation has revolutionized the management of this condition.

The exact nature of the iodide trap is unknown. Autoradiographic studies performed in animals in which organic binding of iodide is blocked by the prior administration of a drug show that the radioiodide is localized in the follicles of the gland at the periphery of the colloid. All attempts to demonstrate a specific iodine-fixing protein have been unsuccessful so far. Many investigators believe that the operation of the iodine trap is dependent upon a continuing supply of metabolically derived energy, for the gland does not concentrate iodide under anaerobic conditions, or when inhibitors of oxidative metabolism are present. According to this view, the concentrating mechanism function is a metabolically driven pump similar to other ion transport systems which maintain an uneven distribution of ions between two fluid compartments of the body.

The blood flow of the thyroid gland is so large and the avidity of the gland for iodide is so great that the normal gland, in spite of its compara- tively small size, is able to retain 20–40% of a tracer dose of I^{131}. By far the largest quantity of the remainder is excreted in the urine, so that an inverse relation exists between thyroid uptake and urinary excretion of I^{131}. Small amounts, however, may appear in the gastric juice (the parietal cells of the stomach epithelium evidently substitute I^- for Cl^- during gastric acid production) and in the saliva and sweat, but 90% or more may be accounted for by the combined thyroid uptake and urinary excretion.

One of the mechanisms by which the thyroid can compensate for a low intake of I^- is by increasing its avidity for iodide. There may be a 10 to 20-fold increase in I^{131} uptake in laboratory animals fed an iodine-free ration for a week or more. The reverse of this is also true, that is, prior ingestion of iodide- or iodine-containing substances may depress the I^{131} uptake by the gland. Knowledge of these facts is of the greatest practical importance in the diagnosis of thyroid disease, for a very high uptake may signify iodine deficiency rather than hyperthyroidism, whereas a low uptake may be the lingering result of the administration of an iodine-containing contrast material used in a radiological examination rather than an indication of hypothyroidism.

Certain pharmacological agents—specifically, thiocyanate and perchlorate—selectively inhibit the operation of the thyroid iodide trap. This can be demonstrated by the use of a drug which blocks thyroid hormone manufacture by interfering with the "organification" of iodine, that is, with the incorporation of iodine into the organic fraction, which consists of the iodotyrosines and the iodothyronines (see below). A gland blocked in this way retains its ability to concentrate I^-, but when it is confronted with thiocyanate or perchlorate it promptly spills its accumulated I^{131} load overboard. The mechanism of this effect is not known, but on the basis of the fact that large doses of iodine re-establish hormone synthesis in an SCN^- blocked gland, it has been suggested that SCN^- and I^- compete with each other for some component of the trapping mechanism.

③ HORMONE CHEMISTRY AND BIOSYNTHESIS

After the iodide is trapped in the gland, it is oxidized to iodine, a reaction which is mediated by a peroxidase enzyme. The amino acid tyrosine

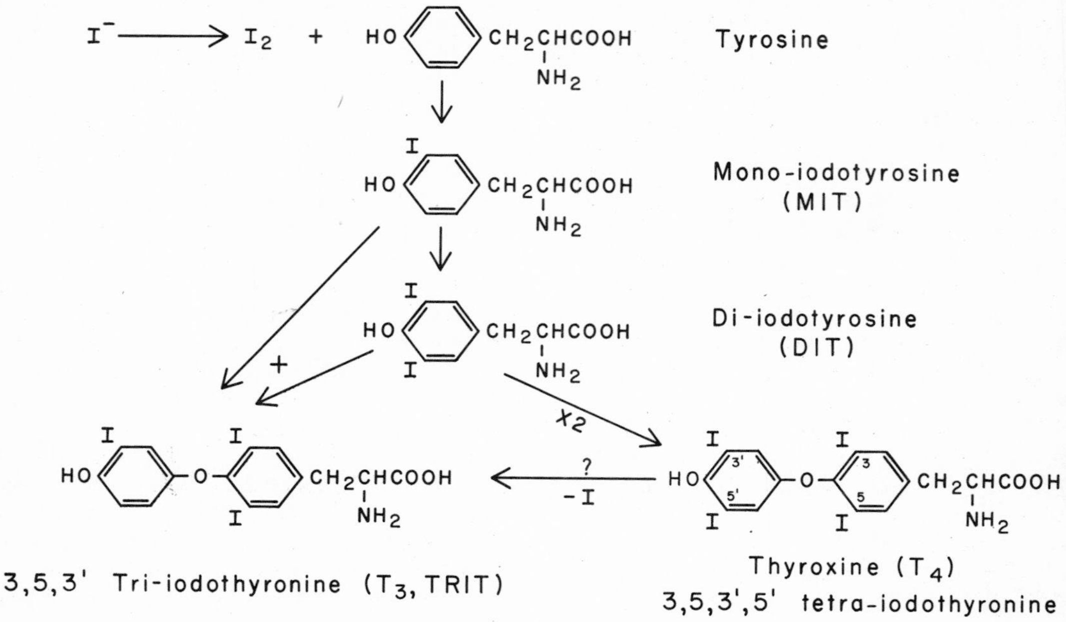

Fig. 6-2.—Biosynthesis of thyroid hormones.

is progressively iodinated, and the iodotyrosines couple to form iodothyronines.

The steps in thyroid hormone biosynthesis are as follows:

1. I^- trapping.
2. I^- oxidized to I_2.
3. Iodination of tyrosine to mono-iodotyrosine (MIT).
4. Further iodination of MIT to di-iodotyrosine (DIT).
5. Condensation of 2 molecules of DIT to form thyroxin.
6. (Possible) condensation of 1 molecule of MIT and 1 molecule of DIT to form tri-iodothyronine (T_3 or TRIT). A summary of these reactions is given in Figure 6-2. On radioautographic evidence, reactions 3, 4 and 5 are believed to occur mainly at the interphase between the thyroid epithelial cells and the colloid.

The formation of MIT (reaction 3) can proceed in vitro at fairly rapid rates in the absence of living tissue. In fact, iodination of casein in alkaline solution can result in the slow formation of thyroactive substances. The thyroid gland cell is particularly well adapted to carrying out this synthetic sequence at rates which insure high production levels of hormone.

The elucidation of this aspect of thyroid physiology has led to the interesting discovery that what used to be considered a single disease—hereditary cretinism—may result from any of several inborn errors of metabolism. Individual cases of cretinism have been described in which there was one of the following: a defective iodine-trapping mechanism, reduced rate of formation of MIT and DIT, and reduced rate of coupling of the iodotyrosines. Some have even been found in which iodotyrosine formation was normal and a "counterfeit" thyroxin was formed which was dutifully transported by the thyroxin-carrying proteins of the serum, so that serum protein-bound iodine levels were normal or above in the face of a tissue deficit of biologically active thyroxin. Wherever the defect occurs, the final result is thyroxin deficiency and in all but very few cases the patient responds to the administration of thyroxin.

All of the compounds that have been described as occurring during thyroid hormone biosynthesis are found in a highly specialized storage protein called *thyroglobulin* ④, which occurs in the form of a colloid aggregate within the acini of the gland. This substance, which is a glycoprotein with a molecular weight of about 680,000, is acted upon by a protease which causes the release from it of MIT, DIT, T_3 and T_4. The latter are available for secretion into the blood stream, but the iodotyrosines (MIT and DIT) are deiodinated in the gland by a sort of scavenger enzyme called deiodinase ⑤, which can be regarded as a part of an intrathyroidal iodine cycle which functions to reclaim iodide and tyrosine for reuse. Thyroidal deiodinase does not act upon either T_3 or T_4, which makes good teleological sense, since these must traverse the thyroid epithelial cell from the acinar side to the blood side in order to be secreted. In the normal gland, T_4 is by far the predominant secretory product, although small amounts of T_3 are readily demonstrable in gland homogenates. In the hyperthyroid gland, much larger amounts of T_3 may be produced and may appear in the blood (see below). It is important to realize that several weeks supply of thyroid hormone may be stored in the acinar colloid in the normal gland. This can be inferred from the fact that when hormone synthesis is specifically blocked by a drug (see below) it takes that long for deficiency symptoms to appear.

ANTITHYROID DRUGS.—An important aspect of the biology of the thyroid is the fact that we have available a number of chemical substances which inhibit or stop thyroid hormone biosynthesis in the thyroid gland. We owe these to a long series of observations in experimental animals and man but especially to a chance observation that was made during the course of a quest for a new rat poison. Richter and Clisby (1942) described goiters in animals given alpha naphthylthiourea (ANTU), and soon afterward Astwood *et al.* described a number of derivatives of thiourea, including the thiouracils, which had the effect of producing a functional hypothyroidism and hypertrophy, hyperplasia, and hypervascularization of the thyroid gland. The thioureas, the aminothiazoles, and the mercaptoimidazoles which inhibit thyroid hormone formation, all contain the following configuration:

Thiocyanate and perchlorate, both of which inhibit the thyroid at the level of the iodide trap, also cause goiter. Their effects may be overcome by the administration of large amounts of iodide. The mechanism of the thiourea type of block is not known with certainty, but there is evidence to suggest that drugs in this group prevent the oxidation of I^- to "active" I and that they may prevent the coupling reaction. Moreover, they probably inhibit the scavenger deiodinase ⑤. There is a persistence of iodine concentrating ability in the thiouracil-blocked gland (Fig. 3-2, p. 33). There is a latent period of several weeks before the inhibiting effect of thiouracil becomes apparent, because the hydrolysis of thyroglobulin and the release of hormones into the blood are not blocked by the drug. The reservoir of stored hormone in the gland must be depleted before the decreased rate of hormone production can be appreciated by the peripheral tissues. In the rat, thiouracil has the additional effect of interfering with the action of exogenously administered thyroxine in the tissues. In microorganisms, the drug acts as an anti-metabolite for uracil and interferes with RNA synthesis, but, so far, no similar effects have been described in mammalian tissues.

The thyroid gland in a thiouracil-treated animal has the appearance of an overstimulated organ. Its size is large, its vascularity is markedly increased, and on histological examination, the epithelial cells are high and show extensive mitotic activity. This has been referred to as an hypertrophy of frustration or desperation, for as the hormone output of the gland falls a signal is set up which elicits the outpouring of increasing amounts of thyroid-stimulating hormone from the anterior hypophysis. This results in an intense stimulation and hypertrophy of the thyroid which has its mechanical analogue in the hypertrophy of the left ventricle that occurs in aortic stenosis. The extent of the thyroid hypertrophy, in fact, can be interpreted as a sort of autobio-assay for TSH. Since one of the biological effects of thyroid hormones is to inhibit the output of TSH by the pituitary, the thiouracil-blocked animal has become a convenient assay preparation for testing this effect and for comparing various thyroactive materials with respect to their ability to shut off the hypophysial TSH faucet.

⑥ Thyroid-Stimulating Hormone (TSH)

The concept of a hormone of pituitary origin which stimulates the thyroid gland goes back to a 1914 observation that hypophysectomized tadpoles do not undergo metamorphosis. Later (in 1922) P. E. Smith showed that metamorphosis could be induced in hypophysectomized tadpoles by injecting them with extracts of bovine pituitary glands. Recently, it has been found that TSH is probably produced by 1 of 3 identifiable basophilic cell types. These cells contain the storage form of the hormone incorporated in dispersed secretory granules, and we must assume that they are specifically responsive to TSH-releasing factor (TRF).

TSH is a glycoprotein with a molecular weight of about 10,000. It has not been purified to the point that amino acid sequence analysis has been possible, but it is sufficiently pure to have been used as an antigen for the production of an antibody which can be employed as a reagent in a radioimmuno-assay. Predictably, this test has revealed high levels of TSH in the blood of thyroidectomized animals and men.

In recent years, the imaginative application of a variety of methods—histochemical, biochemical, autoradiographic, electronmicrographic—has resulted in new insight into the effects of TSH on the thyroid gland. One can imagine the thyroid cell of the hypophysectomized animal as being in a state of torpor or hibernation. Its oxygen consumption is low, its glucose utilization is minimal, its iodide-concentrating ability is low (but still perceptibly higher than that of extrathyroidal tissues), the rate of "organification" of iodine is low and hormone release rate is low. The "resting" cell has a characteristic way of disposing of fatty acids—it is more likely to store them as triglyceride than as phospholipid.

When a "resting" cell is suddenly confronted with TSH, either in vivo or in vitro, things begin to happen within minutes. Among the earliest observable effects are the following:

1. Imbibition of water and sodium
2. Increased oxygen consumption
3. Increased glucose utilization
4. A preferential increase in the appearance of glucose carbon 1 in respiratory CO_2, signifying increased metabolism by way of the pentose phosphate pathway
5. A sudden increase in inorganic phosphate in the cell, possibly signifying a breakdown of some existing phospholipids
6. A marked increase in the rate of incorporation of P_{32} into certain phospholipids, especially into the phosphoinositide fraction.

Later, the radioactive iodine uptake increases and ultimately cell growth, mitotic activity and cell division occur. The vascularity of the gland increases to the point at which it may resemble a blood-filled sponge. It should be emphasized that, although the long-term effects of TSH on the gland obviously involve nuclear and cytoplasmic components of the protein synthetic apparatus, the early effects on oxygen consumption, glucose utilization and proteolysis can be elicited in thyroids pretreated with either actinomycin D or puromycin (see Chapter 12), and thus they do not require *de novo* protein synthesis in order to occur.

It is only possible to speculate on the relationship of these findings to the intracellular events. There is one distinctive reaction in the thyroid cell which is believed to increase the requirement for TPNH, i.e., the reaction involving the de-iodination of MIT and DIT which must precede the salvaging of I and T for re-use by the synthetic machinery of the gland. The increase in the oxidation of glucose by way of its TPN-linked pathway may be secondary to the accumulation of MIT and DIT as a result of thyroglobulin proteolysis. These compounds have been shown to increase glucose utilization by thyroid slices and may be partly responsible for the increase in glucose uptake seen in the acutely stimulated gland.

The morphologic changes in the thyroid follicular cell following TSH stimulation suggest that the hormone produces an intricate, coordinated and complex response. Within a few minutes after exposure to TSH, colloid droplets appear at the apical ends of the cells near the colloidal surface. Luxuriant growths of microvilli proliferate into the colloid, and adjacent processes can be seen to enclose colloid droplets by a process similar to phagocytosis. The material in these droplets has been identified as colloid, both histochemically (it contains carbohydrate just as does the extracellular colloid) and radioautographically (if colloid is prelabelled with I^{131}, the label appears in the apical droplets after TSH stimulation).

While the apical end of the cell begins to ingest colloid droplets, smaller electron dense organelles which can be shown histochemically to contain various phosphatases, esterases and proteases (i.e., lysosomes) can be seen to migrate from the basal part of the cell toward the colloid end within a few minutes after TSH stimulation. Fusion of enzyme-containing granules and colloid droplets occurs near the apex of the cell. Proteolysis occurs in these compound droplets, and, as thyroid hormones and iodinated tyrosines are released, the droplets appear to move back toward the basal part of the cell, becoming more and more electron dense and less full of colloid as they do so. This intense phagocytic activity and elaborate and stylized ballet of organelles which occurs in response to TSH suggests that membranous structures in the cell undergo rapid remodeling. Possibly the changes in P^{32} incorporation into phosphoinositide is related to the structural alteration and biochemical modifications produced by TSH. There is reason to believe that TSH may exert its multiple effects on the thyroid cell through the agency of 3', 5' cyclic adenylic acid (see Chapter 8).

It is worth pointing out that many cells, when aroused to activity from a resting state, show changes in oxygen consumption, glucose utilization pattern (including a greater use of glucose via the pentose phosphate pathway) and an increased incorporation of P^{32} into phosphoinositides. This is a fair description of what happens in an exocrine pancreatic cell stimulated to secrete enzymes by acetyl choline, or of a leukocyte stimulated to phagocytic activity by the presence of polystyrene microspheres.

Pituitary extracts rich in TSH have been found to produce exophthalmos in certain experimental animals, such as the guinea pig and the Atlantic minnow. Recently, however, the hormone has been purified to the point at which it no longer has this effect, and there has been a tendency to belittle the pertinence of observations on minnows and guinea pigs to exophthalmos in the human. Yet some patients with exophthalmos have improved when they were given TSH-suppressing doses of thyroid hormones, and the possibility still exists that some exophthalmos-producing principle may be made and/or released in association with TSH. Certainly the failure to find exophthalmos on the administration of large amounts of TSH to hypothyroid patients may indicate simply that the retro-orbital tissues, which are the end-organ of the exophthalmos-producing factor, may be resistant to stimulation in this condition.

For many years there has been a continuing discussion of the possibility that Graves' disease, or toxic diffuse goiter, may be secondary to a hypersecretion of TSH by the pituitary. Many attempts to demonstrate an excessive amount of TSH in blood by a number of assay procedures have produced conflicting results. Some investigators have found normal levels and some have found elevated levels. It has been pointed out that a normal blood level of TSH does not necessarily rule out an increased rate of production and release, since slices of hyperplastic thyroid gland inactivate TSH added in vitro at a more rapid rate than do normal slices. On the other hand, some of the findings of an increased TSH activity in the blood of hyperthyroid individuals have been called into question because the thyroid-stimulating material has been found to be not TSH but a "long-acting thyroid stimulator" (LATS). Whether this new material will contribute to our understanding of the etiology of Graves' disease remains to be seen. Possibly "Graves' disease" will eventually prove to be as nonspecific a designation as "cretinism" is now.

The use of TSH as a therapeutic substance is neither possible nor necessary. At the present stage of their purification, most TSH preparations stimulate the production of antibodies and would therefore be effective for only a limited time. Moreover, hypothyroidism, whether primary or secondary to failure of pituitary trophic stimulation, is readily manageable with desiccated thyroid, or (as is done more rarely) with purified thyroid hormones. TSH is used diagnostically, however, to determine the competence of the thyroid to respond to stimulation. One measure of responsiveness is the I^{131} uptake after TSH compared with a pretreatment control value.

The inhibition of endogenous TSH secretion rate may be of either diagnostic or therapeutic importance to the physician. Since the secretion of TSH is regulated by the thyroid hormone level of the blood, it can be completely suppressed by the administration of an adequate dose of exogenous thyroid hormone. This effect can be achieved with the equivalent of 300–400 micrograms per day of 1-thyroxin, which is only moderately higher than the replacement dose for myxedema.

Certain patients with no obvious signs of hyperthyroidism show a high I^{131} uptake, possibly due to a prior low iodine intake. The high values revert to normal when endogenous TSH is suppressed by thyroid hormone. In true hyperthyroidism, RAI uptake is not reduced by this test even when the dose of thyroid hormone is increased to 20 times the replacement dose for myxedema. This could be due to a failure of suppression of TSH by the test dose of hormone, or it could indicate that the gland is functioning autonomously.

There has been an experimental use of TSH suppression in certain individuals with metastatic thyroid cancer, particularly when the tumors have consisted of well-differentiated tissue. These metastases have been shown to be under some degree of TSH stimulation, for when TSH is suppressed by the administration of exogenous thyroid hormone, they regress strikingly. These studies are most recent, but it will be interesting to watch new developments in this field.

⑦ Control of TSH Secretion

During embryogenesis, a primitive outgrowth of the pharynx comes into close association with the developing brain, and the adenohypophysis and hypothalamus become linked by a vascular connection, the hypophysial portal vessels. The physiological significance of this anatomical fact has been the subject of intense study, particularly during the past decade. It has now been firmly established that electrolytic lesions of the anterior hypothalamus just behind the optic chiasm in many species result in a fall in thyroid activity, especially as estimated by the reduction in size and the histologic appearance of the glands of propylthiouracil-treated animals. That such lesions may have remarkable specificity is indicated by the fact that fairly "pure" TSH deficits may be seen; the decreased I^{131} uptake may be seen without concomitant gonadal or adrenal disturbances. The significance of these experiments was greatly enhanced by the demonstration (by Harris and Woods in 1958) that stimulation by means of electrodes implanted in the same part of the hypothalamus of the nonanesthetized, unrestrained rabbit produced a striking increase in the rate of I^{131} release from the thyroid. In these experiments, the stimulation was applied by means of a large primary induction coil surrounding the animal's cage.

It is equally clear that the adenohypophysis separated from the hypothalamus either by stalk section (with precautions against the regeneration of the portal blood vessels) or by transplantation to a distant site (usually the anterior chamber of an eye, or under a kidney capsule) retains some degree of TSH control over the thyroid. For while the activity of the end-organ diminishes, the values for I^{131} uptake and the histological appearance are intermediate between those of completely hypophysectomized animals and controls. One of the most convincing demonstrations of the specificity of revascularization by the hypophysial portal vessels was given by Nikitovitch-Winer and Everett (1958), who confirmed the fact that subcapsular kidney pituitary grafts showed only slight TSH activity in the rat. In half of their animals, they retransplanted the renal transplants to the temporal lobe and in the other half to the region just below the median eminence. Although both sets of retransplanted glands were revascularized to the same extent, those placed under the median eminence resumed their normal output of TSH as well as ACTH and gonadotrophins.

Other experiments have been done which suggest that transplanted pituitaries respond to microinjection of thyroid hormones by diminishing their TSH output. But the transplanted gland, or stalk-sectioned gland, cannot respond to cold exposure with an increase in TSH output as occurs in the intact animal. Moreover, the thyroid response to cold is evident within a few minutes, before it is likely that there has been lowering of the circulating thyroid hormone level.

All of these experimental facts make it difficult for us to accept the simple, traditional view of an uncomplicated feedback mechanism of TSH control which involves an increase in TSH output with falling blood thyroid hormone levels and a shutting off of TSH with rising blood hormone concentrations. This is a general description of the operation of the system, but many unanswered questions remain. Do TSH-inhibiting amounts of thyroid hormone work on the hypothalamus as well as on the adenohypophysis? What is the nature of the compound neuroendocrine reflex whose neural afferent component is triggered by some event that occurs during cold exposure and whose endocrine afferent component involves the transmission of a message (presumably chemical in nature) from the hypothalamus to the adenohypophysis via the portal vascular system? How is the information of an excessive thyroxin production rate received and decoded in those chemoreceptor cells which eventually send the TSH shutoff signal? That thyroxin itself is not the signal, but rather the initiator of either a metabolic signal or of a signal such as heat generated by metabolism, is suggested by the fact that dinitrophenol is said to be able to inhibit TSH output. This compound causes a marked hypermetabolism which is secondary to uncoupling of oxidation from ATP production, which means that heat production is greatly increased.

At the present time we can summarize the results of a massive amount of experimental work in this field by stating that the adenohypophysis, separated from the hypothalamus and deprived of any close vascular connection with it, has some autonomous ability to secrete TSH and even to diminish its TSH output in response to thyroid hormone. It cannot, however, participate in the normal thyroid cold-response by increasing its TSH output very markedly. The normal hypophysis, or a transplanted gland revascularized by the hypophysial portal vessels, can do all of these things. We must conclude that there is a direct feedback relationship between the hypophysis and the thyroid, but that the subtle modulation of the function of the gland demanded by complex life siutations requires the participation of the central nervous system. This is rather like focusing your microscope with both a coarse and a fine adjustment.

⑧ Circulating Thyroid Hormone

When the thyroglobulin protease frees thyroxin and tri-iodothyronine from their storage depot in the follicular colloid, they traverse the cell and enter the blood stream. There they are selectively bound by one of several carrier proteins which have been exhaustively studied. By far the largest amount of hormone in the blood is in the form of thyroxin, but very small amounts of tri-iodothyronine are also detectable. In thyrotoxicosis or acute infections of the thyroid, larger amounts of tri-iodothyronine may appear. The nature of the thyroxin-binding proteins has been determined by chemical fractionation of the serum proteins and by ingenious combinations of paper electrophoresis with localization by means of I^{131} labels on the specific compounds under study. It has been found that most of the protein-bound iodine (PBI) migrates with a mobility between that of alpha 1 and alpha 2 globulin. A smaller portion examined under certain precise conditions of buffering and pH migrates with a prealbumin fraction.

There is no evidence that protein-bound thyroxin or tri-iodothyronine can enter cells, so we must presume that the hormone-protein complex dissociates at the tissue sites where the hormone exerts its effect. These may be either in the peripheral tissues (to be discussed below) or in those structures in the nervous system and the hypophysis which participate in the feedback regulation of TSH output regulation. The carrier protein has three times the affinity for thyroxin as it has for tri-iodothyronine, and some investigators suggest that the shorter latency and increased potency of the latter when compared with the former may be due to the fact that ingested or injected thyroxin is more tightly bound to the carrier protein and more slowly released to the tissues.

The estimation of serum PBI has become an important test in the diagnosis of hypothyroidism and hyperthyroidism. Like the RAIU (radioactive iodine uptake) its ability to discriminate deviations from normal thyroid function is far greater than that of the BMR. It should be emphasized that abnormal values for PBI and for RAIU can be due to reasons other than thyroid dysfunction. The normal range for PBI is 4–8 micrograms per 100 ml of serum. Values below 4 are suggestive of hypothyroidism and values above 8 are consistent with the diagnosis of hyperthyroidism. In difficult diagnostic situations the clinical endocrinologist uses a whole battery of laboratory aids (BMR, PBI, RAIU, serum cholesterol) and judges the results in the light of his clinical appraisal of the patient, rather than relying on a single test for an oracular verdict.

In some cases, false high values for PBI may occur when the patient has ingested iodides in one form or another for some time prior to the test. When such artifacts are due to inorganic iodides, they may be eliminated by performing a butanol-extractable iodine (BEI) determination. In this test, alkaline washing of the butanol extract releases inorganic iodide, MIT, and DIT, but not thyroxin. Unfortunately, the BEI is of no particular value when false high measurements are due to organic iodides, such as those that occur in x-ray contrast media. Figure 6-3 shows the relationship of BEI, PBI, total organic iodide, and total iodine in serum. Sterling has devised an ingenious method for measuring the concentration of unbound thyroxin in plasma. This tiny fraction, which represents only about 1/1000 of

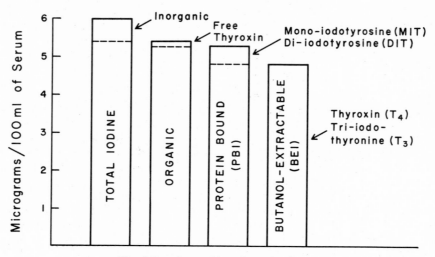

Fig. 6-3.—Composition of serum iodine.

the PBI, can now be measured with sufficient accuracy to separate hyper-, eu-, and hypothyroid patients.

There is one condition in which there is a physiological increase in the PBI accompanied by an increase in uptake of I^{131} and that is pregnancy. In spite of these laboratory findings suggestive of hyperthyroidism, there is no hypermetabolism, nor are there other signs or symptoms suggestive of hyperthyroidism. The explanation rests with the fact that in pregnancy there is a marked increase in the concentrations of a number of serum globulins, among them the thyroxin-binding protein. As the amount of this protein increases the very small fraction of free hormone decreases and an increase in TSH is elicited. This increases the activity of the thyroid and hence its rate of uptake of I^{131}. The increased activity of the gland proceeds just to the point of accommodating the increase in carrier protein, that is, until the free hormone concentration returns to euthyroid levels, and then stabilizes at the new high level of output. After parturition there is a gradual return of all parameters to normal levels. Table 6-1 illustrates the value of performing a battery of laboratory tests in a patient suspected of having a thyroid disorder. It will be seen that nearly any combination of increase or decrease in any of the measurements can be seen. Note especially the patterns that occur when thyroxin or tri-iodothyronine are ingested in excess over a period of time (thyro-

toxicosis factitia). In both instances there are, paradoxically, signs and symptoms of hyperthyroidism in association with a high BMR, but a low RAIU. In the case of thyroxin there is a high PBI, but for some reason (possibly related to its low affinity for carrier protein) tri-iodothyronine administration results in a *low* PBI. This

TABLE 6-1.—PATTERNS OF PROTEIN-BOUND IODINE (PBI), RADIOACTIVE IODINE UPTAKE (RAIU) AND BASAL METABOLIC RATE (BMR)*

CONDITION	PBI	RAIU	BMR
Normal	—	—	—
Hypothyroid	↓	↓	↓
Hyperthyroid	↑	↑	↑
Pregnancy	↑	↑	—
Estrogens	↑	—	—
Thyroiditis	↑ or ↓	↓	↑ or ↓
Iodides	↑	↓	—
Nephrosis	↓	—	—
Cortisone or ACTH	↓	↓	—
Thyroxin	↑	↓	↑
Tri-iodothyronine	↓	↓	↑

*Note that much more information can be obtained from a battery of tests than from a single one. (↑ = increased, ↓ = decreased and — = unchanged.)

is a highly abbreviated list and is presented here only to illustrate the manner of use of the tests under discussion.

An additional test has recently been added to the 3 discussed above by Hamolsky *et al.* This maneuver has the distinct advantages of being rapid, simple, approximately as accurate as the more standard tests, and does not involve giving a radioactive isotope to the patient. Moreover, it can be used with success even in patients with a history of prior administration of either organic or inorganic iodine-containing compounds. It is performed as follows: A tracer amount of I^{131}-labeled tri-iodothyronine is added to a measured amount of whole blood and incubated for approximately one hour. The amount of I^{131}-labeled compound that remains attached to the red cells (corrected to 100 hematocrit) after 5 washings is then determined. The value is high in hyperthyroidism, low in hypothyroidism, and low in pregnancy. The mechanism is not entirely clear, but the test appears to be an estimate of the degree of saturation of carrier proteins with hormone: the more saturated they are, the more of the added labeled tri-iodothyronine is free to combine with the red cells during the incubation period. A similar test, in which a resin is substituted for red cells, is in wide use.

⑨ Effects of Thyroid Hormone

Table 6-2 is a summary of some of the effects of thyroid hormone deficiency and excess that have been noted by observers working at virtually every wavelength of the biological spectrum. The purpose of this discussion is to examine these effects in an effort to discover the extent to which observations made at different levels of organization may either complement one another or confound the passionate searcher after unity.

Gross effects of thyroid hormone lack and surfeit are obvious. In general, the earlier the hormone deficiency appears, the more far-reaching the effects on the central nervous system. If the deficiency in the cretin goes untreated for too long, irreversible damage may be done to the brain, but it is frequently surprising to see the improvement in learning power and general level of awareness that takes place in a child who has been severely hypothyroid for several years when he is first treated with the hormone. While some of the CNS effect of thyroid hormone deficiency

may be regarded as a developmental failure, it is clearly not completely so, for if the deficiency occurs in a previously healthy adult the same kind of mental sluggishness, torpor, and somnolence appear as one sees in a cretinous child, and the clearing away of the mental fog on treatment with replacement doses of thyroid hormone can be nothing less than astonishing. The thyrotoxic patient—restless, anxious, emotionally unstable— not infrequently finds his way to the internist by way of the psychiatrist. These symptoms, too, subside dramatically with successful treatment.

The hypothyroid patient prefers the hot weather and complains bitterly about the cold, while the hyperthyroid individual is just the reverse. It will be recalled that experimental animals adapt to exposure to cold environment by increasing their output of TSH and in consequence, of thyroxin. An intact hypothalamus and hypophysial portal vascular system are essential for this response to occur. The hypothyroid individual is unable to make this adaptation successfully, whereas the hyperthyroid one is inappropriately "adapted" to the cold even at warm temperatures. In effect, he is unable to turn off his cold-adapting machinery; hence, his misery at ambient air temperatures that seem only mildly warm to euthyroid individuals.

One should reflect on the fact that a few micrograms of a rather simple organic chemical substance can cause such profound changes in mood and mentation by its absence or its excessive presence. It seems fair to conclude that variations in the supply of this and other chemical substances within the so-called normal range could help to account at least in part for some of the wide differences in personality structure seen in the "healthy" ambulatory population. While it may be that many of the psychiatrist's patients have only "problems in living" and are not somatically "ill," it seems to at least one biologist that the capacity to solve "problems in living" may depend, to some extent, on the nature of one's inborn endocrine equipment as well as on the functioning of other bits and pieces of the soma.

Among important observations made in the nonbehavioral sphere of the whole person, those on growth are of great interest. Thyroxin is a growth hormone in replacement doses, for growth failure occurs in hypothyroid infants and children and rapid growth spurts regularly follow the treatment of such patients with adequate amounts

TABLE 6-2.—EFFECTS OF THYROID DEFICIENCY AND EXCESS OBSERVED AT
DIFFERENT LEVELS OF ORGANIZATION

LEVEL OF ORGANIZATION	HYPOTHYROID	HYPERTHYROID
Behavior	Mental retardation Mentally and physically sluggish Somnolent Sensitive to cold	Often quick mentally Restless, irritable, anxious, hyperkinetic Wakeful Sensitive to heat
Whole individual	Deficient growth Low BMR Hypercholesterolemia Myxedema	Negative nitrogen balance High BMR Hypocholesterolemia Exophthalmos
Organ systems Cardiovascular	↓ Cardiac output ↓ BP, pulse pressure Weak heart beat ↑ Circulation time	↑ Cardiac output ↑ Systolic BP, pulse pressure Tachycardia, palpitations ↓ Circulation time
G.I.	Hypophagia Constipation Low glucose absorption rate	Hyperphagia Diarrhea High glucose absorption rate
Muscle	Weakness Hypotonia	Weakness Fibrillary twitchings, tremors
Immune mechanism	Infection-susceptible Subnormal phagocytic capacity of leukocytes?	Infection-susceptible (? related to excess protein catabolism)
Tissues	↓ QO_2 of liver, kidney muscle, etc. in vitro Normal QO_2 of brain, testis, retina, etc. Decreased sensitivity of some tissues to epinephrine	↑ QO_2 of same tissues Normal QO_2 of brain and same tissues Potentiation of epinephrine effect on intest. smooth muscle by thyronines
Organelle	Increased no. of mitochondria per cell. No change in P/O ratio	Increased no. of mitochondria per cell. P/O ratio ↓ (uncoupling of phosphorylation from oxidation)
Organelle component	———	Mitochondrial swelling (action on mitochondrial membrane?)
Enzymes	↓ Oxidative enzymes	↑ Oxidative enzymes in chronically treated animals

of thyroid hormone. A surplus of the hormone, on the other hand, produces excessive protein catabolism with tissue wasting in severe cases. The patient with Graves' disease literally burns up his own substance.

In 1895 the great pioneer, Magnus-Levy, discovered that hypothyroid patients were hypometabolic and hyperthyroid patients had high basal metabolic rates. These changes are still most striking, although their specificity is not great, for the BMR can be high or low for many reasons other than thyroid dysfunction. While the test is the least discriminating of the 3 in widespread use

at the present time, it is still useful in the study of patients with thyroid disorders.

Disturbances in lipid metabolism have been associated with altered states of thyroid function for many years. In hypothyroidism there may be lipemia, hypercholesterolemia, and a fatty infiltration of the liver, while in hyperthyroidism there is characteristically a decrease in the serum cholesterol. Recent studies with C^{14} labeled metabolites have revealed that the rate of cholesterol catabolism by the liver may be responsible for the comparative plasma levels. For in hyperthyroidism, in spite of accelerated cholesterol synthesis rates from acetate by liver slices, there is an even greater acceleration of the destruction of cholesterol by the liver, thus contributing to low circulating levels. Another factor which may influence serum cholesterol in the hyperthyroid individual is the fact that even when such people overeat they may be underfed with respect to their total caloric requirement. While the serum cholesterol in adults is so variable that it is not very useful diagnostically in investigating thyroid status, an elevated level in small children may be very helpful in alerting the physician to the possibility of hypothyroidism.

There is no major organ system that is uninfluenced by either the absence or excess of thyroid hormone. We have already discussed some of the behavioral aspects of thyroid physiology and these, in the last analysis, represent expressions of hormone effect on the central nervous system and the neuromuscular apparatus. Just as impressive dependence on thyroid hormone and disturbances due to its presence in excess are seen in many other systems.

In the *cardiovascular system* the cardiac output tends to be proportional to the metabolic rate being low in hypothyroidism and high in thyrotoxicosis. The same generalization can be made about changes in blood volume and in systolic blood pressure. One of the most distinctive findings in hyperthyroidism is a moderate elevation in systolic blood pressure with little change in diastolic, or a marked increase in pulse pressure. This is often associated with vigorous, brisk, and rapid contractions of the heart which are in contrast with the weak heart beat (which often produces low voltage deflections in the ECG) of hypothyroidism. The arm-to-lung or arm-to-tongue circulation time is prolonged in hypothyroidism and shortened in hyperthyroidism.

While the regulation of food intake and food intake behavior are not regarded primarily as local *gastrointestinal tract functions,* it is pertinent to note that altered thyroid status is accompanied by striking differences in the quantity of food ingested. Hypofunction of the thyroid is usually associated with decreased food intake, while thyrotoxic patients often eat voraciously without becoming obese. The mechanisms by which these attempted adjustments of intake to caloric need are made is not known, but some of the implications of these findings for current theories of food intake regulation are discussed in

Chapter 10. It should be realized that the severely thyrotoxic individual often cannot keep up with his huge caloric requirement even if he overeats heroically, and that the machine-tool needs of his overworked biochemical machinery are so high that he is extremely susceptible to the development of avitaminoses, particularly involving thiamine and the other water-soluble vitamins.

A prominent gastrointestinal tract function that is often markedly influenced by thyroid dysfunction is motility. The cretin or adult hypothyroid often suffers from constipation, while diarrhea may be a prominent complaint of the hyperthyroid patient. The mechanism of these effects is not known. They may be due in part to modifications of the central nervous system and in part to alterations in the sensitivity of the gastrointestinal smooth muscle cells to their customary neurohumoral transmitter substances.

The rate of intestinal absorption of glucose parallels the basal metabolic rate and the general level of thyroid activity. Hypothyroidism is associated with slow absorption rates and hyperthyroidism with rapid ones. Since the rate of hepatic and peripheral removal of absorbed glucose also parallels the level of metabolic activity, the oral glucose tolerance curve of a hypothyroid and a hyperthyroid patient may look much the same.

The effects of thyroid hormone lack or excess on *muscle* are extremely complex. Weakness, or the consciousness of diminished muscle strength, is one of the commonest complaints heard by physicians, but the pathophysiology of weakness is not commonly discussed. It is convenient to think of weakness as a derivative of 3 potential contributory factors: (1) the central perception or awareness of weakness, (2) a cardiopulmonary-circulatory component, and (3) the state of the muscle as a contractile machine. The central perception of weakness must be at least as complicated as the perception of hunger, satiety, thirst, or similar sensations, and while thyroid hormone availability or lack may have effects on the perception of the sensation of fatigue, we cannot describe these at present. The cardiopulmonary-circulatory contribution to fatigue in hypothyroidism must be considerable, for the reserves of the heart and lungs in this condition are inadequate to deal with the increased oxygen and fuel requirements even of moderate exercise. In the severely hyperthyroid person the tissue demands may be so outrageously high that even a tachycardia, a high pulse pressure, and a markedly diminished circulation time fail to keep up with them. Moreover, extremely hypermetabolic individuals are susceptible to vitamin deficiencies, so that a sort of beriberi heart syndrome may develop and lead eventually to cardiac failure. If hyperthyroidism occurs in a middle-aged or elderly person and the peremptory demands of a racing metabolic motor are made on a heart which is supplied by narrowed, atherosclerotic vessels, cardiac decompensation may occur. It is interesting to recall that the reverse of this process has been tried clinically in patients with severe and intractable cardiac pain of effort. Such patients have been thyroidectomized or, more recently, treated with thyroid-ablating doses of I^{131} in an effort to lower the metabolic demands on the heart to the point at which an enfeebled pump can meet them.

Both hypothyroidism and hyperthyroidism are characterized by disturbances in the muscle tissue itself. In hypothyroidism, a generalized hypotonia and sluggishness is a characteristic finding. In children and growing animals, the failure of growth is just as apparent in muscle as in other tissues. In hyperthyroidism, there is a negative nitrogen balance, and the presence of creatinuria and a low concentration of creatinine and phosphocreatine in the muscle of hyperthyroid animals suggests that there is a very rapid catabolism of muscle protein. Thus, the weakness of hyperthyroidism is the complicated sum of circulatory failure, local muscle factors and, possibly, heightened perception of fatigue centrally. In addition to these, one should not forget that the fibrillary twitching and tremors seen in a patient with severe hyperthyroidism represent a relentless bombardment of the muscles by nerve impulses, so that in a sense such an individual is always exercising, and any muscle work that he does is superimposed on an existing load.

This constant muscular activity of the hyperthyroid animal or man may not be obvious to inspection but is clearly evident in electromyograms. Since the muscle mass constitutes 50% of the body weight, and since muscle has the widest range of oxygen requirement of any tissue, muscular activity must contribute very substantially to the elevated basal metabolic rate seen in hyperthyroidism even under the conditions of the test, although, as we shall see, other tissues removed from hyperthyroid animals show a high rate of oxygen consumption when studied in vitro.

Hypothyroid patients and animals are said to have an increased susceptibility to infectious disease. This may be related to defective function of the immune mechanism and to the subnormal phagocytic capacity of leukocytes described in this condition. [In recent experiments, P. Reed and I were unable to confirm the suggestion that leukocytes from thyroidectomized rats are phagocytically incompetent.] Hyperthyroid individuals, too, are hypersusceptible to infections, but the mechanism of this susceptibility is not clearly understood. Possibly the general debility resulting from prolonged negative nitrogen balance may account for most of it.

Many studies have been made on the in vitro metabolism of surviving tissues obtained from animals with altered thyroid function. Certain tissues, particularly liver and kidney, accurately reflect the thyroid status of the donor animal, for they show high oxygen consumption if they are obtained from a hyperthyroid animal and a low consumption if they are taken from a hypothyroid animal. These effects are not seen immediately: a week or more of treatment of the donor animal is required before the tissue effects are seen. The events that occur during the latent period will be discussed below.

Just as impressive as the high "tissue BMR" of the tissues of hyperthyroid animals is the fact that certain other tissues—particularly brain, testis, retina, and others—do not show decreased or increased rates of oxygen consumption when they are obtained from animals with thyroid hormone lack or excess. Since altered thyroid hormone availability has unmistakable effects on the function of the brain in situ, our inability to detect an obvious metabolic aberration (though admittedly a gross one) is an arresting finding. After McIlwain had pointed out that there are clearly disparate effects of certain drugs on the oxygen consumption of the "resting" brain slice as compared with that of the electrically or potassium stimulated brain slice, I attempted to demonstrate effects of modified thyroid function on the potassium-stimulated moiety of brain slice oxygen consumption, but the results were negative (unpublished observations). We are left with the conclusion that thyroid hormone effects on the brain can occur without a change in oxygen consumption, which leaves plenty of other possibilities to explore.

One of the characteristic features of the hyperthyroid state in the whole animal is the apparent exaggerated response to the autonomic neurohumors. On the adrenergic side, anxiety, wakefulness, tachycardia, increased contractile force of the heart, susceptibility of the heart to arrhythmias, and increased systolic blood pressure, all suggest a kind of hyperepinephrinism. Diarrhea and sweating suggest increased cholinergic activity.

The relationship between thyroxin and epinephrine has been studied especially by Brewster *et al.* who found that either surgical or pharmacological blockade of the adrenergic division of the autonomic nervous system prevented the calorigenic and cardiac effects of overdosing the dog with thyroid hormone. They suggest that the thyroid hormones cannot exert their effects without at least permissive amounts of epinephrine, and that therefore the two hormones collaborate to produce the results seen. In another sort of experiment it has been found that the fatty acid mobilizing activity of epinephrine is not demonstrable in the hypophysectomized monkey without the prior administration of a thyroid hormone. It had been shown previously that the glycogenolytic effect of epinephrine is greatly increased in hyperthyroidism or after thyroid hormone administration. While there is some difference of opinion as to whether hypersensitization to catecholamines occurs in hyperthyroid states, there is strong evidence to suggest that it does. T. S. Harrison points out that, in 1865, hyperthyroidism was thought to be "a neurosis of the cervical sympathetic nerve"! The mechanisms involved in the interplay between catecholamines and thyroid hormones are still only dimly understood. It seems to me that a most promising approach to the problem was opened up by the observation (made in adipose tissue) that the level of adenyl cyclase activity is higher in hyperthyroid animals than in normals (Brodie et al., 2nd Catecholamine Symposium, 1966). Surely this kind of study will be extended to other tissues. If it should prove to be true that thyroid hormone in some way participates in setting the level of activity of adenyl cyclase a molecular mechanism will have been found for an ancient and perplexing puzzle. (For more information on this problem the reader should consult Chapter 8 and also the review on Adrenal Medullary and Thyroid Relationships by T. S. Harrison.)

A mechanism of the hypermetabolism of hyperthyroidism can be discerned one step below the cellular level; namely, at the level of the mitochondrion. The mitochondria function as energy transducers in the sense that they can convert an electron flow into a chemical storage form of energy, or ATP. Usually, a fixed molar ratio of 3:1 obtains between the rate of formation of ATP by the mitochondrion and its rate of oxygen consumption (P/O). Preparations from tissues of hyperthyroid animals, or mitochondrial suspensions treated in vitro with rather high concentrations of thyroid hormone, show a depressed P/O ratio. That is to say, the process of phosphorylation is less efficient because it takes a larger oxygen consumption to produce a given amount of ATP. So far, no one has demonstrated that hypothyroid tissues are *more* efficient than normal ones, but these results at the level of the cell organelle are of extraordinary interest when related to observations to cold exposure in the whole animal. The effect of uncoupling of oxidative phosphorylation (whether by thyroxin or dinitrophenol) is to produce less stored chemical energy but to produce more heat. If the total caloric expenditure is markedly increased, as it is in cold adaptation which is characterized by a marked increase in spontaneous food intake, there would be more than enough ATP produced, but the uncoupled phosphorylation machinery would produce much more heat. This biochemical stoking of the furnace would, of course, diminish the strain on the heat conservation mechanisms of the body which are probably working overtime. It is a fact that, uncoupled or not, the hyperthyroid animal produces a larger net amount of ATP than does a euthyroid animal. Thus, while it is extremely difficult to explain the signs and symptoms of hyperthyroidism or the role of the thyroid hormones in differentiation on the basis of phosphorylation uncoupling, this effect can be related teleologically to cold adaptation, which, while it involves a functional hyperthyroid state, cannot be regarded as a thyrotoxic condition.

Agents (like thyroxin) which modify the performance of the mitochondrial energy transducer might conceivably do so in one of several ways. First, they might act at the level of the oxidative

Normal   **Hyperthyroid**

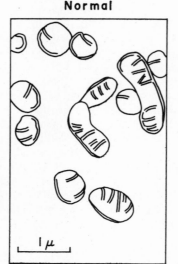 

Fig. 6-4.—Effect of thyroxin on liver mitochondria. Tracing of electronmicrographs published by Schulz, H., *et al.* in *Electron Microscopy*, Proc. Stockholm Conference (New York: Academic Press, Inc., 1957).

phosphorylation machinery itself; or they might produce indirect effects on the machinery by exerting a primary effect on the *mitochondrial membrane* which can be seen readily with the aid of an electron microscope. It has been found by students of mitochondrial physiology that uncoupling agents fall into two general categories— those which have an uncoupling effect even when the mitochondrial membrane is broken and those which require an intact mitochondrial membrane for the uncoupling to be effected. Dinitrophenol is an example of the former, while the thyroid hormones are examples of the latter. Both thyroxin and tri-iodothyronine cause swelling of mitochondria, and it is presumed that they do so by virtue of an effect on the permeability of the membrane to water and solutes. The swollen mitochondria have the appearance of having been pumped full of fluid under pressure (Fig. 6-4). The swelling presumably modifies the intramitochondrial environment in such a way as to produce uncoupling. It is of interest that the swelling can be reversed by the addition of ATP to the system. Thyroid hormone also stimulates mitochondrial protein synthesis. Whether this is due to a primary effect on the protein synthetic machinery or whether it is secondary to a primary effect on the mitochondrial membrane is as yet unknown.

A large body of literature exists on the general subject of the effect of thyroid hormones on various *enzyme activities* of tissues. In general, certain mitochondrial enzymes (succinoxidase, fatty acid oxidizing system, Cytochrome C, Cytochrome oxidase) are increased per unit of tissue, due probably to the increased number of mitochondria. On the other hand, a group of Krebs cycle dehydrogenases may be diminished in activity, which may be an expression of a disordered intramitochondrial environment. No specific interaction between thyroid hormone and any single enzyme has been described as a primary effect from which all other observed effects could logically flow. We must presume that the many effects on enzymes seen in thyroxin-treated animals represent adaptive changes that occur during a period of days and that they are secondary to some primary effect which stimulates the manufacture of new mitochondria by a mechanism that has yet to be discovered.

The complexity of the control mechanisms that determine the size of the aggregate mitochondrial mass are well illustrated by the recent report of Gustafsson *et al.* (1965) on the effects of thyroidectomy and thyroid hormone treatment on the mitochondria of rat skeletal muscle. In their artistic electron micrographic study, these authors showed, surprisingly, that *both* thyroid hormone deprivation and thyroxin cause an increase in the total number of mitochondria. Parallel studies of the activities of certain representative mitochondrial enzymes showed a decrease in the former case and an increase beyond that accounted for by increased mitochondrial mass in

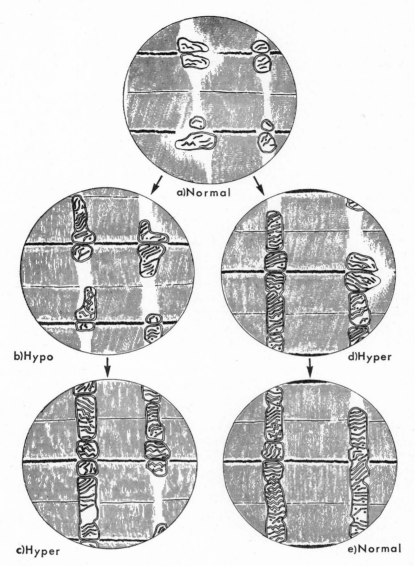

Fig. 6-5.—Schematic summary of the structural changes in skeletal muscle mitochondria accompanying alterations in their metabolic activity induced by thyroidectomy and treatment with L-thyroxin. The terms "normal," "hypo," and "hyper" refer to the thyroid state. For explanation see text. (Reproduced with permission from Gustafsson, R., Tata, J. R., Lindberg, O., and Ernster, L.: J. Cell Biol. 26:557-578, 1965.)

the latter. This means that, in the hypothyroid state, mitochondrial enzyme activities per unit of mitochondrion are even lower than we had imagined them to be, while, after thyroid hormone, there are not only more mitochondria but also a higher concentration of enzymes per unit of mitochondrion. The authors suggest that the mitochondrial "hypertrophy" of the hypothyroid state represents a compensatory phenomenon,

stimulated by a mitochondrion-replicating signal that can operate in the absence of thyroid hormone. The mitochondrial proliferation of hyperthyroxinism is regarded as a direct response to the hormone. The hypertrophic mitochondria of the hypothyroid animal could be made to increase in size and number by treatment with thyroid hormone, and, in the process, they assumed the enzyme activity characteristics of the hyperthyroid state. It was of great interest that cessation of treatment with thyroxin caused a disappearance of hypermetabolism and of elevated mitochondrial enzyme activities, while electron micrographs still showed very striking increases in mitochondrial size and number. These studies are summarized schematically in Figure 6-5.

In summary, we have examined effects of thyroid hormone at many levels of organization, from behavioral to enzymatic, from organ system to an organelle of an organelle, we have seen how some of the fragments fit together and how others fail to do so. A brief discussion of the biochemical mechanism of action of thyroid hormones will be found in Chapter 12.

Thyroid Hormone Analogues

We have already noted the fact that certain drugs, such as thiocyanate, the thioamides, and others are useful both in the analysis of thyroid gland physiology and as therapeutic agents. The tranquilizers (as chlorpromazine), too, are of interest because they have a striking effect in wildly excited patients with hyperthyroidism. (They are so effective, in fact, that they may camouflage the true diagnosis if they are used indiscreetly.) More recently the symptoms and signs of hyperthyroidism have been markedly ameliorated in patients given the adrenergic blocking agent, guanethidine (see Chapter 8).

In another dimension of thyroid pharmacology, the organic chemist has built a large number of variants of thyroxin and tri-iodothyronine in an attempt to discover compounds of potential therapeutic interest. Some of this work was inspired by the desire to find a substance that would produce a serum cholesterol-lowering effect without exerting a calorigenic effect; some of it was part of a search for a thyroid hormone analogue that would competitively inhibit the effect of thyroid hormone at the target tissue. The acetic acid derivatives (TETRAC and TRIAC) apparently have a more marked effect on the elevated serum cholesterol than they do on calorigenesis. The extraordinary potency of the propionic acid analogues in the tadpole tail-shortening assay has now been found to be due to the method of administration (intra-aquarial) which requires percutaneous absorption, for when the various thyroactive materials are injected into tadpoles their relative potencies on differentiation parallel effects on other parameters in other species. Literally hundreds of compounds have been assayed comparatively in dozens of systems. Table 6-3 is a representative sample of a few of the results.

The Thyroid and Autoimmunity

In very recent years, studies on the thyroid gland have contributed to our understanding of an increasingly important subject; namely, autoimmunity and autoimmune disease. One of the most important events that occurs during the differentiation of the embryo is the development by the immune mechanism of the "knowledge" of "self" and "not-self" (in Burnet's phrase). It is well known that an individual embryo can be

TABLE 6-3.—HANDY THYROID HORMONE ANALOGUE GUIDE FOR THE PERPLEXED

NAME	ABBREVIATION	CYCLIC STRUCTURE	SIDE CHAIN	DISTINCTIVE FEATURE(S)
Tetra-iodothyroacetic acid	TETRAC	As in T_4	CH_2COOH	? Immediate calorigenic effect
Tri-iodothyroacetic acid	TRIAC	As in T_3	CH_2COOH	Selective lowering of serum cholesterol
Tetra-iodothyropropionic acid	TETPROP	As in T_4	CH_2CH_2COOH	Most active in tadpole maturation assay
Tri-iodothyropropionic acid	TRIPROP	As in T_3	CH_2CH_2COOH	
Tetra-iodothyramine	T_4 amine	As in T_4	$CH_2CH_2NH_2$	Potentiate epinephrine effect on intestinal smooth muscle in vitro
Tri-iodothyramine	T_3 amine	As in T_3	$CH_2CH_2NH_2$	
3, 3′, 5′ Tri-iodothyronine		3, 3′, 5′ I	As in T_3	Competitive inhibitor of T_3 in tissue

fooled into accepting a fragment of "not-self" as "self" if it is presented to the organism at an early enough stage of its development. This is the basis for the tolerance of freemartin twin calves (i.e., fraternal twins with pooled placental circulations) for each other's blood cells when they belong to different immunological types. Human fraternal twins of this type have been discovered who not only have mixed blood groups but also accept skin grafts from one another just as if they had been monovular, and therefore genetically identical, twins.

Ehrlich expressed the widely held view that one's own proteins cannot be antigenic, and that great Latin phrase maker said it in two words, "horror autotoxicus." But in the case of the thyroid, evidence of autoimmunization has been found in the clinic, and a beautiful experimental animal model of a human disease has been described in which animals are stimulated to produce antibodies which react with their own substance.

In 1912, Hashimoto first described the disease that bears his name. Most often the patient with Hashimoto's disease (also called lymphocytic thyroiditis) exhibits a diffuse goiter that is accompanied by hypothyroidism, although there may be some evidence of hyperthyroidism, including a high PBI, in the early stages. In 1956, appreciable amounts of thyroglobulin-precipitating antibody were discovered in the sera of patients with Hashimoto's disease. Shortly afterward a second antigen of thyroid origin was implicated in Hashimoto's disease and was found to be particularly plentiful in the microsomes of homogenates of thyroid glands surgically removed from thyrotoxic patients, although it can also be demonstrated in extracts of normal glands. White (1957), who used Coons' fluorescent antibody technique, treated a frozen section of thyroid of a patient with Hashimoto's disease with the patient's own serum globulin which had previously been made fluorescent. He was able to show specific fluorescence in the colloid and in scattered locations within the epithelial cells.

At about the same time these studies were being made, Witebsky and his colleagues produced a disease in rabbits, guinea pigs, and dogs which closely resembled Hashimoto's disease in the human. They succeeded by slowly releasing thyroid extract from one rabbit into the circulation of another. The result was the appearance of antibodies which produced destruction and lymphocytic infiltration of the thyroid gland. In other experiments, thyroidectomized rabbits developed antibodies when they were injected with extracts of their own thyroid glands.

Many investigators are now working on the general hypothesis that, long after the individual has decided what is "self" and what is "not-self," antigens (thyroglobulin, microsomal intracellular antigen, or a combination) leak from the gland. (The cause of the proposed leak is not known, but virus infection will do as well as any other for the moment.) The immune mechanism "decides" that this circulating material (which normally does not circulate) is "not-self" and proceeds to manufacture antibodies against it. These then gain access to the gland, combine with the antigens fixed there, and damage the structure. The inflammatory response is secondary to the tissue destruction caused by the antigen-antibody interaction. Although this proposed sequence doubtless represents an unforgivable oversimplification of the facts, it has proved to be a useful and stimulating construct.

The importance of the concept of autoimmune disease goes far beyond the terrain of thyroid physiology, for it involves the whole complicated field of that aspect of the physiology of differentiation which has been discussed so provocatively by Burnet and Medawar. Furthermore, there is the possibility that other proteins which are normally sequestered in cells may gain access to the circulation and stimulate the production of antibody which would then have a deleterious effect on the tissue of origin of the antigen. A number of diseases—among them, certain collagen diseases such as systemic lupus erythematosus, rheumatoid arthritis and others, as well as acquired hemolytic anemia—are believed to have a component of autoimmunity in their etiology. There is reason to hope, then, that studies of this nature on the thyroid gland will prove to be of general biological interest.

REFERENCES

Burnet, F. M.: Immunological recognition of self, Science 133:307–311, 1961.

Cassano, C., and Andreoli, M. (eds.): *Current Topics in Thyroid Research*. (Proceedings of the Fifth International Thyroid Conference [New York: Academic Press, Inc., 1965].)

Hamolsky, M. W., and Freedberg, A. S.: The thyroid

gland, New England J. Med. 262:23–28, 70–78, 129–137, 1960.

Harrison, T. S.: Adrenal medullary and thyroid relationship, Physiol. Rev. 44:161-185, 1964.

Hoch, F. L.: Thyrotoxicosis as a disease of mitochondria, New England J. Med. 266:446–454; 498–505, 1962.

Medawar, P. B.: Immunological tolerance, Science 133:303–306, 1961.

Myant, N. B.: The thyroid gland, Brit. M. Bull. 16: 89–170, 1960.

Pitt-Rivers, R., and Tata, J. R.: *The Chemistry of Thyroid Disease* (Springfield, Ill.: Charles C Thomas, Publisher, 1960).

Pitt-Rivers, R., and Trotter, W. R. (eds.): *The Thy-roid Gland,* 2 vols. (Washington, D.C.: Butterworth Inc., 1964.)

Rawson, R. W.: Modern concepts of thyroid physiology (Symposium), Ann. New York Acad. Sc. 86: 311–676, 1960.

Rosenberg, I. N., and Bastomsky, C. H.: The thyroid, Ann. Rev. Physiol. 27:71–106, 1965.

Smith, R. E., and Hoijer, D. J.: Metabolism and cellular function in cold acclimation, Physiol. Rev. 42: 60–142, 1962.

Stanbury, J. B.: Familial Goitre in *The Metabolic Basis of Inherited Disease,* Stanbury, J. B., Wyngaarden, J. B., and Fredrickson, D. S. (eds.) (New York: McGraw-Hill Book Company, Inc., 1966).

Werner, S. C.: *The Thyroid* (New York: Paul B. Hoeber, Inc., 1955).

7

The Adrenal Cortex

THE PHYSICIAN'S INTEREST in adrenal cortical physiology covers a wide spectrum of disorders. Adrenal insufficiency (Addison's disease) and adrenal hyperfunction (Cushing's disease) are not very common, but with increasingly accurate diagnostic methods in the face of our population explosion they can no longer be considered rare. In addition, there are certain well-recognized inborn errors of metabolism of the adrenal cell which manifest themselves as a group of syndromes called adrenal virilism. Like the cells of other endocrine glands, adrenal cells sometimes undergo metaplasia and form tumors which may cause a number of different clinical disturbances, depending on the predominant hormonal product of the tumor cell. One tumor cell type produces an excess of the salt-retaining hormone aldosterone which will be discussed below. Others may produce an excess of androgenic steroids, or estrogenic steroids with manifestations appropriate to internal "overdoses" of these substances.

In addition, the adrenals are believed to play an important role in adaptation to many kinds of "stresses," such as trauma (accidental or surgical), severe infectious disease, severe intoxication, and other similar challenges. The mechanism of the participation of adrenal hormones in these complex events is not known and the role of many other hormonal, neural and nutritional influences in them is just beginning to be appreciated, but current and future studies of these phenomena must involve an understanding of the hypophysial-adrenal cortical machinery.

During the past 15 years the clinical manage-ment of certain types of cancer—particularly cancer of the prostate and of the breast—has been revolutionized by the idea that one can manipulate the hormonal environment of hormone-dependent cancer cells in ways that are beneficial to the host. Adrenalectomy, both surgical and, more recently, "medical" (i.e., by suppressing corticotrophin secretion with adrenal hormone), has been one of a number of weapons in the therapist's armamentarium.

Since 1949, adrenal cortical hormones, and various modifications of the naturally occurring materials that have been made by the organic chemist, have been used for their anti-inflammatory effect in the treatment of many diseases. The ability of these substances to suppress inflammation is one of their most fascinating attributes, and the importance of this effect in the management of patients with rheumatoid arthritis, disseminated lupus erythematosus, and various allergic states is well-recognized though not well understood. The successful use of these compounds in the fields of dermatology and ophthalmology alone would have justified the work that went into discovering and producing them.

The student whose primary interest is in the behavioral aspects of biology should understand that there are important effects of adrenal cortical insufficiency and excess on mood and even on adjustment to reality. Patients with Addison's disease are often depressed or anxious, and these symptoms are ameliorated by proper hormonal replacement therapy. The use of pharmacological doses of adrenal steroids in the long-term man-

SOME LANDMARKS IN ADRENAL CORTICAL CHRONOLOGY

DATE		INVESTIGATOR
1563	Adrenals described	Eustachius
1855	Adrenal insufficiency in man	Addison
1856	Adrenalectomy fatal in the dog	Brown-Séquard
1895–1904	Discovery of epinephrine (work on cortex inhibited)	Oliver, Schaefer, Abel, Takamine, Stolz
1910	Hypoglycemia of Addison's disease	Porges
1923	Adrenal atrophy in hypox. rats	P. E. Smith
1927	First active adrenal cortical extract	Hartman, Pfiffner, Swingle
1927	Low serum Na, high serum K in dogs. Prolonged life in adrex. dog with NaCl	Bauman, Kurland, Marine
1932	Life of patients with Addison's disease prolonged by salt	Loeb et al., Harrop et al.
1932–1938 et seq.	Carbohydrate metabolism defect in adrenal insufficiency in animals	Britton et al., Long et al.
1936	The "alarm reaction"	Selye
1938	Synthesis of desoxycorticosterone	Reichstein
1948	Partial synthesis of cortisone	Sarett et al.
1949	First anti-inflammatory use of cortisone in rheumatoid arthritis	Hench, Kendall
1952	Discovery of aldosterone	Simpson and Tait
1954	Amino acid sequence analysis of ACTH	Bell
1955	Discovery of primary aldosteronism	Conn
1961	Synthesis of ACTH peptide	Hofmann

agement of patients with arthritis or other diseases may result in euphoria or even overt psychosis in certain individuals who are presumably predisposed to such a condition. In some instances the central nervous system effects can be correlated with changes in the character of the electroencephalogram. Thus, there is scarcely a medical field of interest in which a knowledge of the adrenal cortex is without pertinence.

Effects of Adrenalectomy

Adrenal ablation in animals or man causes a far-reaching metabolic disturbance that has repercussions in virtually every area of physiology. The untreated condition is characterized by *weakness* and *easy fatigability*, by *hypotension*, by a variety of *gastrointestinal disturbances* including anorexia, nausea, vomiting, abdominal pain, and diarrhea, by various ill-defined *emotional* difficulties including anxiety and depression, and (in man) by increased *pigmentation* of the skin. There may be a striking intolerance to fasting and there is certainly decreased ability to withstand trauma, infections, hemorrhage, or other similar insults. In man, the untreated deficiency may lead to a condition known as "adrenal crisis," which is characterized by prostration and peripheral circulatory failure. There are certain analogies between the diseases diabetes mellitus and adrenal insufficiency in man; both are due to a hormone deficit; both require careful, long-term week-to-week management; both kinds of patients may be made worse by a sudden, unexpected event, such as an injury or an infection; and both may lead to a kind of collapse that can be described only as a medical emergency (adrenal crisis and diabetic acidosis).

It is traditional to separate the sequelae of adrenal ablation into two general physiological compartments: one associated with the metabolism of carbohydrate and protein, and with the capacity to withstand stresses of many types; the other, with water and electrolyte metabolism and the ability to reabsorb sodium from the glomerular filtrate, and thus conserve this ion when it is available only in limited amounts. While this compartmentalization is sometimes useful it can also be misleading, for a primary effect on electrolyte and water excretion may lead to a severe circulatory disturbance which, in turn, may have a devastating effect on carbohydrate and protein metabolism. For example, the sequence of events following adrenalectomy may be as follows: Loss of aldosterone → sodium loss in urine → dehydration → peripheral circulatory failure → tissue hypoxia → protein catabolism. The integrity of metabolic processes in cells depends in part on their blood supply and a serious hemodynamic derangement may result in a profound metabolic disturbance.

One of the most constant characteristics of the adrenalectomized animal or the patient with adrenal insufficiency is the inability to excrete a large water load and the susceptibility to water intoxication. This defect persists even when the salt-wasting tendency has been corrected hormonally or compensated for by an increased salt intake. It is corrected not by the typical salt water adrenal steroids like desoxycorticosterone but by steroids of the cortisol type which are active in organic metabolism.

The two general areas of activity of adrenal hormones—salt conservation and organic metabolism—can be affected differentially or unequally in both animals and man. Aldosterone, which is the main salt-retaining hormone of the adrenal cortex, is synthesized in the glomerulosa layer of cortical cells, while cortisol (in man) and corticosterone (in the rat), which are the principal glucocorticoids of adrenal vein blood, are made primarily in the fasciculata layer. When tuberculosis was a prominent cause of bilateral adrenal destruction, far more pronounced defects in salt conservation were seen than are observed in idiopathic adrenal insufficiency which may sometimes express itself as an almost pure glucocorticoid deficiency. The hypophysectomized animal shows many of the organic metabolic defects of the adrenalectomized animal, but it does not die of adrenal insufficiency because the glomerulosa appears to be able to secrete a sufficient amount of aldosterone to fill its limited needs. The trophic control of secretion from the different zones of the adrenal will be discussed later.

The *electrolyte-water* defect of adrenal insufficiency is far more complex than a simple renal incontinence for sodium. The most prominent feature of the defect is an inability to reabsorb sodium and chloride from the tubular urine sufficiently rapidly to prevent a net sodium loss from the body under conditions of normal or reduced sodium intake. (The ability of the intact animal to do this doubtless had great evolutionary survival value, and no doubt countless species which moved away from the sea became extinct when salt was in short supply.) This is accompanied by potassium retention and rising concentrations of this ion in the extracellular fluid. The increase in serum potassium is due to a combination of the animal's inability to excrete it and an accompanying discharge of potassium from the intracellular into the extracellular fluid compartment of the body which may be partly the result of an effect of adrenal cortical hormone deficiency on cell membranes generally and partly the tissue hypoxia which develops as a result of the hemodynamic disturbance of the untreated deficiency state. As the dehydration becomes more severe due to the loss of progressively more sodium, the ensuing hypotension and diminished renal blood flow contribute to an accumulation of phosphate and nonprotein nitrogen in the blood as well as potassium. Associated with this sequence of events there may be gastrointestinal disturbances, such as vomiting and diarrhea. These accentuate the salt and fluid loss, and may tend to telescope the events described above within a shorter time just as they tend to accelerate the development of diabetic acidosis.

Although the renal aspects of salt conservation have been studied most extensively, effects of adrenalectomy and salt-water adrenal hormone treatment on salt escape from the body by other routes are also striking. Desoxycorticosterone, a powerful salt-retaining hormone, can not only promote the reabsorption of sodium by the renal tubule but also diminish the sodium concentration of sweat, saliva, and intestinal secretions. The effect on sweat adds a new dimension to our thoughts about the adrenal cortex and evolutionary survival value, for heat exposure is a powerful stimulus to aldosterone secretion, and we can assume that the additional aldosterone secreted functions to diminish the sodium concentration of sweat as desoxycorticosterone has been shown to do. Thus, the salt-retaining activity of the adrenal hormones is of adaptive value not only when there is less salt available in the environment for ingestion but also when a hot environment leads to increased salt loss through sweating.

The adrenals are essential to life because their salt-retaining function is a vital one. The lives of hypoadrenal animals and patients can be prolonged by feeding them large amounts of sodium chloride. A salt-maintained adrenalectomized animal, or a similar animal maintained with just a salt-water hormone such as desoxycorticosterone lives a precarious life because it lacks those hormones which function primarily in the sphere of organic metabolism.

The *organic metabolic defects* of adrenal insufficiency are extremely complicated and it is impossible to give a tidy or appealing summary of them at this time. Some of the metabolic effects of adrenalectomy that have been described are due to glucocorticoid hormone deficiency; others, to hemodynamic effects of salt loss on metabolism; and still others to the fact that adrenalectomized animals do not eat well and have an abnormally low rate of total metabolism.

Adrenalectomized animals show a rapid fall in blood glucose and tissue glycogen levels on fasting. Patients with Addison's disease often show a typical reactive hypoglycemia, or overshoot, during the performance of a glucose tolerance test, suggesting that the intact individual uses his adrenal steroids as a sort of brake on the falling blood glucose concentration (see Chapter 9). In fact, insulin sensitivity is a prominent feature of adrenal insufficiency. Pancreatic diabetes is ameliorated by adrenalectomy partly because the insulin is compensated for by the absence of adrenal hormones. There are many experiments which suggest that the fasting adrenalectomized animal is unable to adapt to carbohydrate deprivation by drawing upon its muscle protein and lymphoid tissue stores for the process of gluconeogenesis. While there is much experimental evidence to support the view that peripheral tissue protein, particularly that of muscle and lymphoid tissue, is not readily available for gluconeogenesis in the adrenally deprived animal, other evidence suggests that the liver cell in such an animal may not be able to convert amino acids to glycogen at a normal rate.

In addition to the effects described, the adrenal glucocorticoids often appear to play a "permissive" role in metabolism. This simply means that many cells which are responsive to a variety of humoral and neural influences only perform well when they are exposed to a certain baseline concentration of adrenal cortical steroids. For example, the adrenalectomized animal does not respond to trauma or hemorrhage with an increased nitrogen excretion as the normal intact animal does. Comparatively small doses of a cortisone-like compound "permit" this response to occur.

It now seems that the hepatic effect of glucocorticoids on gluconeogenesis, like the effect of these substances on peripheral protein mobilization, is basically a permissive one. Exton and Park (1967) have described a failure of the isolated perfused liver of the adrenalectomized rat to respond to a gluconeogenic stimulus such as glucagon, epinephrine or 3′, 5′ cyclic adenylic acid. Pretreatment of such an animal with glucocorticoids results in a restoration of the normal gluconeogenic response to these agents. Partial restoration of the response can even be achieved by perfusing the hormone deficient livers with an adrenal glucocorticoid (dexamethasone) in vitro. Adrenal insufficiency does not result in a diminished production of 3′, 5′ cyclic AMP in response to the gluconeogenic stimulus (see Chapter 8 for a full discussion of this substance). It apparently interferes with the capacity of a component of the gluconeogenic machinery to respond to the cyclic nucleotide. (A more complete treatment of the role of glucocorticoids in hepatic gluconeogenesis will be found in Chapters 9 and 12.)

In human adrenal insufficiency pigmentation of the skin is a prominent finding. The possible role of the high hypophysial corticotrophin output that is characteristic of this condition in the mechanism of the hyperpigmentation will be discussed.

The behavioral and emotional disturbances seen in Addison's disease and the fact that these may be accompanied by abnormal electroencephalographic tracings has already been referred to. These changes can be reversed by the administration of glucocorticoids.

Design of the Neurohypophysial-Adrenocortical System

The fasciculata zone of cells in the adrenal cortex is trophically controlled by hypophysial corticotrophin (ACTH) ⑤ which stimulates them to produce steroids such as cortisol ③ which are concerned especially with organic metabolism. The aldosterone-producing cells in the glomerulosa zone ⑦ are controlled separately by other trophic substances ⑧ which may require permissive concentrations of ACTH in order to raise secretory activity to high levels. It has been suggested that adrenal androgens ⑨ arise predominantly in the cells of the reticularis, or juxtamedullary, portion of the cortex, but this is not proved. The glomerulosa cells have a degree of freedom from ACTH direction, for the glomerulosa zone does not become depleted of lipid on ACTH stimulation as the fasciculata does, and it can be shown to vary in width with salt depriva-

Fig. 7-1.—Neuroendocrine control of adrenal cortical function.

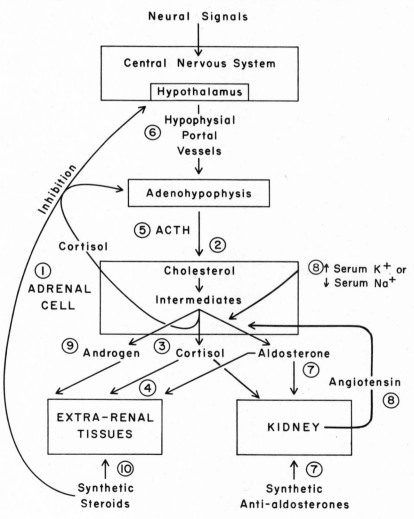

tion and repletion even in the hypophysectomized animal. Thus, there are at least 2 feedback systems which regulate the activity of the adrenal cortex: one which involves principally ACTH and cortisol, and the other, aldosterone and its own trophic substances. In the case of the former, the level of output of cortisol in adrenal vein blood is almost entirely determined by the intensity of the ACTH stimulus. The cortisol produced then feeds back on the trophic tissues and "instructs" them to decrease ACTH release ⑥. The rate of ACTH production at which the shutoff signal is perceived and acted upon apparently can be reset at higher or lower levels in a manner that is not now understood. The regulation of aldosterone secretion will be considered in a later section of this chapter.

The adrenal androgens ⑨ and their regulation have not been studied as extensively as the other categories of adrenal steroids have been. From observations made on female patients who receive very large doses of cortisol, we can conclude that hypophysial gonadotrophin secretion is inhibited either by the cortisol or by its biotransformation into androgenic steroids.

If we use Figure 7-1 as a diagrammatic outline of the entire neurohypophysial-adrenocortical end-organ system we will be able to see how each of the following subdivisions of the discussion fits into the larger picture.

① The Adrenal Cortical Cell: Hormone Biosynthesis

Adrenal cortical cells have no visible innervation; therefore, the marked variations in activity that occur in these cells are due to varying amounts of chemical stimuli that are brought to them in the blood stream. Of these stimuli corticotrophin (ACTH) has been most studied. In the absence of ACTH the adrenal cortex narrows, the glands become small and the production of glucocorticoids falls to negligible levels. Aldosterone production decreases somewhat, but remains sufficiently high to prevent serious salt loss.

Unlike the islets of Langerhans, the hypophysis, and the thyroid, adrenal cortical cells do not store large quantities of hormone. The glands are extremely vascular and the cells appear to secrete hormone into the blood as soon as it is made. In order to extract milligram quantities of cortisol or aldosterone from adrenal glands it is necessary to process very large amounts of material. A large number of steroids (25–30) have been extracted from adrenal tissue and identified but most of these are believed to be metabolic intermediates in the synthesis of the few final hormonal products. With the perfection of paper chromatographic techniques it is now possible to detect and even quantify steroids that appear in adrenal vein blood on ACTH stimulation. The main glucocorticoid in man and the dog is cortisol (hydrocortisone, Kendall's Compound F); in the rat it is corticosterone.

As a result of the application of a large number of methods (histochemical, analytical chemical, radioactive tracer studies, paper chromatography, adrenal perfusion, study of urinary excretion products, and others) it is now possible to reconstruct a plausible account of hormone biosynthesis in the adrenal cell. Although the adrenal cell does not store large amounts of finished hormone, it does contain very large amounts of what is presumed to be hormone precursor, esterified cholesterol. When the cell is suddenly confronted with ACTH, the concentration of cholesterol falls within minutes, and associated with this fall an increased concentration of cortisol is detectable in adrenal venous blood. Many of the intermediate steps in the synthesis of cortisol from the starting material are known and the coenzyme requirements of many of the reactions involve hydroxylations at carbons 11, 17, or 21 of the steroid nucleus and these are especially important for an understanding of the mechanism of action of ACTH on the whole process of hormone production. Figure 7-2 illustrates a typical postulated reaction sequence for the synthesis of adrenal steroids. The hydroxylation reactions are designated by the symbol TPNH, for all of these reactions have an obligatory requirement for reduced triphosphopyridine nucleotide. The importance of this scheme transcends the fasciculata cells of the adrenal cortex, for similar events doubtless take place in all steroid hormone-producing cells, whether the final product is cortisol, aldosterone, estrogen, androgen, or progesterone. All of the structures that produce these materials (adrenals, ovarian cells, testicular cells) are embryologically derived from the primitive urogenital ridge and eventually differentiate to specialize in the production of one steroid hormone (see Fig. 5-5, p. 67). Whether the final product turns out to be one or another steroid

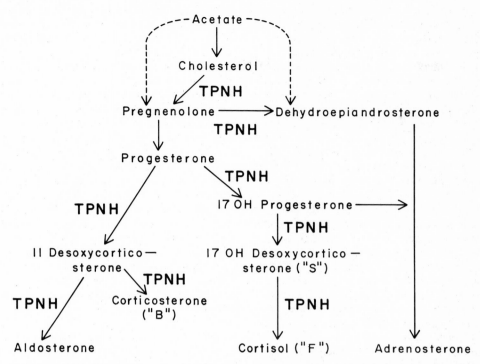

Fig. 7-2.—Steroidogenesis in the adrenal cortical cell, showing the marked dependence of cortical hormone formation on the availability of TPNH.

depends on the enzyme profile of the hormone-producing cell. For example, the manufacture of cortisol depends on the presence of 11-hydroxylation machinery. The mechanisms involved in this extraordinarily subtle differentiation of cells with closely related functions are not known. We are familiar with the idea of morphological and functional differentiation, but this is a problem in the physiology of differentiation at the enzyme level.

The way in which ACTH stimulates the comparatively dormant adrenal cell of the hypophysectomized rat to a high level of activity is now beginning to be understood ②. Epinephrine and glucagon both cause glycogenolysis in the liver by eliciting the appearance of a substance closely related to ATP called cyclic adenylic acid (or 3′, 5′ AMP). This material participates in the activation of the enzyme phosphorylase, which in turn is believed to promote glycogenolysis. (For a discussion of this subject see Chapter 8.)

An entirely analogous situation has been found in the adrenal cortical cell, for here ACTH releases cyclic adenylic acid which activates phos-phorylase. This is a highly specific effect, for ACTH does not activate liver phosphorylase, and neither epinephrine nor glucagon has an ACTH-like effect on the adrenal. The adrenal cell has an extremely active direct oxidative pathway (hexose monophosphate or pentose shunt) for glucose. Hence, the glycogenolysis promoted by the phosphorylation activation insures that much of the glucose-6 phosphate will traverse the direct oxidative pathway. It will be recalled that the oxidation of glucose by this route results in the generation of TPNH which (as can be seen from inspection of Fig. 7-2) is required at many of the intermediate steps in hormone biosynthesis.

It is difficult to conceive how the mechanism just described could account for a *continuing* stimulation of hormone production beyond that which could be achieved by the breakdown of the small amount of glycogen which is present in the gland at the time of exposure to ACTH. Fortunately, other workers have shown that ACTH stimulation is accompanied by an increase in the rate of utilization of glucose which, they postulate, is based on an effect on transmembrane transport of glucose similar to that of insulin in muscle. Although the details of the relationship of phosphorylase activation and the increased permeability of the cell for glucose are imperfectly understood, we can begin to see the general outline of a cellular mechanism of action of ACTH based on the distinctive biochemical characteristics of a tissue whose metabolic apparatus appears to be peculiarly adapted to provide energy in a form in which it can be used most efficiently for reductive steps in hormone biosynthesis. For an expanded discussion of the mechanism of action of ACTH see Chapter 12.

When the striking fall in adrenal cholesterol following ACTH administration was first observed, similar tests were conducted on ascorbic acid which is present in extremely high concentrations in the adrenal cortex. The experimenters were somewhat surprised when adrenal ascorbic acid concentration fell just as sharply, and slightly more rapidly, than the cholesterol had done. Since the chemical estimation of ascorbic acid was less cumbersome than the analytical methods for cholesterol of the time, ascorbic acid depletion became the basis for a widely used assay method for ACTH. It had the considerable advantage that it could be used either as a measure

of exogenously administered ACTH (as in the Sayers' test, which is done in the hypophysectomized rat) or of endogenously secreted ACTH; in other words, as an indication of the magnitude of ACTH response to various stresses in the intact animal. Recently, direct determinations of hormone output, often on adrenal venous blood, or by fragments of surviving adrenal glands in vitro, have been widely used. But in spite of the fact that ascorbic acid depletion and increased hormone output do not always parallel each other, the ascorbic acid test has been of enormous historical importance and is still extremely useful.

The mechanism of ascorbic acid depletion of the adrenals on ACTH stimulation is not known. Unmodified ascorbic acid has been found in the venous effluent from the adrenals after ACTH stimulation. It is possible that some of the depletion may be due to an overboard leak of the vitamin which is related to a nonspecific increase in the bidirectional permeability of the adrenal cell membrane that occurs on treatment with ACTH.

There has been an almost immediate practical yield from the beautiful basic studies on the pathways of steroid transformations in the adrenal gland, for it has been possible to identify and, in

Fig. 7-3.—Inborn errors of metabolism in adrenal cortical cells. Enzyme defect at **I** produces virilism without hypertension. Block at **II** results in virilism with hypertension. (After Bongiovanni, A. M., and Eberlein, W. R.: Pediatrics 16:628, 1958.)

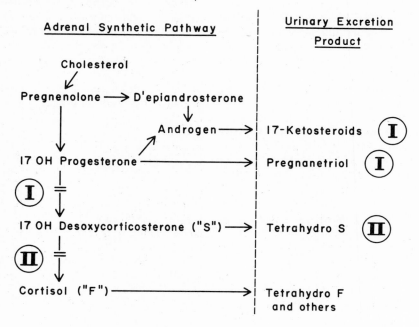

many cases, to treat very successfully patients with certain *inborn errors of metabolism* of adrenal cells. Several types of patients have been found who exhibit virilism and adrenal hyperplasia. This can manifest itself as masculinization in the female or precocious puberty in the male. In 2 of these types the precise biochemical locus of the metabolic defect is known; moreover, it can be identified simply by chemical analysis of the urine. In type I (Fig. 7-3) the block is in the 21-hydroxylation reaction from 17-OH progesterone to compound "S," and the condition is characterized by virilism *without* hypertension or disturbances in water and electrolyte metabolism. The urine contains abnormally large amounts of pregnanetriol and 17-ketosteroids. In type II (Fig. 7-3) there is a deficiency of 11-hydroxylase activity by which "S" is normally converted to cortisol. Patients with this inborn metabolic error have virilism *and* hypertension, and their principal urinary excretion product is tetrahydro "S."

In these and similar kinds of patients there is a deficiency in cortisol production caused by the genetic enzyme defect. This, in turn, is interpreted by the ACTH-producing department as a need for more ACTH, which is secreted in large amounts. The analogy between this situation and the "hypertrophy of frustration" of the thiouracil-blocked thyroid is obvious. The net effect of the increased outpouring of ACTH is to increase the production of substances *behind* the block, ketosteroids and pregnanetriol in type I and tetrahydro S in type II. The virilization is due to the fact that some of these may have pronounced androgenic activity. The hypertension may be due to the accumulation and secretion of large amounts of desoxycorticosterone. The remarkable fact is that if replacement doses (25 mg per day) of cortisol are given to these people all symptoms and signs of disordered adrenal function disappear within a very short time.

In addition to these conditions, many kinds of hormone-producing tumors of the adrenal cortex have been described, and some of these produce excessive amounts of androgens, estrogens, aldosterone, and other substances. The metabolic pathways in such tumors are being worked out, and this work has already advanced to the point at which the presence of at least one kind of tumor can be detected by a chemical examination of the urine. Tumor-bearing patients excrete large amounts of dehydroepiandrosterone while patients with diffuse adrenal hyperplasia and virilism do not. If virilization is due to a tumor, neither the signs nor the elevated urinary 17-ketosteroids disappear on treatment with replacement doses of cortisol.

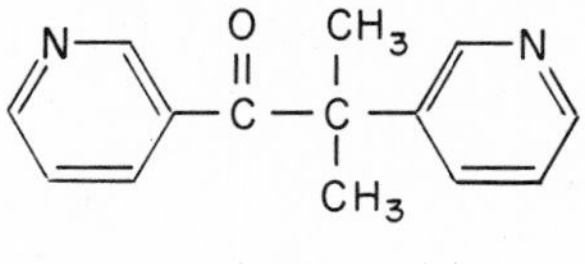

Recent advances in the pharmacological inhibition of adrenal cortical cell metabolism are of great biological interest, although clinical application of these findings is not as yet widespread. A compound known as *amphenone B* has been found to interfere with the later stages of steroid hormone synthesis, particularly at the hydroxylation steps and thus can be regarded as a sort of thiouracil for the adrenals. A markedly increased ACTH secretion can be elicited by treatment with this and similar drugs, and one drug in this series has, in fact, been used to test the competence of the pituitary to secrete ACTH. This experimental drug (Metopirone, Fig. 7-4) inhibits primarily the 11β hydroxylating mechanism, and thus effectively shuts off the production of cortisol, corticosterone, and aldosterone. The uninhibited pituitary of the treated animal pours out ACTH, which stimulates the adrenals to produce large amounts of certain potent salt-retaining hormones which are normally only intermediates in the synthesis of the final products. Thus, this chemical inhibition closely mimics the type II adrenal virilism-cum-hypertension syndrome described above.

③ Cortisol

As soon as cortisol (Fig. 7-5) is synthesized it is released into the blood stream and transported both to the tissues on which it acts and to the brain and pituitary which regulate the rate of release of ACTH. Transport of cortisol is accomplished by means of a specific serum protein which has been called *transcortin*. It is interesting to note that the blood concentration of transcortin, like that of the thyroxin-carrying protein, is elevated in pregnancy.

Cortisol is the prototype of the so-called "glucocorticoid," or adrenal steroid whose predominant function is on organic metabolism, as opposed to the "mineralocorticoid," or salt-and-

Fig. 7-4.—Metopirone (Methopyrapone).

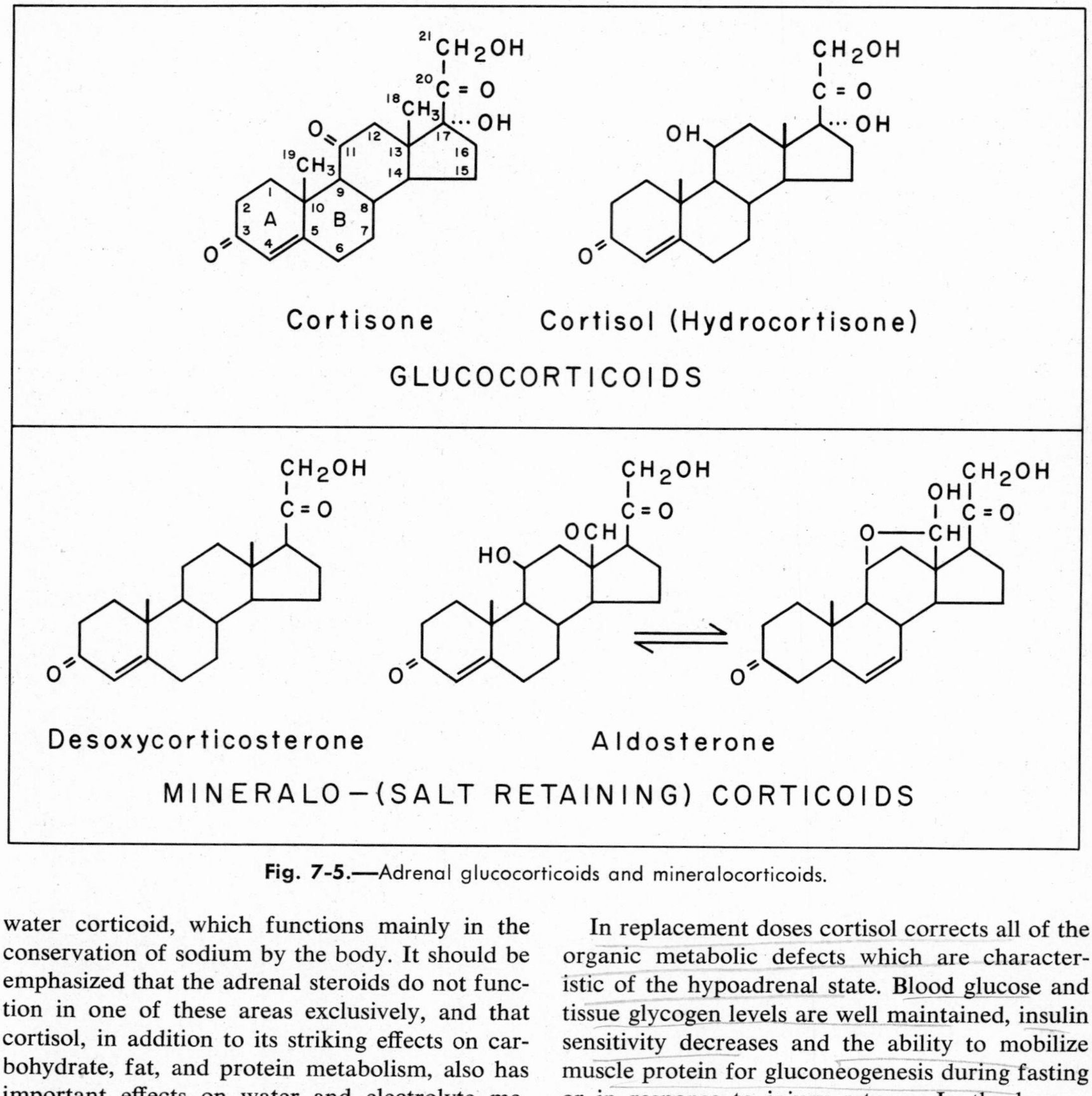

Fig. 7-5.—Adrenal glucocorticoids and mineralocorticoids.

water corticoid, which functions mainly in the conservation of sodium by the body. It should be emphasized that the adrenal steroids do not function in one of these areas exclusively, and that cortisol, in addition to its striking effects on carbohydrate, fat, and protein metabolism, also has important effects on water and electrolyte metabolism.

When one discusses the biological effects of cortisol one must distinguish between the effects of replacement doses in deficiency states and "pharmacological" doses which are used clinically for their anti-inflammatory effects. The hormone may be secreted in excess also in Cushing's disease. Indeed, overdoses of the hormone used thereaputically cause a condition which has been called "iatrogenic (or physician-induced) Cushing's disease." It is not too early to begin to become sensitized to the concept of iatrogenic disease in the first year of medical school.

In replacement doses cortisol corrects all of the organic metabolic defects which are characteristic of the hypoadrenal state. Blood glucose and tissue glycogen levels are well maintained, insulin sensitivity decreases and the ability to mobilize muscle protein for gluconeogenesis during fasting or in response to injury returns. In the human skin pigmentation diminishes and weakness disappears. Blood pressure stabilizes at a more nearly normal level and the psychological condition of the patient improves. In the animal, a return of normal food intake is apparent and restoration of normal growth rates is re-established in young animals.

The effects of overdoses of cortisol often represent exaggerations of the responses which, at lower doses, tend to compensate for an insufficiency of the hormone. Thus, large doses cause a very marked deposition of glycogen in the liver, sometimes to the point at which 15% of the weight of that bulging opalescent organ can be accounted for as glycogen (normal 3–5%). The blood glucose may be elevated above normal levels; indeed, if the insulin reserves of the animal are low, a state of diabetes can be induced by administering cortisol over a period of days. In animals like the rat and the mouse, which have virtually indestructible islets of Langerhans, the hyperglycemia produced by chronic overdoses of cortisol causes a very striking hypertrophy and hyperplasia of the islets which is presumably associated with markedly increased rates of insulin production. The insulin so produced greatly enhances deposition of the glucose in the fat depots and its conversion there into fatty acids. Ultimately, this may lead to marked obesity, and this sequence of events (observed primarily in the mouse) is the best mechanistic description we can give at present for the obesity of Cushing's disease (see Chapter 10).

Associated with these changes in glycogen and blood glucose are marked effects on protein metabolism. A negative nitrogen balance may develop, and greatly increased levels of creatine (signifying muscle breakdown) and uric acid (due to dissolution of lymphocytes and other cells?) are seen in the urine. Skeletal muscle mass decreases and muscular weakness appears. The skin may become atrophic and, where it is subjected to stretching, it may show striae or bands which are due to the breaking of its collagenous supporting structures. Such striae are prominently seen in Cushing's disease. Similarly, osteoporosis may occur either during long continued administration of pharmacological doses of cortisol or in Cushing's disease. This development has been attributed to a defect in the metabolism of the protein matrix of bone caused by the steroid excess.

Cortisol effects on the blood and lymphoid tissues of the body are especially noteworthy. The injection of a corticoadrenal hormone of the cortisol type causes a very prompt decrease in the number of circulating eosinophils and lymphocytes. Moreover, there is a marked decrease in the size of the lymphoid tissue mass of the body wherever such tissue is found, as in the thymus, spleen, lymph nodes, and intestinal tract. Curiously, cortisol increases the number of circulating platelets in patients with idiopathic thrombocytopenic purpura, but has no such effect in normal men. There is, however, a high incidence of thromboembolic disease in patients treated with cortisone, and such patients do show a decreased venous blood clotting time for unknown reasons.

An important group of cortisol effects represents the clinical basis of the use of compounds of this sort in a very wide variety of diseases; namely, the collagen diseases, or diseases of mesenchymal overshoot. The hormones under discussion modify in a most dramatic way the whole sequence of events that we describe as the inflammatory response and tissue repair. When a tissue is injured—mechanically, chemically, or by parasite invasion—there is (1) an extravasation of fluid from the intravascular compartment into the tissue spaces, (2) an infiltration of the area with leukocytes, and (3) the beginning of the healing process which is characterized by the synthesis of connective tissue, frequently (in the case of a surgical or traumatic wound) in association with a previously formed blood clot. Pharmacological doses of cortisol and its congeners astonishingly inhibit all phases of this sequence—extravasation, cellular infiltration, and wound healing. This can be demonstrated by producing a standard sterile inflammation in the paw of a rat and then observing the effect of cortisol treatment on the developing inflammation (Fig. 7-6). The hormone inhibits the swelling of the limb, and histologically a markedly diminished cellular infiltration is seen in the treated paw. It is this effect of cortisol which is related to the clinical occurrence of serious, masked infections in patients who receive this and similar substances over a long period of time. A discussion of the mechanisms involved in the anti-inflammatory effects of glucocorticoids will be found in the following section.

Many demonstrations have been made of the inhibition of wound healing by large doses of cortisol. Presumably this is related to an inhibition of the ability of collagen-producing cells to produce the ground substance of connective tissue.

Cortisol is also useful for its antiallergic properties. It can prevent anaphylactic shock in the guinea pig, as well as control a severe attack of asthma in the human. Histamine formation from histidine is not blocked by adrenal hormones, nor is the ability of antigen and antibody to interact. It appears likely that the antiallergic effect is somehow associated with the anti-inflammatory effect; i.e., the antigen-antibody transaction pro-

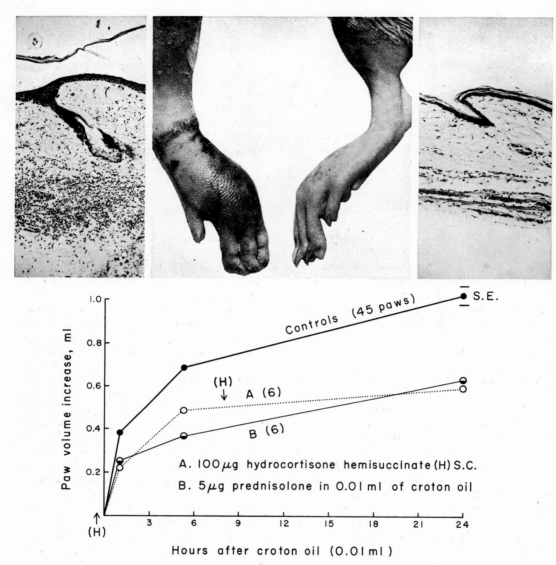

Fig. 7-6.—Gross and histological appearance of standard sterile (croton oil) inflammation used in assay for anti-inflammatory activity of adrenal and related steroids. The paws are depilated and 0.010 ml of irritant oil is injected subcutaneously in the anesthetized (pentobarbital) rat. The change in volume of the paw is followed for 24 hrs. The photographs show a normal paw (right) and a paw 24 hrs after croton oil injection (left). The chart shows the anti-inflammatory effects of hydrocortisone hemisuccinate injected systemically and of prednisolone dissolved in 0.010 ml of croton oil. Both procedures produced highly significant suppression of inflammation. (From Green, A., Riemenschneider, P., and Tepperman, J., unpublished.)

vokes an inflammatory response which is suppressed by cortisol. One must confess that the hypotheses that have been advanced to explain these phenomena somehow seem drab and unexciting in comparison with the dramatic clinical events they are designed to explain.

The effect of cortisol on electrolyte and water excretion is qualitatively similar to that of aldosterone, although its potency is very much less. Sodium retention by the kidney and potassium excretion are promoted, and certain addisonian patients whose salt-losing defect is not serious can be managed very well on cortisol alone. More specifically, cortisol assists in the excretion of a water load and prevents water intoxication on water loading. This is not strictly a renal effect; rather, it is likely that the hormone influences the distribution of water between the intracellular and extracellular fluid compartment and prevents the intracellular sequestration of water that occurs in the untreated adrenally insufficient animal which is suddenly confronted with a large excess of water for disposal.

The central nervous effects of cortisol have already been referred to. Often patients given a cortisol-like compound become euphoric, and some show a marked increase in appetite and weight gain. Many of these people had been chronically ill and anxious and some of their feeling of well-being may justifiably be attributed to the relief of symptoms. Some of it, however, is doubtless due to a direct effect of the cortisol on the cells of the central nervous system. That steroids can have profound effects on neurones is illustrated by the fact that some of them, when given in large doses, are anesthetics. Electroencephalograms of some patients on large doses of adrenal cortical steroids show disturbances in alpha activity and "runs" of slow waves.

Most of our knowledge of the effects of cortisol have been obtained at the physiological level. There is as yet insufficient information at the cellular level to use as the basis of a theory of cellular mechanism of action. The prevention of the protein catabolic effect of cortisol by large amounts of carbohydrate suggests that the peripheral tissue effects on protein in metabolism may be secondary to influences on carbohydrate utilization. Current discussion of this problem centers on the liver as the primary end-organ of the glucocorticoids. Recently, the addition of hormones of the cortisol type have been shown to enhance gluconeogenesis from amino acids by surviving liver slices in vitro. This may be related to the observation that the transport of a nonutilizable amino acid into liver cells is enhanced by cortisol. It seems unlikely that the effect of cortisol on concentrative transfer of amino acids into the liver is the primary action of the hormone, for such an effect cannot be demonstrated in muscle although the steroid obviously has profound metabolic influences on that tissue. The presentation to the liver of large amounts of peripheral tissue protein for disposal following cortisol administration results in the adaptive formation of a number of enzymes, particularly those concerned with gluconeogenesis. This may be the basis of the observed *increase* in protein synthesis in the liver in the face of peripheral tissue breakdown. A more complete discussion of this interesting subject will be found in Chapter 12.

A definitive description of the intracytologic site of action of cortisol must embrace at least the following: (1) its effect of hepatic gluconeogenesis, (2) its depressing effect on protein synthesis in muscle, (3) its capacity to stimulate protein synthesis in liver, (4) its lytic action on lymphocytes and eosinophils, (5) the mechanism of its antiallergic and anti-inflammatory actions, (6) the mechanism by which it influences the distribution of water across all membranes, and (7) the manner of its effect on cells or synapses of the central nervous system. Obviously, no such description can be given at this time.

④, ⑩ THE ANTI-INFLAMMATORY EFFECT OF GLUCOCORTICOIDS: HORMONES AND LYSOSOMES

One of the most characteristic biologic effects of the glucocorticoids is their ability to inhibit the development of an anti-inflammatory response and to reverse an established inflammation. Dramatized by the 1949 discovery by Hench and Kendall of their remarkable effects in patients with rheumatoid arthritis and rheumatic fever, the anti-inflammatory effect of adrenal cortical hormones and related 11-hydroxylated compounds has been extensively studied in experimental animals and in the clinic. Until recently, no very plausible hypotheses were advanced to explain the mechanism of this action of the steroids, but several investigators have now proposed some fresh and attractive theories which, at least, help us to conceptualize the problem of the role of adrenal hormones in inflammation.

Rarely, an illuminating idea stimulates students of many apparently unrelated problems to re-examine old facts in a new light. Such an idea was the lysosome concept, first enunciated by De Duve in about 1955. De Duve discovered that certain acid hydrolases which were capable of breaking down many of the cell's normal constituents (including proteins, fats, glycogen, nucleic acids and mucoproteins) were associated with a readily identifiable particulate fraction of liver homogenates. When this fraction, or whole homogenates, were treated in a variety of ways (freezing and thawing, exposure to detergents, sonication, etc.) much more acid hydrolase activity which had formerly been associated with a sedimentable fraction now appeared in the supernatant. De Duve brilliantly deduced that this destructive group of enzymes had been sequestered in the cell in membrane-wrapped packages, and that these packages had been unwrapped, so to speak, by the various experimental maneuvers he had used. By means of histological, histochemical, and electron micrographic techniques, De Duve's granules, which he called lysosomes, were quickly shown to be identical with granular organelles which the histologist has been seeing for decades in all sorts of cells, but most particularly in leukocytes.

A small army of investigators suddenly began to re-examine their problems in the light of the new and beautiful lysosome concept. Fell and Dingle, who were interested in a curious dissolution of cartilage that occurs in organ cultures of bone and in droopy-eared rabbits under the influence of toxic doses of vitamin A, found that the vitamin disrupted lysosomal membranes and that this was probably responsible for the release of cartilage-dissolving enzymes. Cohn and Hirsch demonstrated that the granules of polymorphonuclear leukocytes were authentic lysosomes in good standing and that they are part of the intracellular digestive apparatus of the white blood cell which had first been postulated by Metchnikoff. Ingested material was found to affiliate itself with lysosomes and the membrane-bound aggregate then effectively kept foreign substances undergoing digestion outside the cell in the same sense that the contents of the gastrointestinal tract are outside the body. Moreover, it was found that cell injury and disruption of lysosomes result in the release of inflammation-producing and -sustaining molecules, substances which cause vasodilation, increased vascular permeability and cellular infiltration. Thus, inflammation is similar to a chain reaction: a noxious substance injures cells, lysosomes are ruptured and their contents injure adjacent cells while they cause the typical vascular and cellular responses to injury; then, perhaps, some of the very cells that were attracted to the inflamed area are overwhelmed by the challenge—either a bacterial toxin or endogenously derived toxins—and succumb, thus releasing more acid hydrolases and inflammation-eliciting peptides of various sorts. The kinins (bradykinin and related peptides) may be among these.

Weissman and Thomas and their colleagues have suggested one way in which glucocorticoids might interrupt this vicious circle. They discovered that cortisol treatment protected animals against some of the toxic manifestations of an overdose of vitamin A, and, since vitamin A had been shown to "labilize" lysosomal membranes and free intralysosomal enzymes, they tested cortisol and related compounds in similar systems. They found that lysosomes prepared from the tissues of glucocorticoid-treated animals resist disruption by a number of agents. Moreover, lysosomes from normal animals are stabilized by the addition of admittedly high concentrations of cortisone or cortisol to the fluid in which they are incubated.

That these are not nonspecific effects is suggested by the fact that other steroids—notably etiocholanolone—which produce local inflammation and fever when they are injected intramuscularly have exactly the opposite effect on lysosomes in vitro. They, in fact, render lysosomes more fragile and release intralysosomal enzymes into the non-sedimentable phase of a homogenate. Cortisol is capable of antagonizing this effect of etiocholanolone on the lysosomal membrane.

Thus, it is possible that part of the anti-inflammatory effect of glucocorticoids is related to the ability of these compounds to stabilize lysosomal membranes, perhaps by interacting with lipid components of the membrane in an as yet unspecified way. However, I am persuaded that this is not the whole explanation of mechanism of action of adrenal hormones in inflammation. The effect of locally applied cortisol in an inflamed conjunctiva, for example, is so rapid that it is difficult to conceive of it as due entirely to lysosomal membrane stabilization. It is much more likely that there is a sudden interruption in the production of a pain and/or inflammation-producing peptide. Therefore, the suggestion of Melmon is particularly attractive. This investigator has demonstrated that glucocorticoids inhibit the production of kinins from their α-globulin precursor, a reaction which is mediated by the enzyme kallikrein. Since there are very active kininases in tissue the kinins are evanescent peptides, and the interruption of their production would effectively reduce their concentration sharply. Of course, this hypothesis requires that the kinins play an active role in inflammation—a proposition on which there is not yet general agreement.

The impact of the lysosome story on endocrinology has gone far beyond the antiphlogistic effect of glucocorticoids. There is scarcely a branch of the subject that has remained untouched by the hypothesis. The role of lysosomes in the intracellular digestion of thyroglobulin has already been discussed. The participation of lysosomes in a variety of catabolic processes which involve hormones includes mobilization of fat from adipocytes; gluconeogenesis in the liver, either in fasting or stimulated by glucagon; the involution of embryonic or larval structures, such as androgen-induced resorption of the mullerian ducts or thyroxine-induced shortening of the tadpole's tail; the involution of hormone-supported cells when the hormone is removed, i.e., in the prostate gland after castration. These are just a few examples of many that could be given of the surprisingly varied findings that have resulted from De Duve's happy inference of the lysosome idea.

④ CORTISOL AND THE STRESS CONCEPT

One of the dominant themes in adrenal cortical physiology has been the theory that the pituitary-adrenal axis participates prominently in the "nonspecific systemic reactions of the body which ensue upon long exposure to stress." In 1936 Selye called attention to the fact that "diverse nocuous agents" produced a rather stereotyped response in rats. At the time, the main features of this response were adrenal hypertrophy, atrophy of the lymphoid tissue of the body, and lymphopenia. Subsequently it was found that the earliest detectable change following trauma,

heavy muscular exercise, infections, hemorrhagic shock, cold exposure, hypoxia, burns, and even severe psychological trauma is a depletion of cholesterol and ascorbic acid in the adrenals which is associated with an increased output of 11-oxygenated adrenal corticoids in adrenal vein blood. In some experiments the increased hormone output has been inferred from a characteristic hormone effect, such as eosinopenia, liver glycogen deposition, or diminished thymus or spleen size. More recently, 17-OH steroid estimations in urine and blood have confirmed earlier experiments based on indirect estimates of hormone output. There may also be some degree of sodium retention and an increased excretion of potassium. A negative nitrogen balance is characteristic of the response, but this can be largely inhibited in many instances by force-feeding carbohydrate. The sequence of events cannot occur in the absence of the hypophysis, and hypophysectomized or adrenalectomized animals and men are notoriously vulnerable to such stresses as those enumerated above.

Selye referred to the earliest stages of his general adaptation syndrome (which he abbreviates as GAS) as the "alarm reaction," because he interpreted the changes he observed as part of a "call to arms," by analogy with the "fight-flight" adrenomedullary sympathetic discharge pattern which had been described earlier by Cannon. With the passage of time the GAS theory was developed, expanded, pruned, modified to accommodate new discoveries and used as the basis for explaining the pathogenesis of many diseases of unknown etiology which were visualized as the result of a disordered adaptive response. For example, salt-retaining steroids were found to enhance inflammatory responses and cause certain necrotic changes in the heart which resembled those of the human disease, periarteritis nodosa. Therefore, it was suggested that an abnormal alarm reaction in which glucocorticoids and mineralocorticoids were delivered by the adrenal in an improper ratio might contribute to the etiology of certain human diseases.

The GAS theory has had its articulate partisans as well as its able critics, and it is impossible here to give a detailed account of its history. Since the broad outlines of the theory constitute more of a poetic concept (this is intended as a compliment to its originator) than a definitively described biologist's equivalent of the periodic table, reactions to it tend to be personal, and sometimes even emotional. The student is urged not to accept the following estimate as anything more than one observer's opinion.

The alarm reaction aspect of the general adaptation syndrome has proved to be an enormously valuable construct, and it has stimulated a large amount of useful experimental work and fruitful dialogue. It is a remarkable fact that the pituitary-adrenal axis is activated by such a variety of potentially harmful stimuli, and it is certainly possible, though not yet proved, that the increased amount of cortisol secreted immediately after injury, or even in anticipation of injury, may assist in the vital redistribution of amino acids, that must occur in order for repair to proceed. A possible locus of participation of cortisol in the nonspecific injury response as well as the possible evolutionary survival value of a generalized injury response is suggested by the following quotation from Cuthbertson:

From teleological considerations the present writer early suggested that the general reaction by which labile protein is catabolized as a result of injury may serve to provide energy, or amino acids, or both, for the healing process, and that this is a primitive response independent of food, for a wounded animal is necessarily reduced in its capacity to feed itself.

Historically one of the most important effects of the alarm reaction discussion has been a widespread awakening of the surgeon's interest in the metabolic response to trauma, both accidental and surgical. Of course, this development has not been due entirely to theories concerning the participation of the adrenals in the response to stress, but there is no doubt that such theories have stimulated much study of the metabolism of patients postoperatively and that the care of surgical patients has been, and is being, much improved as a result.

In some ways, the alarm reaction and GAS concepts with their emphasis on nonspecificity have had a stultifying effect on adaptation theory. For even in its earliest stages the responses to injury or anticipation of injury show striking specificities. In cold exposure, for example, both ACTH *and* TSH secretions are elicited, while in other circumstances only ACTH appears. Certain stresses present unique problems in adaptation almost from the start. Extensive burns, for example, create complex problems in heat loss due to evaporation from the burned surface, and blood loss, with its immediate lowering of oxygen-carrying capacity, elicits responses that may not appear in an acute infection. The tendency to think in terms of a massive, undifferentiated response has had the effect of obscuring some of these differences, and each kind of stress must finally develop a "personality" of its own.

But it is during the repair stages of stress response that preoccupation with adrenal participation in the over-all response has been least helpful to our understanding. Here, the exquisite appropriateness of each response is the most striking feature of it; there is nothing 'nonspecific" about any of them. Specific antibodies are not formed in response to broken bones, and an increased rate of new red blood cell production is not stimulated by fright. Much of the capacity for repair is resident in the tissues themselves. Unicellular organisms, like yeast and bacteria, adapt to different conditions of oxygenation and nutrition without benefit of a pituitary-adrenal system, and analogous processes that occur in mammalian cells are only beginning to be explored. Moreover, when the endocrine system does play a role in tissue adaptation it is not just the adrenals that are involved. Thyroxin, insulin, and possibly somatotrophin may also be featured prominently.

The hypothesis that many diseases may be caused in part by a disordered alarm reaction, or by the production of unusually large amounts of mineralocorticoids during the adrenal stress response, has not been widely accepted. There is as yet no evidence that certain pathological lesions which can be produced in experimental animals by treatment with mineralocorticoids are in any way related to similar lesions which are seen in the human.

In summary, the alarm reaction and the general adaptation syndrome have proved to be heuristically valuable theories, but the adaptive significance of the increased output of 11-oxygenated adrenal steroids in the nonspecific response to stress is not yet understood: On the occasion of the silver anniversary of the theory we can point to it as evidence that biologists are hungry for unifying concepts, of which they have all too few.

⑤ ACTH

After the demonstration of adrenal cortical atrophy following hypophysectomy by P. E. Smith, crude hypophysial extracts were found to

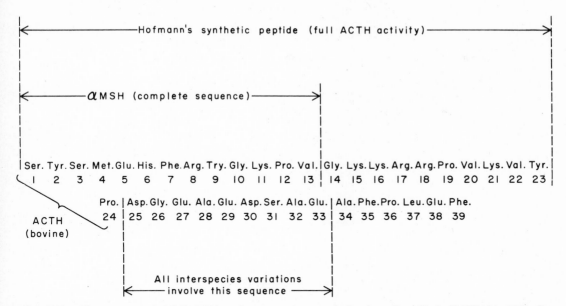

Fig. 7-7.—The structure of ACTH, MSH, and a synthetic peptide (Hofmann) with full ACTH activity. ACTH: Bell, P. H.: J. Am. Chem. Soc. 76:5565-5566, 1954. MSH: Lerner, A. B.: Ann. Rev. Med. 11:187-194, 1960. Synthetic ACTH peptide: Hofmann, K., et al.: J. Am. Chem. Soc. 83:487-489, 1961.

produce adrenal hypertrophy. These were progressively purified, partly owing to the development by Sayers of the ascorbic acid depletion method of assay for ACTH activity. This procedure consists of removing one adrenal of a hypophysectomized rat, injecting the ACTH unknown, and then removing the other adrenal after a specified time. The difference in ascorbic acid concentration between the two glands is proportional to the ACTH activity of the unknown.

The elucidation by Sanger of the amino acid sequence of the insulin molecule and the studies of DuVigneaud on posterior pituitary peptides stimulated similar work on many proteins and peptides, among them ACTH. The complete amino acid sequence of 2 corticotrophins (alpha and beta) from a number of species has now been described. Both of these are straight chain polypeptides, 39 amino acids long, with a MW of about 4500. The structure of bovine corticotrophin is shown in Figure 7-7.

Recently, a 24 amino acid peptide prepared by enzymatically splitting β corticotrophin was shown to have full ascorbic acid depleting potency of the complete peptide. More recently, Hofmann and his colleagues first synthesized *de novo* a 23 amino acid peptide (No. 1–23) with all of the ACTH activity of the naturally occurring material. Then they succeeded in synthesizing the entire 39 amino acid peptide, beginning with individual amino acids. This feat preceded by several years the total synthesis of insulin, which has now been accomplished by three separate groups of investigators. These are historically important accomplishments, for they foreshadow the total synthesis of even more complex molecules in the future.

The structure of ACTH suggests a possible contributory mechanism for the pigmentation of Addison's disease. The sequence of the first 13 amino acids of ACTH is identical with that in the structure of α melanophore-stimulating hormone (MSH) which arises from the pars intermedia of the hypophysis and has striking pigment-intensifying properties which are seen most dramatically in amphibia. The shared sequence of amino acids in the 2 hormones suggests either that ACTH itself may have MSH properties or that an MSH-active peptide can be split from the longer ACTH peptide. Since the ACTH-releasing mechanism is uninhibited in Addison's disease, large amounts of the hormone are produced and released. The clearing of skin pigmentation on administration of replacement doses of adrenal glucocorticoids is consistent with this theory, for adrenal hormones strongly inhibit ACTH release.

MSH output is also inhibited by cortisol and is elevated in adrenal insufficiency (see Chapter 3).

The level of metabolic activity of, and hormone production by, the fasciculata cells of the adrenal cortex is set by the intensity of ACTH stimulation. In the hypophysectomized animal or human there is a striking atrophy of the fasciculata layer of cells, but the glomerulosa layer is much less affected. Conversely, on stimulation with ACTH (or, in the intact animal subjected to a stress) there is a marked depletion of sudanophilic lipid in *fasciculata* layer, but no such change in the glomerulosa. Measurements of the hormone content of adrenal vein blood have shown that aldosterone secretion is only slightly reduced after hypophysectomy and fluctuates in response to appropriate stimuli. This comparative independence of the glomerulosa cells from ACTH stimulation, at least when the requirement for aldosterone is low or moderate, is the basis for the fact that adrenalectomy is fatal, whereas hypophysectomy is not.

If a radioactive label is attached to pure ACTH, it can be shown that an intravenously injected dose stays in the blood for a very short time—only 1 min in the rat, 5–15 min in man. Concentration and tissue fixation occur mainly in the adrenals and, curiously, in the kidneys. Whether this kidney-bound material can be split free and recirculated to the adrenals is at present a matter of conjecture.

⑥ REGULATION OF ACTH SECRETION

If one adrenal gland is removed, the contralateral gland hypertrophies to the point at which the total adrenal cortical cell mass is the same as it was in the paired glands. This does not occur in the absence of the hypophysis. Similarly, if the glands are surgically enucleated, so that only a thin layer of cortical cells remains attached to the capsule which is left in the animal, the cells proliferate up to a total mass approximately equal to the preoperative level. In this case, however, hypertension may develop, particularly on high salt diets. This may be explained by the fact that in developing adrenal cells proliferate from the capsule inward, and as they migrate they differentiate enzymatically so that the preponderant hormonal product shifts from aldosterone to corticosterone or cortisol. Newly formed cells

in the regenerating gland apparently do not differentiate fast enough, so that they maintain an inappropriately high level of aldosterone production which may be partly responsible for the hypertension. Some circumstantial evidence in support of this hypothesis is afforded by the observation that certain aldosterone antagonists (i.e., substances which competitively inhibit the salt-retaining effect of aldosterone in the kidney) have been shown to prevent adrenal regeneration hypertension. Adrenal regeneration, like compensatory hypertrophy, requires ACTH.

In normal men and unstimulated animals the amount of ACTH in the blood is too small to detect by the Sayers test. When a stressful stimulus is applied to an animal (hemorrhage, skin burn) there are small but clearly detectable amounts of ACTH in the blood. If this amount is designated as 100, the ACTH levels of the blood of unstimulated adrenalectomized rats is 200. If an adrenalectomized rat is subjected to a stress, the blood ACTH may reach levels of 800–1000. These experiments of Sayers and his colleagues summarize much of what we know about ACTH release, for they say, in effect, that ACTH is released in response to a lowering of corticosterone or cortisol blood levels (as in adrenalectomy) but that they may be increased when there can be no change in the adrenal hormone level of the blood. Furthermore, they demonstrate the braking effect of adrenal hormone on the releasing system, since the largest amount of ACTH is secreted when the corticosterone brake is not applied, for instance, in the adrenalectomized animal.

That the central nervous system participates in ACTH release is an established fact. Very striking increases in the 17-OH corticoid concentration of the blood can be provoked by the technique of traumatic interview in man (which consists of deliberately insulting or embarrassing subjects in conversation) and by frightening or frustrating monkeys in various ways. The route by which the information reaches the anterior hypophysis and signals ACTH release is the hypophysial portal system of blood vessels. Many experimental maneuvers which ordinarily trigger release of ACTH fail to do so in the animal whose hypothalamic median eminence has been destroyed by the placing of electrolytic lesions. Stimulation through electrodes in the same area, or in other, higher parts of the brain, promptly elicits a rise in the blood 17-OH corticoid (glucocorticoid) level.

Harris deduced from the anatomical relationships of the median eminence, the hypophysial portal blood vessels, and the adenohypophysis that some chemical substance may be produced in the region of the median eminence, transported to the hypophysis and there signal the release of ACTH into the venous effluent of the gland. Now several groups of workers have isolated substances from the hypothalamus (but not from other parts of the brain) which cause the release of ACTH in the median eminence-lesioned animal in extremely small (microgram quantity) doses. These substances are called corticotrophin releasing factors (CRF) and they have been isolated from commercial vasopressin preparations as well as from hypothalamus extracts. They are now being brought to a high state of purity, and are believed to be peptides of approximately the size and amino acid composition of vasopressin. There has been some evidence in favor of vasopressin itself as a physiological CRF, but the amounts of this material required to release ACTH in the lesioned animal seem too large for this view to be accepted (see Chapter 3).

At another level of organization the observation has been made that the cells of an anterior pituitary gland grown in tissue culture dedifferentiate (i.e., lose their usual staining characteristics) and do not produce detectable amounts of ACTH in vitro. If small amounts of hypothalamic tissue (but *not* other parts of the brain) are added to the tissue culture system as late as the seventeenth day, the cells redifferentiate into recognizable acidophils and basophils and the tissue produces detectable amounts of ACTH in vitro!

There is a certain analogy between ACTH and TSH. As in the case of the thyroid, the adrenal fasciculata does not atrophy to the state seen in the hypophysectomized animal when the adenohypophysis is transplanted to a site remote from the median eminence. Although adrenal function is diminished, it is well above bottom and, in fact, the transplanted gland can either be inhibited by cortisol or induced to put out more ACTH by unilateral adrenalectomy or even by certain types of stress. Therefore, it cannot be stated with certainty where the inhibitory effect of cortisol or corticosterone occurs in the hypothalamic-hypophysial complex which is responsible for

ACTH output. Inhibition may occur directly in the pituitary, in the hypothalamus, or in both places. It is also possible that suprahypothalamic structures may be involved in the control of ACTH release and production.

The reader should reflect that ACTH release is not the only event which is triggered by injury, fright, pain, noise, and so on. The neurohypophysial antidiuretic hormone (ADH) pours out under the same circumstances and adrenoglomerulotrophin (see later section), which may participate in the regulation of aldosterone secretion, also appears in large amounts. One wonders how many other materials are involved in this response and what significance this cornucopia of hormonal goodies has for adaptation and survival.

From the behavioral point of view one of the most fascinating aspects of this story is the fact that fear, or anticipation of physical injury or pain, can trigger precisely the same sequence of endocrine responses as pain itself or actual physical injury. These anticipatory responses are similar to those described by Cannon as being characteristic of a sympathoadrenomedullary discharge in anticipation of fight or flight. All of these responses taken together illustrate vividly the functional relationships that exist between higher cerebral processes and autonomic responses, whether of the sympathetic nervous system or of the endocrine system. It is now easy to imagine how emotional disorders can bring about serious derangements in somatic function by exerting effects through the "wired" and "wireless" communications systems of the body.

⑦ The Salt-Retaining Hormones— Mineralocorticoids

The first potent salt-retaining hormone, desoxycorticosterone acetate (DCA) (Fig. 7-5), was synthesized before it was isolated from adrenal cortical tissue where it is present in very small amounts. In extensive studies in man and animals it was soon found to correct the salt-losing defect of adrenal insufficiency, and thus markedly to prolong life. It did not, however, correct the carbohydrate and protein abnormalities of either the addisonian patient or the adrenalectomized animal. The correction of the salt-losing defect prevents or reverses the whole sequence of events beginning with hemoconcentration and ending in peripheral circulatory failure which are seen in the untreated adrenally deficient animal or man. The effects of salt-retaining hormones at sites of salt loss other than the kidney, such as the sweat glands, the salivary glands, and the gastrointestinal glands, have already been mentioned.

Large doses of DCA promote the renal excretion of potassium and may cause a net potassium deficiency with depletion of intracellular potassium stores and their partial replacement by sodium. This may manifest itself as muscle weakness, or in characteristic changes in the electrocardiogram. It is possible that the islands of necrosis and fibrosis seen in the cardiac and skeletal muscle of animals chronically treated with DCA may be related to potassium loss and the derangement of cellular function incident to it.

Animals maintained on large doses of DCA and physiological saline as drinking water develop severe hypertension which is believed to be similar to the adrenal regeneration hypertension mentioned previously. If the hypertension is allowed to persist, cardiac hypertrophy and renal hypertrophy are seen in addition to the patchy muscle necrosis referred to above. DCA-treated animals drink large amounts of fluid and produce correspondingly large amounts of urine. Presumably, thirst caused by sodium retention is the primary event to which the high urine volume is secondary. The mechanism of the hypertension is unknown, for it occurs without detectable expansion of the circulating blood or extracellular fluid volumes. The fact that it can be ameliorated by treatment with tranquilizers suggests that there is a prominent central nervous system component in it.

The high salt-retaining potency of the so-called amorphous fraction of commercial adrenal extracts encouraged Tait, Simpson and their colleagues to search for the "physiologic DCA." As a result of the development of highly sensitive paper chromatographic methods by others they were enabled to isolate and identify a new adrenal steroid which resembled cortisol and cortisone in its chromatographic mobility but differed from them in forming a diacetate on acetylation. The compound was first called electrocortin, but is now universally known as *aldosterone*. Its most distinctive chemical characteristic is an aldehyde group at C-18 which is masked by the formation of the hemiacetal form of the compound.

While aldosterone was being extracted and identified another exceedingly active salt-retaining factor (SRF) was isolated from the urine of certain edematous patients by Leutscher *et al.* The identity of SRF and aldosterone has now been proved.

Aldosterone is certainly the "physiological DCA" that was sought, for it has been found in the adrenal vein blood of a number of species and it is an extremely potent salt-retainer. Life can be maintained in the adrenalectomized dog with as little as 1.5–2.0 *micrograms* of aldosterone per kg of body weight injected daily. Addisonian patients may require as little as 100–200 *micrograms* per day. Aldosterone has from 5 to 100 times the salt-retaining potency of DCA, depending on the assay method used.

Since aldosterone is oxygenated at C-11 it is not surprising that it has considerable glucocorticoid activity. It is, in fact, one-half to one-third as active as cortisone in such tests as liver glycogen deposition and eosinophil depletion. In the blood, however, the concentration of aldosterone is less than one hundredth that of cortisol (0.08 microgram/100 ml of blood versus 8–15 mcg for cortisol) and its glucocorticoid activity is therefore physiologically negligible. These figures illustrate the point that an animal can have life-maintaining amounts of aldosterone in his circulation and at the same time be grossly deficient in glucocorticoids.

PRIMARY ALDOSTERONISM

In 1955, Conn described a new disease—primary aldosteronism. The original patient, a 35-year-old woman, complained of weakness, which is hardly a promising beginning for a brilliant research exploit. But Conn was struck by the association of excessive renal loss of potassium with hypokalemia, moderate hypernatremia, and mild hypertension. Bio-assay of the urine revealed large amounts of a highly active salt-retaining material which was identified as aldosterone. Exploration of the patient revealed an adrenal cortical tumor, which was removed. Weakness, hypertension, and electrolyte abnormalities disappeared and the patient has remained well. Over 100 such patients have now been studied and most of them have had aldosterone-producing adenomata, although a few have had diffuse adrenal hyperplasia with excessive aldosterone production. This development illustrates the short latent period that sometimes occurs between the discovery of basic physiological facts and their application in the clinic.

SECONDARY ALDOSTERONISM

The discovery by Leutscher of large amounts of a potent salt-retaining factor in the urine of many patients with various kinds of edema and the identification of the material as aldosterone has been confirmed many times. Increased urinary excretion of aldosterone has been seen in edematous patients with congestive heart failure, nephrotic syndrome, hepatic cirrhosis, and toxemia of pregnancy. In others, as primary aldosteronism, some patients with Cushing's disease, malignant hypertension, and postoperative or posttraumatic patients, high urinary levels of aldosterone or salt-retaining factor are seen in the absence of edema. The lack of edema in the latter group suggests that hyperaldosteronism probably is not the primary factor in the initiation of the edema seen in the first group. Obviously, however, when an increase in aldosterone secretion is elicited in an edematous patient it tends to perpetuate the edema by interfering with salt excretion. That this is the case is suggested by recent experience with certain synthetic steroid analogues of aldosterone, called spirolactones, which competitively inhibit aldosterone at the renal tubular cell and prevent its salt-retaining action (Fig. 7-8). Some patients resistant to the action of diuretics respond to the antialdosterones with a prompt diuresis.

The mechanism of the hypersecretion of aldosterone in edematous states remains uncertain. Various speculations have included the possibility that these conditions may be characterized by a diminished effective circulating blood volume, that this signal is perceived by volume receptors which relay it to the juxtaglomerular cells which, in turn, respond by releasing renin. This results in the production of angiotensin II, which stimulates the glomerular cells to produce aldosterone. (See following section for a more complete account.) In the case of liver disease it has been suggested that there may be a decreased inactivation of aldosterone which results in its accumulation. A full understanding of this interesting phenomenon must await an elucidation of the problem to be discussed in the following paragraphs.

⑧ REGULATION OF ALDOSTERONE SECRETION

Early histochemical work by Deane and others seemed to indicate that the glomerulosa cells of the adrenal cortex, in which aldosterone is produced, are relatively independent of the action of ACTH. It was pointed out that hypophysectomized animals and men do not die of salt loss and that the glomerulosa of rat adrenals widens in response to a low salt intake even in the absence of the hypophysis. More recently, this view has been recognized as an oversimplification. It is now generally conceded that ACTH plays an important role in aldosterone regulation but that its status as a major stimulus to the secretion of the hormone varies greatly among the species. At one end of the spectrum, ACTH is probably the major trophic hormone for aldosterone secretion in the frog, particularly following salt depletion. At the other, the importance of ACTH in aldosterone secretion in man is more likely related to its ability to maintain the glomerulosa cells in such condition that they can respond maximally to the stimulatory effects of other substances. In the dog, ACTH is essential for a full aldosterone

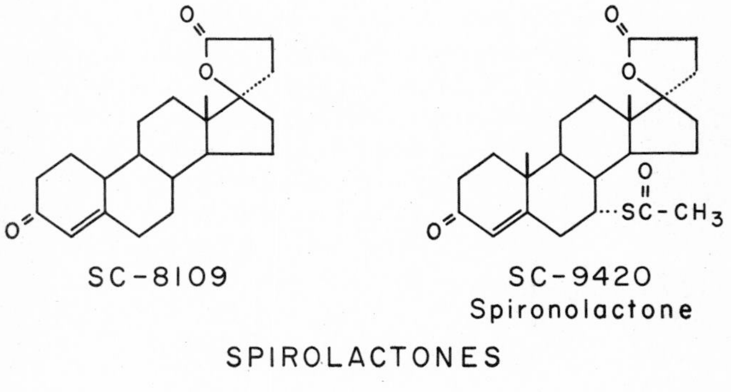

SC-8109

SC-9420
Spironolactone

SPIROLACTONES

Fig. 7-8.—Spirolactone aldosterone antagonists. (See review by Streeten, D. H. P., in Clin. Pharm. Therap. 2:359-373, 1961.)

response to many stimuli. However, in this species, as Mulrow has shown, aldosterone output is not increased appreciably by injected ACTH unless very large doses (100-1000 mU) are used, whereas a striking increase in the output of 17-hydroxycorticoids occurs at a dose of 5 mU and a maximal increase occurs at the 10 mU level. This suggests that ACTH is acting more permissively with respect to aldosterone but that its major function is to elicit the secretion and synthesis of glucocorticoids.

Perhaps some clues about the nature of the signals which elicit aldosterone secretion can be obtained from contemplating the circumstances in which increased excretion of aldosterone occurs (and therefore, presumably, increased rate of production). A prime stimulus is *acute hemorrhage,* with its sudden sharp decrease in circulating volume. *Diets low in sodium* or *high in potassium* also cause increased aldosterone output in the urine. The clinical condition of *hyperaldosteronism secondary to edema* may have its experimental animal counterpart in the increased aldosterone secretion that occurs in dogs with chronic *constriction of the inferior vena cava.* A powerful stimulus to aldosterone production is *prolonged heat stress* associated with profuse sweating and its concomitant salt loss. Thus, one can infer that the signal or signals for aldosterone release either involve alterations in the concentrations of serum electrolytes or changes in effective circulating blood volume or both.

In fact, there is good evidence that both of these kinds of signals are operative. In addition to earlier histological observations on the widening of the glomerulosa in animals on Na^+ poor or K^+ rich diets, studies with isolated perfused adrenals have confirmed earlier suspicions that concentrations of electrolytes perfusing the adrenals directly influence the output of aldosterone by the glands. Either lowering the Na^+ concentration or raising the K^+ concentration increases aldosterone production. In the case of K^+, Davis has found that increases as small as 1.3 mEq/L are effective and it has been suggested by Laragh and Stoerk that this direct effect of K^+ on the glomerulosa cells is a primary defense of the body against a sudden increase in K^+ intake such as occurs after the ingestion of K^+ rich foods. Decreases in serum Na^+ are, perhaps, less likely to figure prominently in the regulation of aldosterone secretion.

A happy confluence of ideas beginning in about 1960 has resulted in the elucidation of the *renin-angiotensin mechanism of aldosterone regulation.* Prior to that time, there had been extensive speculation, largely stimulated by the imagination of John P. Peters, about the existence and possible anatomical localization of certain "volume receptors" which, somehow, were able to monitor changes in circulating blood volume and send messages to appropriate buffer systems. At about the same time that J. O. Davis and colleagues and Ganong and Mulrow proved that the kidney is a source of a powerful aldosterone stimulating substance, Genest *et al.,* and J. Laragh independently demonstrated that the intravenous infusion of synthetic angiotensin II resulted in a marked increase in aldosterone secretion in man. Many of the details of the renin-angiotensin mechanism had already been worked out by Braun-Menendez *et al.,* by Page *et al.,* and by others in the context of studies on experimental hypertension. This line of work can be traced back to the classical studies by Goldblatt on renal hypertension.

Studies on the juxtaglomerular cells of the kidney, which have been shown by immunochemical methods to be the source of renin, indicated a striking parallelism between degranulation (presumably, renin secretion) and widening of the glomerulosa zone of the adrenals. Although the authorities on this subject are not in unanimous agreement on every issue, I have attempted to present a diagrammatic summary of current thought on the control of aldosterone secretion in Figure 7-9.

A poorly defined signal—possibly set up by a change in blood volume—instructs the juxtaglomerular cells to release renin, a proteolytic enzyme. The renin then acts on a circulating α_2-globulin (sometimes called angiotensinogen) and produces a decapeptide, angiotensin I. A circulating converting enzyme then splits 2 amino acids from angiotensin I to produce the physiologically active angiotensin II. This substance has two known physiological effects: (1) it is a powerful vasoconstrictor and (2) it is a potent stimulator of the glomerulosa cells of the adrenal cortex to produce aldosterone. Angiotensin II is a sort of ACTH for the glomerulosa cells, but, as we have indicated, there is some evidence in some species that the stimulating effect of angiotensin II on the glomerulosa cell is maximally

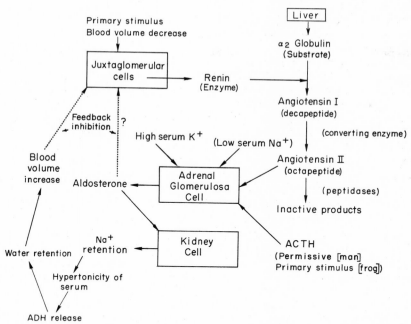

Fig. 7-9.—A schematic description of renal aldosterone regulation. (Adapted from descriptions of J. O. Davis, P. Hartroft, P. J. Mulrow, J. Genest, J. Laragh, I. Page and others.)

effective only if the cell is under the influence of ACTH. Circulating angiotensin II has only a fleeting existence, since it is quite susceptible to inactivation by unspecified peptidases which are ubiquitously distributed.

The biochemical mechanism of action of angiotensin II in the glomerulosa cell has not been studied in as much detail as has that of ACTH in the fasciculata cell. It will be of great interest to discover whether or not angiotensin II selectively stimulates the glomerulosa cell to produce 3'5' cyclic AMP by analogy with the effect of ACTH on the glucocorticoid-producing cell.

The aldosterone produced under the stimulus of angiotensin II increases sodium and water reabsorption in the distal tubule of the kidney. A short review of the biochemical mechanism of action of aldosterone is given in Chapter 12. It is sufficient here to say only that sodium and water retention result in a correction of the initial blood volume disturbance that initiated the demand for aldosterone in the first place and that this has the effect of removing the stimulus to the juxtaglomerular cells. Laragh believes there is evidence to suggest that aldosterone itself may have a direct feedback relationship with the juxtaglomerular cells. P. M. Hartroft (1966) has

suggested that changes in sodium availability may influence the function of the JG apparatus when blood volume changes are prevented. Figure 7-9 also shows that elevation of serum K^+ and decrease of serum Na^+ independently stimulate the glomerulosa cells to produce aldosterone.

The problem of the role of the central nervous system in the regulation of aldosterone secretion remains unresolved. There has been a tendency, in recent years, to belittle the contribution of the CNS as a major determinant of aldosterone secretion rate, largely on the basis of Davis' demonstration that marked fluctuations in secretion rate occur in the decapitated animal. The existence of a specific adrenoglomerulotrophin of CNS origin has been questioned by many of the leading investigators of this problem. However, we are still left with the problem of providing mechanistic explanations for clinical observations of hypernatremia after hypothalamic injury and salt diuresis following a variety of CNS insults (see Rauschkolb and Farrell, 1958). If these vaguely defined syndromes involve aldosterone regulation they may do so secondarily by way of changing blood flow patterns through various vascular beds in such a way that the renin-angiotensin mechanism might be tricked into either discharging or withholding renin inappropriately.

If aldosterone is secreted at inappropriately rapid rates, as it appears to be in secondary hyperaldosteronism, it may also accumulate because it is inactivated too slowly in edematous states. Again, Davis has demonstrated by means of H^3 labeled aldosterone that failure of inactivation of the hormone may occur in edematous states in which liver function is impaired. This obviously exaggerates the effect of the aldosterone that is being overproduced.

Aldosterone, like glucocorticoids, is produced in a recurrent diurnally variable pattern; i.e., in a circadian rhythm. More of the hormone is excreted in the forenoon than at other times of the day. Wolfe, Liddle and associates (1966) have found that the rhythmic fluctuations in aldosterone excretion (and, presumably, secretion) are due to postural changes, for they can be suppressed by having human subjects remain in a recumbent posture through the 24 hours. In their experiments, changes in plasma renin activity were parallel with those in aldosterone excretion. This finding is of some importance in the clinical evaluation of aldosterone excretion patterns.

The discovery of the importance of the renin-angiotensin system as a trophic complex for aldosterone secretion has stimulated an enormous amount of imaginative clinical investigation. Now, methods are available for measuring fluctuations in the renin concentration in blood and these, coupled with aldosterone measurements, should make possible distinctions between primary and secondary aldosteronism.

⑨ Adrenal Androgens

The role of adrenal androgens in physiology is unknown. Although they are believed to be the source of approximately three fifths of the aggregate urinary androgen excretion product, 17-keto-steroids, they are obviously unable to maintain the secondary sex characteristics of either castrated men or animals. In the female they may be associated with the growth of pubic and axillary hair, and some cases of idiopathic hirsutism are believed to be due to the production of excessive amounts of abnormal kinds of adrenal androgen. It has been asserted that androgens produced by the adrenals are important in maintaining normal libido in the female, for while libido may persist in the ovariectomized woman it does not survive adrenalectomy. The physician's interest in adrenal androgen has been devoted largely to the problems of virilization in the female and precocious puberty in the young male as a result either of an inborn metabolic error or of an androgen-producing tumor. A detailed discussion of the adrenal androgen problem has appeared in a recent review (Munson, 1961).

⑩ The Adrenals and Molecular Roulette

The widespread use of adrenal cortical steroids as anti-inflammatory agents has stimulated searches for compounds which would have certain desirable qualities exaggerated and undesirable qualities suppressed or eliminated. Organic

TABLE 7-1.—APPROXIMATE COMPARATIVE POTENCIES OF CERTAIN NATURAL AND SYNTHETIC STEROIDS IN MAN**

COMPOUND	SALT-RETAINING ACTIVITY DCA = 1	GLUCO-CORTICOID ACTIVITY Cortisol = 1	ADRENAL SUPPRESSION mg/day	ANTI-INFLAMMATORY Cortisone = 1
Aldosterone	30	0.3	?	0.3
9 α Fluorohydrocortisone	20	10–20	2–5	10*
Δ^1-Hydrocortisone	minimal	3	10	4
Δ^1-9 α F'hydrocortisone	20	3(?)	1.5	10+*
2-Methyl hydrocortisone	1	1	4	3
2-Methyl 9 α F'hydrocortisone	100	10	6	10+*

*Used for local anti-inflammatory effect only.
**Modified from Prunty, F. T. G., in *Modern Trends in Endocrinology*, Gardiner-Hill, H. (ed.) (New York: Paul B. Hoeber, Inc., 1958).

chemists appear to be able to play an almost infinite number of variations on the structure of the naturally occurring hormone, and their modified compounds are then subjected to batteries of tests to ascertain their spectrum of activities. This approach to experimental therapeutics has been described as molecular roulette by Modell. A number of extremely useful compounds have been developed in this way, among them the spirolactone aldosterone antagonists which were discussed above.

The *halogenated steroids* were originally prepared as intermediates in the laboratory synthesis of cortisone from bile acids. When cortisol was fluorinated at the 9 α position, both salt-retaining potency and glucocorticoid activity were remarkably enhanced. This is a case in which the organic chemist improved on nature, for one of the fluorinated steroids (2 methyl 9 α fluorocortisol) is more than three times as potent as aldosterone in mineralocorticoid activity, and is effective as replacement therapy in man at a dose of only 25 micrograms per day by mouth. It is possible that the halogenated compounds owe some of their potency by the oral route to the fact that they resist detoxification in the liver.

The Δ^1 compounds, prednisone and prednisolone, are analogues of cortisone and cortisol respectively. In each case the only difference from the parent compound is the addition of a double bond in the 1,2 position. This apparently minor modification changes the characteristics of these substances so that their glucocorticoid activity is enhanced by a factor of 3–5 times, while there is no increase in salt-retaining potency. Since the early clinical experience with cortisone and cortisol was marred by the frequent occurrence of salt and water retention, mild hypertension and even congestive heart failure, the Δ^1 compounds represented a real advance, for it was possible to achieve equivalent anti-inflammatory effects with smaller doses which were less likely to cause unwanted salt and water retention. Similar high inflammatory potency compounds with low salt-retaining activity have been achieved by methylating the B ring at the 6 position. The most widely used compound in this series is 6 methyl-Δ^1 hydrocortisone, or methyl prednisolone.

Fig. 7-10.—Synthetic analogues of adrenal cortical steroids. 9α fluorocortisol is powerfully salt-retaining, but the 16α hydroxy substituted compound (triamcinolone) and the 16α methyl substituted compound (dexamethasone) are predominantly anti-inflammatory glucocorticoid substances.

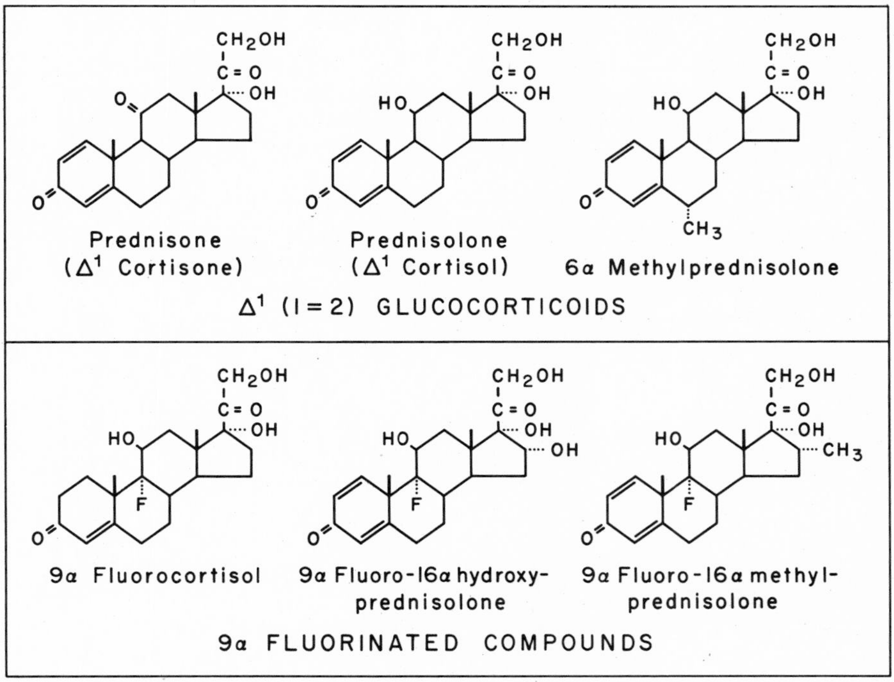

Prednisone
(Δ^1 Cortisone)

Prednisolone
(Δ^1 Cortisol)

6α Methylprednisolone

Δ^1 (1 = 2) GLUCOCORTICOIDS

9α Fluorocortisol

9α Fluoro-16α hydroxy-
prednisolone

9α Fluoro-16α methyl-
prednisolone

9α FLUORINATED COMPOUNDS

It should be emphasized that though there has been some degree of success in producing compounds which are preferentially anti-inflammatory rather than salt-retaining, the newer compounds do not have a specific increase in anti-inflammatory activity without an increase in other typical glucocorticoid activities. Thus, although the salt-retention risk has been diminished to a certain extent, many of the other unwanted side effects of long-term administration of steroids are as likely to appear with the smaller doses of the new synthetic compounds as they were with the parent substances. Osteoporosis, masking of infections, central nervous stimulation, and asthenia on withdrawal due to ACTH suppression have not been eliminated by increasing the anti-inflammatory potency of the compounds, for so far these effects have not been separable from anti-inflammation. The structures of some of the synthetic steroids are shown in Figure 7-10. The nonhalogenated compounds are useful not only for their anti-inflammatory effect but also as replacement treatment for missing hormones and for ACTH suppression in adrenal virilism. The fluorinated substances are used with success in Addison's disease and for their local anti-inflammatory effects. The comparative potencies of some of these compounds in different assays are given in Table 7-1.

REFERENCES

Asboe-Hansen, G.: Hormonal effects on connective tissue, Physiol. Rev. 38:446–462, 1958.

Bartter, F. C., *et al.*: Studies on the control and physiologic action of aldosterone, Recent Prog. Hormone Res. 15:311–344, 1959.

Bunim, J. J.: A decade of anti-inflammatory steroids, from cortisone to dexamethasone (Symposium), Ann. New York Acad. Sc. 82:797–1014, 1959.

Bush, I. E.: Chemical and biological factors in the activity of adrenocortical steroids, Pharmacol. Rev. 14:317–445, 1962.

Chart, J. J., and Sheppard, H.: Pharmacology and biochemistry of some amphenone analogues and other adrenal cortical inhibitors, J. Med. & Pharm. Chem. 1:407–441, 1959.

Davis, J. O.: Mechanisms regulating the secretion and metabolism of aldosterone in experimental secondary hyperaldosteronism, Recent Prog. Hormone Res. 17:293–352, 1961.

Eisenstein, A. B. (ed.): *The Adrenal Cortex* (Boston: Little, Brown & Co., 1967).

Hayano, M., *et al.*: Some aspects of the biogenesis of adrenal steroid hormones, Recent Prog. Hormone Res. 12:79–123, 1956.

Lipsett, M. B., Schwartz, I. L., and Thorn, N. A.: Hormonal control of sodium, potassium, chloride and water metabolism, in *Mineral Metabolism,* Comar, C. L., and Bronner, F. (eds.) (New York: Academic Press, Inc., 1961) vol. 1, pt. B, pp. 473–549.

Moon, H. D.: *The Adrenal Cortex* (New York: Paul B. Hoeber, Inc., 1961).

Moore, F. D.: *Metabolic Care of the Surgical Patient* (Philadelphia: W. B. Saunders Company, 1959).

Skelton, F. R.: Adrenal regeneration and adrenal regeneration hypertension, Physiol. Rev. 39:162–182, 1959.

Soffer, L. J., Dorfman, R. I., and Gabrilove, J. L.: *The Human Adrenal Gland* (Philadelphia: Lea & Febiger, 1961).

Sorkin, S. Z.: The centenary of Addison's disease, Bull. New York Acad. Med. 32:819–843, 1956.

Stempfel, R. S., Jr., and Tomkins, G. M.: Congenital virilizing adrenogenital hyperplasia, in *The Metabolic Basis of Inherited Disease* (New York: McGraw-Hill Book Company, Inc., 1966).

Streeten, D. H. P.: The spirolactones, Clin. Pharmacology & Therapeutics 2:359–373, 1961.

Weissman, G., and Thomas, L.: The effects of corticosteroids upon connective tissue and lysosomes, Recent Prog. Hormone Res. 20:215-245, 1964.

Wolstenholme, G. E. W., and O'Connor, M.: *Metabolic Effects of Adrenal Hormones,* Ciba Foundation Study Group No. 6 (Boston: Little, Brown & Co., 1960).

8

The Adrenal Medulla

THE ADRENOMEDULLARY PRODUCT, epinephrine, was the first hormone to be chemically identified and synthesized. Appropriately, it was the first hormone for which the outlines of a plausible biochemical mechanism of action were developed. If the latent period of approximately half a century that occurred between these events represents par for the course, we still have several decades in which biochemical mechanisms of action for other hormones may be worked out.

Like the posterior pituitary, the adrenal medulla is a functional part of the nervous system. It can be regarded as a specialized sympathetic ganglion which is innervated by the customary long preganglionic neurone. In the gland there is a cholinergic synapse with chromaffin cells which, on activation, discharge stored epinephrine and norepinephrine directly into the blood. Thus, a nerve-borne preganglionic message is converted into a blood-borne postganglionic one. It is characteristic of the sympathetic, or adrenergic, division of the autonomic nervous system that a single preganglionic neurone synapses with many postganglionic ones, and thereby contributes to the massiveness of the adrenergic discharge that occurs in a variety of physiological or psychological (anticipatory) emergencies. No doubt, the blood-borne character of the adrenomedullary postganglionic message provides an additional dimension of pervasiveness to the flooding of the organism with chemical alarms in the form of epinephrine and norepinephrine. The effects of adrenomedullary discharge constitute the first in a timed series of adaptive responses to meet an emergency.

The importance of the adrenal medullary response for survival is a matter of conjecture. It is certainly true that the adrenal medullae are not essential for life, as the cortices are. But if one adrenal is removed and the other demedullated the magnitude of the usual adrenergic response is diminished, although a massive sympathetic discharge still occurs if the animal is challenged. It would be extraordinarily difficult to design an experiment to evaluate whether or not the absence of the adrenal medullae is ever critical for survival.

The adrenal medullae are stimulated to release their hormones in amounts 1000-fold larger than those released by the gland under resting conditions. It is interesting to reflect that this auto-injection with medullary hormones occurs in precisely the same circumstances in which the secretion of ACTH, ADH, and (in many cases) aldosterone is also stimulated. When specific loci in the medulla, spinal cord, and hypothalamus are electrically stimulated an efferent message is carried via the preganglionic adrenomedullary nerves and a discharge of hormone is brought about. Afferent neural orders for epinephrine discharge may be carried as *pain* messages, or as perception of *cold,* or (as in the case of ADH and aldosterone) volume receptors in the circulatory system may be fired by hypotension secondary to *hemorrhage. Emotional* states (rage, extreme anxiety) can trigger the glands to release their hormones.

In another category, a change in the chemical composition of the blood traversing the brain may cause the release of the medullary substances

SOME LANDMARKS IN ADRENAL MEDULLA CHRONOLOGY

DATE		INVESTIGATOR
1856	Adrenals stained green with ferric chloride	Vulpian
1895	Pressor activity of adrenal gland extracts	Syzmonowicz and Cybulski; Oliver and Schafer
1899	Similarity noted between effects of adrenal extract and sympathetic nerve stimulation	Lewandowsky
1901	Adrenal extracts active even after sympathetic denervation	Langley
1900 et seq.	Isolation, purification, identification, and synthesis of epinephrine	Abel; von Furth; Takamine
1904	First enunciation of neurohumoral theory of nerve transmission: epinephrine postulated as sympathetic transmitter	Elliott
1904–1905	Synthesis of epinephrine	Stolz; Dakin
1910	Synthesis of norepinephrine	Studied by Barger and Dale
1921 et seq.	Role of epinephrine-like substance as neurohumoral mediator established	Loewi; Cannon
1929	"Fight-flight" theory of adrenomedullary discharge	Cannon
1931	Metabolic effects of epinephrine summarized	Cori
1951	Evidence for identity of norepinephrine and sympathetic humoral transmitter marshalled	von Euler

from the adrenals. *Oxygen lack* may cause reflex discharge of epinephrine by acting directly on the brain and it may also act locally in the glands themselves to release hormone. *Insulin hypoglycemia* also provokes a powerful adrenomedullary response; here, there is absolutely no question about the physiological appropriateness and usefulness of the sympathetic discharge, for it tends to restore the blood glucose to the equilibrium level.

Many *drugs* and *poisons* elicit the response; among them are the general anesthetics and convulsants as a group. Since the physiological stimulus of the chromaffin cells is mediated by acetylcholine parasympathomimetic drugs (like acetyl beta methylcholine or carbaminoylcholine), stimulating doses of nicotine and acetylcholine potentiators (like the cholinesterase inhibitors) may stimulate or magnify the adrenomedullary response by acting in the vicinity of the secretory cells themselves.

Storage and Release of Epinephrine and Norepinephrine

In recent years, ingenious combinations of the techniques of differential centrifugation, electron microscopy, and other methods have yielded interesting new information about the nature of the chromaffin storage granules in the adrenal medulla. The pioneer studies of Blaschko and Welch (1953) led to the development of centrifugation methods by which it is possible to separate chromaffin granules from the mitochondria, and to show that these granules are identical with the dense osmiophilic granules seen in electronmicrographs of adrenal medulla (Fig. 8-1). Thus, the medullary cell contains discrete packets of material which represent the storage form of the catecholamine hormones. This powerful medicine is conveniently sequestered in a form in which it cannot embarrass the secretory cell, and it is only spilled overboard into the venous effluent of the

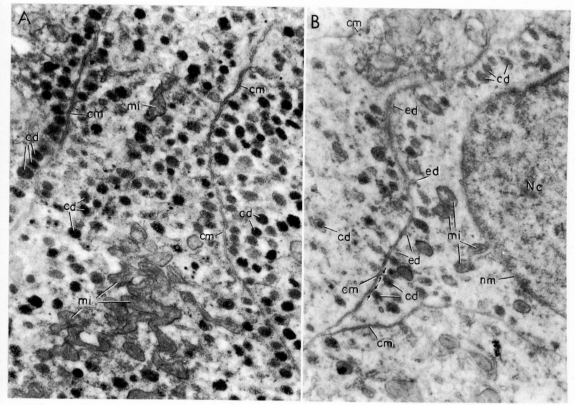

Fig. 8-1.—Electronmicrographs (×41,000) or (rabbit) adrenal medulla, **A** before and **B** after stimulation of the splanchnic nerve: cd, catechol-containing droplets; cm, cell membrane; mi, mitochondria; ed, empty droplets; Nc, nucleus; nm, nuclear membrane. Note that the stimulated cell is nearly free of catechol droplets (cd) and those which remain are at the periphery of the cell. Several empty droplets (ed) can be observed attached to the cell membrane (marked with arrows). (Reprinted with permission from DeRobertis, E. D. P., and Sabatini, D. D.: Fed. Proc. 19 (Suppl. 5): 70-78, 1960.)

gland on demand. By now, the maneuver of packaging a hormone in this way is beginning to seem familiar, for one can recall similar packaging of acetylcholine, posterior lobe peptides, (probably) anterior pituitary hormones, and a powerful mixture of histamine, heparin and 5-hydroxytryptamine (in mast cells). Insulin exists in beta cells in the form of secretory granules. All of this is reminiscent of the storage of the lysozyme group of enzymes in cells, and the activation of these enzymes only when their "envelopes" are broken. In a manner of speaking, thyroglobulin could be considered to be a sort of king-size secretory granule.

There have been suggestions (based on histochemical and electronmicroscopic grounds) that there are two cell types in the medulla: one predominantly epinephrine-secreting, and the other norepinephrine-secreting. In this connection it is of some interest that granules have been isolated which have more of either one or the other catecholamine in them. Indeed, according to one report insulin hypoglycemia elicits a predominantly epinephrine discharge from the adrenals, while the animal in hemorrhagic shock somehow manages to signal for norepinephrine. This seems almost too good to be true, for epinephrine is more powerfully hyperglycemic than norepinephrine, while the latter is the better vasoconstrictor agent. These studies, together with cytologic observations of medullary cell types and granules, open the possibility that the body has ways of differentiating between the two forms of emergency and of despatching an order for just the right remedy for each!

Little is known about the actual mechanism by

which acetylcholine stimulation effects release of the catecholamine hormones from the medullary cell. Hillarp made the fascinating discovery that the isolated chromaffin granules contain astonishingly large amounts of ATP. According to his analyses the chemical composition of the granules is as follows: 68% water, 6.7% catecholamine, 11.5% protein, 4.5% adenine nucleotide (mostly ATP) and 7% lipid. It has been found that there is a molar relationship between total catecholamine and total adenine nucleotide in the resting gland. When the gland is stimulated to discharge its stored material, there is a marked, but uneven, drop in *both* catecholamine and ATP. This curious relationship between catecholamine and ATP also obtains in the norepinephrine granules found in sympathetic nerve fibers. Hillarp has suggested that the hydrolysis of ATP in the granules by an adenosinetriphosphatase might play a role in hormone release. It is certainly esthetically appealing (though highly speculative) to think of the ATP as somehow acting to keep the catecholamine granule intact; that acetylcholine stimulation of the cell activates an adenosinetriphosphatase; and that the hydrolysis of ATP is the equivalent of breaking the string that holds the package together. Acetylcholine added directly to preparations of the isolated granules does not release the catecholamines; apparently it requires some component of the intact cell for its releasing effect. On the other hand, tyramine, a sympathomimetic amine which is believed to act by releasing norepinephrine, does liberate catecholamines from isolated chromaffin particles.

Adrenal Medullary Hormone Chemistry and Biosynthesis

By a combination of radioactive tracer methodology and chromatography students of the adrenal medulla have worked out the biosynthetic scheme shown in Figure 8-2. The amino acid tyrosine is converted to dihydroxyphenylalanine (dopa) which, in turn, is converted to dopamine in a reaction catalyzed by the enzyme L-dopa decarboxylase. Dopamine is the first pharmacologically active compound to be formed in this sequence of reactions; it has many of the pharmacological effects of epinephrine and norepinephrine, but it is far less potent than these com-

Fig. 8-2.—Synthesis of catecholamine hormones.

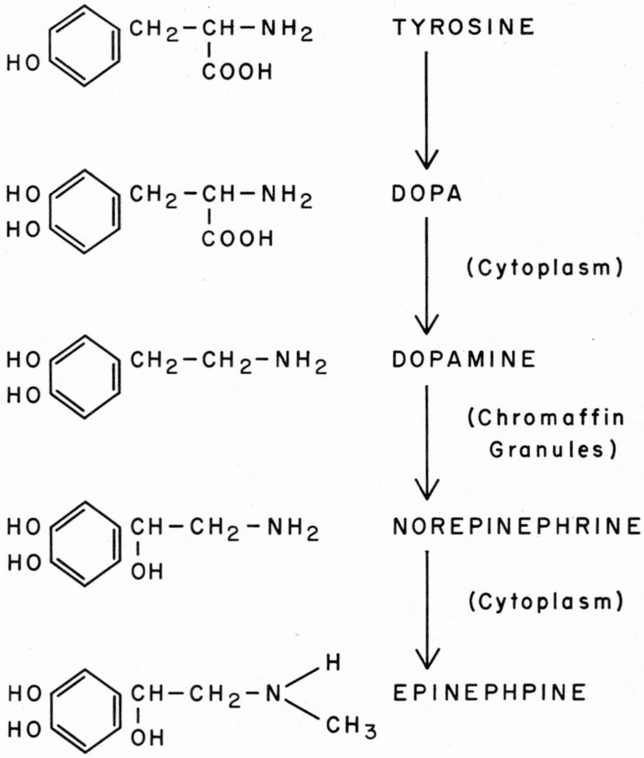

pounds. Dopamine is a minor constituent of the chromaffin granules in the adrenal medulla, but in sympathetic nerve fibers, where it may be present to the extent of 50% of the total catecholamine (the other 50% being norepinephrine) it is outside the granules. The synthetic reactions shown in Figure 8-2 were worked out for adrenal medulla, but the same reactions are thought to occur in sympathetic nerve fibers. One of the key enzymes, L-dopa decarboxylase, has been found in sympathetic nerves. In that locus, a ready supply of dopamine appears to be stored as a norepinephrine precursor, whereas the concentration of dopamine in the adrenals is low. Incidentally, dopamine occurs in secretory granules in odd places all over the body—lung, liver, jejunal mucous membrane, colon—many of which are virtually without innervation. What this pharmacologically active material is doing in these sites, if anything, is at present a deep mystery.

The beta hydroxylation of dopamine to norepinephrine is the only reaction of the biosynthetic sequence which is believed to occur in the secretory granules. The N-methylation of norepinephrine to epinephrine occurs in the cytoplasm of the cell. Since epinephrine is a prominent constituent of the granules when they are separated from the rest of the cell, we must assume that these units have some way of abstracting epinephrine from the surrounding cytoplasm.

After the gland discharges its stored hormone, resynthesis must occur. In this process the innervation of the gland plays a crucial role. Schumann and his colleagues took advantage of the fact that the drug reserpine has the capacity to cause a very marked depletion of catecholamine hormones from the medulla, and studied the rate of restorage following the emptying of hormones from the gland by means of this drug. They found that denervation markedly slowed the rate of resynthesis of epinephrine.

METABOLISM OF THE CATECHOLAMINES

Among many reasons for examining the fate of epinephrine and norepinephrine are the following: (1) An understanding of the intermediary metabolism of these substances is now proving to be of great practical importance in the diagnosis and management of certain patients with catecholamine-producing tumors; (2) the mechanism of the quick termination of the action of these substances (by analogy with the effect of cholinesterase on acetylcholine) is of great interest.

The principal metabolic route of both medullary hormones is by way of O-methylation. Figure 8-3, a diagrammatic summary of an immense amount of work by many individuals, is a representation of our present information about the

Fig. 8-3.—Metabolic fate of catecholamine hormones. The numbers in parentheses signify the per cent of an administered dose of labeled epinephrine that appeared in the urine in the form indicated. Monoamine oxidase and aldehyde dehydrogenase *both* participate in the reactions indicated by upper and lower arrows. (From Axelrod, J., in *Adrenergic Mechanisms*, Ciba Foundation Symposium, Vane, J. R., Wolstenholme, G. E. W., and O'Connor, Maeve [eds.] [Boston: Little, Brown & Co., 1960].)

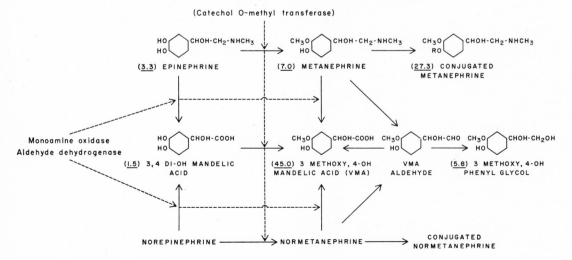

metabolism of epinephrine and norepinephrine.

O-methylation of the hormones occurs extremely rapidly; when labeled material is injected, a preponderance of O-methylated compound is found within 2 min. That this reaction is an inactivating one is suggested by the fact that the physiological effect of the hormones is prolonged when inhibitors of the enzyme O-methyl transferase are present. Formerly, the enzyme monoamine oxidase was suggested as a possible candidate as the "cholinesterase" for epinephrine, but it has now been found that monoamine oxidase inhibitors (such as iproniazid) do not in fact affect either the metabolism of or the physiological response to the catecholamine hormones. The inactivation of these substances can be visualized as occurring in two phases, a rapid one and a more prolonged one. The former is mediated by O-methyl transferase and the latter (in part) by monoamine oxidase.

CATECHOLAMINE HORMONE AND METABOLITE ASSAYS

Until about 10 years ago the only methods widely available for catecholamine hormone assay were bio-assay methods. A variety of quite sensitive assay methods were devised in which the responses of specific tissues to an unknown and to standard solutions of known epinephrine concentration were compared. For example, epinephrine added in vitro to a properly mounted strip of rabbit intestine or isolated hen rectal cecum causes a sudden relaxation of the muscle and an interruption of rhythmic contractions. Such an effect can be obtained with as little as 100–200 millimicrograms of norepinephrine. Among other epinephrine-sensitive biological systems that have been adapted for use in assay methods are the following: (1) acceleration in rate of the isolated frog or toad heart, (2) dilation of the pupil of the enucleated frog or toad eye, (3) contraction of the nictitating membrane of the cat, and (4) vasoconstriction of the denervated rabbit ear. The last method is exquisitely sensitive; with it one can detect epinephrine in a concentration of 10^{-11} Gm/ml or less. Its extreme sensitivity is based on the well-recognized fact that denervated structures are much more sensitive to the action of their appropriate neurohumoral transmitter substances than are similar structures with an intact innervation. This may be related to the fact that when the nerve is cut, not only is the neurohumor lost, but also the enzymatic means for its rapid destruction. The cholinesterase content of denervated cholinergic structures is very low. It would be interesting to know the O-methyl transferase activity of denervated adrenergic structures.

A number of older *colorimetric* procedures for catecholamines are now being replaced by *fluorimetric* methods, for epinephrine and related substances have the property of fluorescence in alkaline solutions. While the fluorimetric methods are far more sensitive than the colorimetric ones they lack specificity unless they are used in conjunction with chromatographic separation methods. The use of column and especially paper-chromatographic methods has made possible the separation and identification of individual catecholamines and their metabolites. One of the most prominent of these is 3-methoxy, 4-hydroxy-mandelic acid or VMA, which is excreted by normal children in amounts ranging from 0.5 to 2.0 micrograms per day. This is the form in which 45% of an injected dose of epinephrine is excreted (Fig. 8-3).

SYMPATHOMIMETIC AMINES

A few naturally occurring compounds and a large number of synthetic ones mimic the action of epinephrine and norepinephrine in one or another way. These are structurally related to the adrenal catecholamine hormones and are commonly used in the clinic and in countless over-the-counter proprietary preparations. One of the most ancient of these is the compound *ephedrine,* an active substance derived from a medicinal plant that has been used in China for millennia. Although ephedrine is less potent that epinephrine, it can be given by mouth and its effect lasts for hours rather than minutes. It is said not to work in denervated structures, and it is therefore a potentiating agent for the natural substances rather than a substitute for them.

Benzedrine, or amphetamine, is a sympathomimetic amine which acts powerfully as a central nervous system stimulant but has little or no obvious effect on the circulatory system when given in the usual doses. It produces a feeling of euphoria in some individuals and it can be an addicting drug. In many metropolitan subcultures it is the first substance taken in a progression of more and more seriously incapacitating habit-forming drugs by adolescents of both sexes.

There are countless other sympathomimetic substances many of which are used for shrinking the swollen nasal mucosa of head-cold sufferers. An example is *paredrine*. All of these substances do indeed shrink the swollen membranes of the nose temporarily, but when the effect wears off there is often a reactive overshoot and the nasal mucosa is more swollen than it was before treatment.

Tyramine (1-(4'-hydroxyphenyl)-2-amino ethane) is a very interesting sympathomimetic amine which resembles epinephrine in its stimulating effect on blood pressure and uterine muscle. As we have seen, it has the property of releasing bound hormone from isolated chromaffin granules in vitro. In structure it closely resembles the compounds of tri-iodothyramine and tetra-iodothyramine, the tyramine analogues of the thyroid hormones. These substances have also been reported to potentiate the effect of epinephrine on intestinal muscle strips in vitro. It would be extremely interesting to know whether they too have the capacity to release catecholamine hormones from their storage granules.

ADRENERGIC BLOCKING AGENTS

In early studies on epinephrine, Dale discovered that certain derivatives of ergot—ergotoxine and ergotamine—had the interesting property of blocking the pressor effects of epinephrine and sympathetic nerve stimulation without blocking the vasodilator effect of the hormone. These compounds also block the hyperglycemic effect of epinephrine. They were the first of a series of substances that have been discovered to function as *adrenergic blocking agents*. Compounds which prevent the effects of sympathetic nerve stimulation are known as *sympatholytics,* while those which prevent the effects of injected epinephrine are called *adrenolytics*. One agent often exhibits both properties. Research in the area of the adrenergic blocking agents was markedly stimulated by the need to develop new and better methods of managing hypertensive patients. The demonstration that surgical sympathectomy caused an amelioration of symptoms in some hypertensives naturally stimulated a search for drugs which could effect a pharmacological sympathectomy.

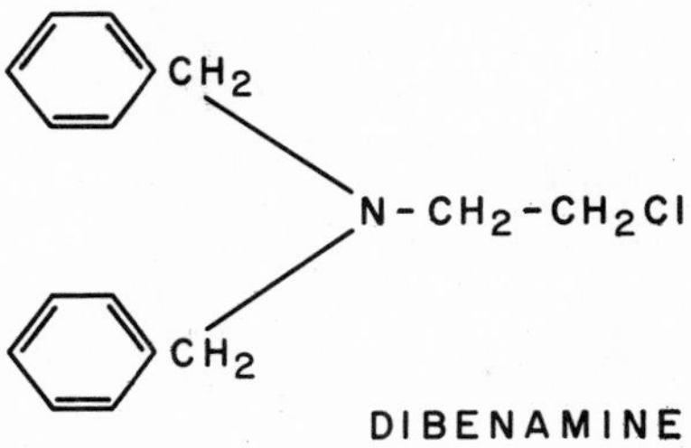

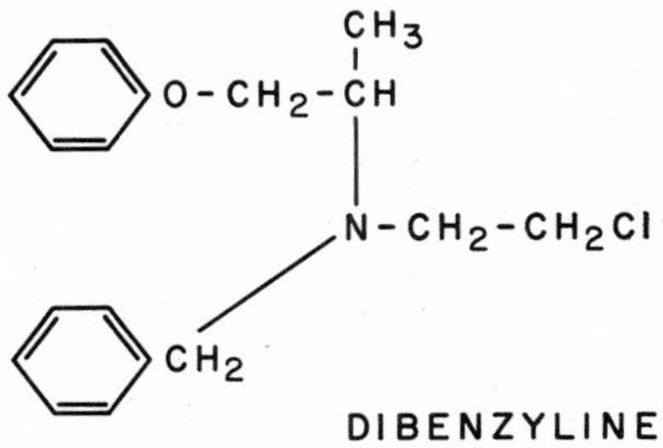

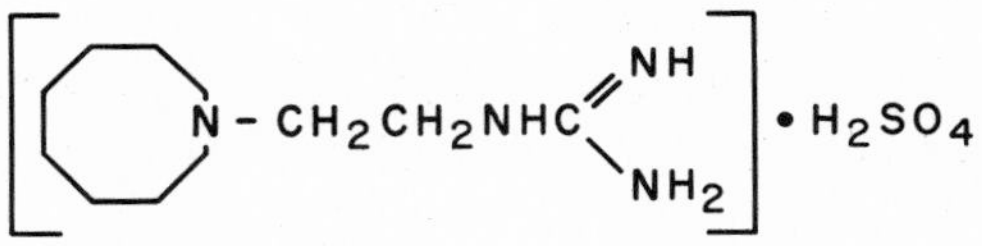

Fig. 8-4.—Adrenergic blocking agents (dibenamine and dibenzyline) and a norepinephrine depleting agent (guanethidine).

Two compounds that have been extremely useful as tools in animal experiments are *dibenamine* and *dibenzyline* (Fig. 8-4). These substances powerfully and specifically block the effects of both sympathetic nerve stimulation and epinephrine administration. Like the ergot alkaloids, they do not block the vasodilator component of epinephrine's effect, and therefore the dibenamine-primed animal shows a paradoxical fall in blood pressure after epinephrine. They differ from ergotoxine in their failure to block the hyperglycemic action of the epinephrine. When these compounds were first studied intensively there was great hope that they could be used in hypertensive patients, especially in view of the fact that they have a very long duration of action. Although they proved to be too toxic for such use, they were very important historically in the development of agents which are now used diagnostically and therapeutically in patients with high blood pressure.

Among the short-acting adrenergic blocking agents are the *benzodioxanes,* or Fourneau compounds. Some of these substances have been particularly valuable in the diagnosis of pheochromocytoma (see p. 150), for the intermittent hypertension characteristically seen in patients with this catecholamine hormone-producing tumor is abruptly interrupted when one of the benzodioxanes is given.

A variety of ganglionic blocking agents, including the *ethylammonium* compounds and the methonium substances, have been studied extensively. These agents interfere with ganglionic transmission in both types of ganglia and, so far as is known, they do not act on the postganglionic neurone. In 1959, a prototype of a completely new blocking agent has been described— *guanethidine.* This extraordinarily interesting substance has been shown to be an effective antihypertensive substance of some promise. While it shows definite ganglionic blocking properties, there is an additional component in its sympatholytic action which has not yet been fully characterized but appears to be related to a functional impairment in the release-storage mechanism for neurohumoral substances in the postganglionic sympathetic nerves. It causes a reduction in catecholamine content of tissues similar to that seen with the rauwolfia alkaloid reserpine, and it also prevents the action of substances like tyramine, which are believed to act by releasing stored catecholamine. No doubt the student will learn much more about these substances in his future studies. They are presented here for the reason that they have an obvious relevance both to fundamental biological mechanisms on the one hand and to practical considerations on the other.

Physiological Effects of the Adrenomedullary Hormones

The effects of epinephrine and norepinephrine are ubiquitous; there is scarcely a field of physiology which does not have its own private preoccupations with these agents. Their effects on the brain, on the heart and circulation, on smooth muscle of the gastrointestinal tract, uterus, eye, and bronchi, on the central nervous system, on skeletal muscle, on blood clotting, on the spleen, on the redistribution of stored calories in the body, and on many other physiological functions are so rich and varied that they can scarcely be known in detail by any single person. There is, however, a discernible theme that is detectable in many of these effects. Although people who are disturbed by teleologically "impure" thinking in biology are sometimes made uncomfortable by Cannon's "fight-flight" characterization of the sympathoadrenomedullary discharge, the fact is that the over-all effect of such a discharge is to mobilize the individual to meet an emergency. This generalization may not be philosophically chic in some quarters, but it is certainly true that one can frequently recall what epinephrine does to an organ or tissue by reflecting on whether or not a particular response serves a useful adaptive purpose in a "fight-flight" emergency.

The over-all response to the effects of simultaneous sympathetic discharge and adrenomedullary secretion involves cardiocirculatory responses which are qualitatively similar to those seen at the beginning of exercise—an increase in cardiac output, increase in pulse rate, rise in blood pressure. In addition, after a brief initial period of apnea, there is an increased minute volume of respiration. Splanchnic vascular constriction (including a reduction in renal blood flow) and dilation of the skeletal muscle vessels produce a redistribution of the enlarged cardiac output which anticipates muscle work. The central nervous system arousal effect of the catecholamine substances results in alertness and quick responsiveness. Hepatic glycogenolysis, its attendant hyperglycemia, and the mobilization from the fat depots of a large supply of free fatty acids (FFA), all collaborate to provide a quick charge of readily available energy to muscles that may be called on. Chemical changes in the muscles themselves increase their capacity for work and possibly diminish the generation of a fatigue signal by the muscle. The central nervous system effects of the substances may, at the same time, diminish central perception of fatigue. As if in anticipation of blood loss, the spleen contracts and adds volume and red cells to the circulation while the coagulability of the blood increases. If a committee of expert physiologists were appointed to draw up specifications for a set of physiological responses that would meet emergency needs it would be difficult for them to devise a more interesting or effective set than that described here.

Central Nervous System

The injection or endogenous release of epinephrine produces a striking excitatory effect on the central nervous system which is sometimes accompanied by a feeling of euphoria. This effect may be characterized generally as a sharpening of cortical alertness and awareness and a facilitation of the passage of information into and out of the brain. Such facilitation can be shown for postural reflexes and also in experiments in which reaction time to a stimulus is measured. According to one currently prominent hypothesis, much of the cortical arousal reaction and the central facilitation can be accounted for on the basis of an action of epinephrine on a small part of the brain which includes the place where the reticular activating system adjoins the posterior hypothalamus. The arousal reaction disappears in experimental animals after the destruction of this part of the brain. The finding (by Vogt) of large amounts of norepinephrine in the same region of the brain is circumstantial evidence in favor of the view that central adrenergic mechanisms may play a prominent role in physiological arousal mechanisms. One guesses that inhibitory influences playing upon such circuits could very well be involved in the mechanism of normal sleep. It should be stressed that the reticular core hypothesis of the mechanism of epinephrine arousal is not universally accepted, but the experiments on which it is based must be consistent with any future hypotheses that may be developed.

A Biochemistry of Hope and Despair?

Recent studies have suggested the possibility that alterations in catecholamine metabolism may be associated with disorders of mood (depression and elation). These affective disorders are obviously complicated and difficult to study; they may, in fact, be a collection of only superficially related syndromes. What has been called "the catecholamine hypothesis of affective disorders" is based on several general kinds of observations: (1) Certain drugs such as *reserpine* which cause a demonstrable depletion of brain catecholamines are associated with sedation or depression in some human subjects and sedation in animals. (2) Other drugs (i.e., monoamine oxidase inhibitors) increase brain catecholamine concentrations by preventing destruction of the compounds. (An abbreviated review of a few drugs which have demonstrable effects on mood is given in Figure 8-5.) (3) In some patients, the urinary norepinephrine excretion has been reported to be diminished in depressed patients and increased in manic patients. Similar observations have been made on urinary normetanephrine, both in patients with spontaneous mood disorders and in those in transition from one mood (depression) to another (absence of depression) under the influence of the drug imipramine. Other attempts to correlate VMA excretion patterns with affective states, like some of the observations on catecholamine excretion pattern,

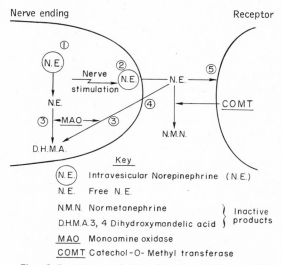

Fig. 8-5.—Presumed loci of action of drugs which affect catecholamine metabolism in brain.

Drug	Effect	Animal Behavior
Reserpine	Depletes N.E. ① and ②	Sedation
Amphetamine	Releases N.E. ① and ②	Excitement (followed by reactive sedation)
	Inhibits uptake of N.E. at ④	
MAO inhibitors	Inhibit destruction of N.E. at ③	Excitement
Imipramine	Inhibits uptake of N.E. at ④	Excitement
	? Potentiates effect of N.E. at ⑤	

(Suggested by Schildkraut, J. J.: The catecholamine hypothesis of affective disorders, Am. J. Psych. 122:509-522, 1965; and by Axelrod, J.: Methylation reactions in the formation of catecholamines and other biogenic amines, Pharmacol. Rev. 18(part I):95-113, 1966.)

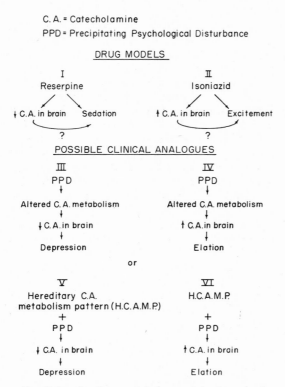

C.A. = Catecholamine
PPD = Precipitating Psychological Disturbance

Fig. 8-6.—Possible models for participation of catecholamines in affective disorders.

are complicated by the fact that the catecholamine metabolism of the brain represents only a very small fraction of the total catecholamine metabolism of the body. Therefore, urinary excretion studies of metabolic products can hardly be expected to illuminate so subtle an event as a mood swing, unless one is willing to concede that gross alterations in catecholamine metabolism may parallel metabolic events in the brain.

In any case, this is an enormously important area of research which is being pursued vigorously by people who are stimulated by interesting experimental animal models. The basic questions in the field are posed in diagrammatic form in Figure 8-6. In the drug models (paradigms I and II), changes in C.A. concentration in brain are seen in association with sedation and excitement. While it is not permissible to conclude that the two events are necessarily causally related, we will assume, for heuristic purposes, that the altered C.A. concentration in each case is the proximate cause of the altered behavior pattern. The diagrammatic descriptions of possible clini-

cal analogues are deliberately nonspecific. It could easily take several thousand words to describe all of the possible biochemical sites which might be involved either in the phrase "altered C.A. metabolism" or "hereditary C.A. metabolism pattern." Some of these can be inferred from an inspection of Figure 8-5. It is only necessary to point out that a precipitating psychological disturbance (PPD) might result in a drastic mood change by working through an altered C.A. metabolism (paradigms III and IV) or that inborn patterns of C.A. metabolism might make certain individuals vulnerable to the mood modifying potentiality of a PPD (paradigms V and VI). Moreover, these same inborn patterns could determine the direction of the mood swing.

As I have indicated elsewhere, other hormones powerfully influence mood. The euphoria of patients maintained on anti-inflammatory doses of adrenal glucocorticoids is well known. Both hyper- and hypothyroid patients may show profound behavioral disturbances. Patients with insulin-producing adenomas may be seen first by psychiatrists because their complaints may be perceived by them as "problems in living." It is not now known whether any or all of these hormonal effects—some of which, like insulin-induced hypoglycemia, may be quite secondary to the original action of the hormone—operate through the "final common pathway" of disturbed catecholamine metabolism in the brain or elsewhere in the body.

At this time in history, these speculations may appear to be gratuitous to some. However, I am persuaded that this is an extremely important field for future study, and I hope that these few words will stimulate some students to explore these ideas in greater depth. The ancient mind-body problem and the biochemistry of hope and despair can be contemplated profitably from the vantage point of a metabolic map of intermediary catecholamine metabolism.

EFFECTS OF BLOOD VESSELS

Epinephrine and norepinephrine differ in their effects on blood vessels and the former, especially, constricts cutaneous and renal arterioles, but dilates skeletal muscle vessels and (probably) the coronary vessels. The vasodilatory aspect of epinephrine's action can be seen best in an animal in which its vasoconstrictor effect is blocked by an adrenergic blocking agent. The local vasoconstrictor effect of epinephrine is used to prevent the rapid systemic absorption of local anesthetics which are injected subcutaneously. Norepinephrine (though less potent as a skin vessel vasoconstrictor) is by far the more potent general vasoconstrictor, being at least 50% more powerfully hypertensive than is epinephrine. The extraordinary potency of norepinephrine in increasing peripheral resistance and maintaining blood pressure is attested to by its frequent use (in a continuous intravenous drip) in surgical situations in which hypotension threatens. In recent years this has become one of the most important uses of the catecholamine hormones.

CARDIAC EFFECTS

The effects of the two catecholamines on the heart are quite different. In general, most of the cardiac effects we associate with the adrenal medulla are produced by epinephrine, and not by norepinephrine. There are 3 main categories of response caused by epinephrine:

1. An increased rate of cardiac contraction (positive chronotropic effect).

2. An increased force of contraction (positive inotropic effect).

3. A sensitization of the myocardium to the fibrillation-inducing effects either of sympathetic nerve stimulation or of various chlorinated cyclic compounds, such as cyclopropane or the insecticide DDT.

The first 2 of these are the basis of the increased cardiac output seen after epinephrine injection. Naturally, the increased work of the heart raises the oxygen requirement of the myocardium, and epinephrine injection may therefore elicit cardiac pain in an individual with coronary artery insufficiency.

RESPIRATION

Both hormones accelerate the rate and increase the depth of respirations after a brief period of apnea which is believed to be mediated through the carotid sinus mechanism as a result of the rising blood pressure. The respiratory stimulation may be the result of the central nervous system excitation induced by these compounds.

SMOOTH MUSCLE

The variable effects of epinephrine and norepinephrine on the vascular smooth muscle in different parts of the circulatory system are seen again in an analysis of the responses of other kinds of smooth muscle to their administration. Much of the smooth muscle of the body—including the nonsphincteric muscle of the gastrointestinal tract, the bronchioles, the urinary bladder—is relaxed by epinephrine or by sympathetic nerve stimulation. Many other types of smooth muscle—including that associated with the splenic capsule, the sphincters of the gastrointestinal tract, the ureters, the *erectores pili* apparatus of the skin, the nictitating membrane of the cat, the *dilator pupillae* of the iris, and others—are stimulated by epinephrine. Some structures, like the uterus, vary in their response according to species and the presence or absence of pregnancy. In some species, including man, uterine smooth muscle is stimulated whether or not pregnancy is present. But in the cat, rat, mouse, and guinea pig the nonpregnant uterus is relaxed while the pregnant uterus is stimulated by epinephrine.

On the basis of much information of this sort elaborate theories have been constructed to account for the interaction of the hormone with its cell receptor. Since no one knows precisely what or where the hypothetical receptor site is, the classification of receptors is purely descriptive and based on empirically observed responses of different tissues to the catecholamine hormones. According to one such scheme *alpha* (or Lands' Ac) receptors are associated with excitatory responses and are blocked by adrenergic blocking agents while *beta* (Lands' Ar) receptors are characterized by relaxation or inhibition and are not blocked by the blocking agents. Since the heart muscle and intestinal muscle are not readily classifiable according to this scheme, the suggestion has been made that these structures contain undifferentiated receptors (Lands' Acr). If one accepts the idea of specificity of response on the basis of the cell receptor specificity, the turnabout in response from relaxation to stimulation that occurs in the uterus during pregnancy in some species would require that the specificity of the receptor site be modified in some way by the state of pregnancy. Rather than rely on elaborate receptor hypotheses, the variation in response of smooth muscle is just as easy to visualize if we imagine that the initial interaction between hormone and receptor may be similar in all of the circumstances enumerated, but that the specificity of response pattern is built into the cell and may, in fact, change as different metabolic events (for example, those associated with pregnancy) occur in the cell. It is even possible that the metabolic characteristics of the cell could determine whether or not an adrenergic blocking agent could work effectively.

SKELETAL MUSCLE

It was shown long ago that the contractions of a stimulus-driven skeletal muscle could be markedly prolonged by epinephrine, and that this substance had the capacity to increase the force of contraction in a fatigued muscle preparation. That these effects are at least partially independent of the neuromuscular transmission apparatus are shown by the fact that they are obtainable even when the stimulus is applied directly to the muscle cells in in vitro preparations. One of the most prominent metabolic effects of epinephrine is seen in skeletal muscle as well; namely, a rapid glycogenolysis with the accumulation of sufficient lactic acid to raise the level of lactate which is carried to the liver where it is resynthesized into glycogen and recirculated as glucose. It also travels to the heart which uses lactate very efficiently as an energy source. According to one hypothesis, the dilation of the blood vessels of the skeletal muscles may be brought about in part by the local accumulation of lactic acid. A number of commentators have observed, however, that this accumulation would have to occur in the wall of the blood vessel itself to be effective, for in the ordinary course of things one would expect little back diffusion of muscle-produced lactate to vessels of a size which are known to dilate after epinephrine.

THE LIVER

One of the most striking effects of epinephrine is the production of hyperglycemia which, in some instances, is sufficiently high to result in glycosuria. That this hyperglycemia is mainly due to hepatic glycogenolysis is indicated by the following facts: (1) it does not occur in the liverless preparation, (2) it does not occur in the previously starved (or deglycogenated) prepara-

tion, and (3) it does not occur in certain patients with forms of glycogen storage disease which are characterized by inborn deficiencies in certain enzymes which are associated with glycogen breakdown in the liver. The absence of a hyperglycemic response to epinephrine is a valuable datum in the diagnostic evaluation of such patients (see p. 150). Norepinephrine has only about one-fifth the glycogenolytic-hyperglycemic effect of epinephrine. This phenomenon can be demonstrated nicely with surviving liver slices incubated in vitro. A very similar response occurs following the administration of the pancreatic alpha cell hormone glucagon (see Chapter 9).

There are certain experimental circumstances when epinephrine administration produces a rise in liver glycogen rather than a fall, especially when the initial glycogen level was low. This is due to the formation of glycogen from lactate derived from muscle glycogenolysis; after the initial hepatic glycogenolytic effect has stopped, the continued resynthesis of lactate may raise the glycogen in the liver above the control level.

CALORIGENIC ACTION

Oxygen consumption may increase by about 30% in the epinephrine-treated subject, human or animal. The CO_2 production is likely to rise even more, resulting in a high respiratory quotient, or RQ. Much of this calorigenic effect is due to the metabolism of the lactate which accumulates as a result of muscle glycogenolysis, and the liver is one of the major sites in which this occurs, for the calorigenic effect of epinephrine is much reduced in the liverless preparation. But in the intact unanesthetized individual, some of the increase in metabolism is due to increased work of the heart and muscles of respiration and to increased muscle tone. The disproportionate rise in CO_2 production is not due to any major shift in the character of the metabolic mixture but rather to the fact that the lactacidemia constitutes a metabolic acidosis which liberates CO_2 from the blood.

ADIPOSE TISSUE

We now realize that the mobilization of carbohydrate from the liver is only the smaller part of the mobilization of caloric reserves that occurs when epinephrine is given. One of the largest and most important end-organs for epinephrine and sympathetic nerve stimulation is the aggregate adipose tissue organ. The catecholamine hormones act on the cells of this tissue to produce a release of free fatty acids (FFA) which are transported in the blood lightly bound to albumin. There is little doubt that this effect of norepinephrine released in the adipose tissue plays an important role in the fat mobilization that occurs on fasting, and now that we know about the

TABLE 8-1.—COMPARISON OF THE EFFECTS OF INTRAVENOUS INFUSION OF EPINEPHRINE IN MAN*

	EPINEPH-RINE	NOREPINEPH-RINE
Heart		
Rate	+	−
Positive inotropic effect	+ + +	0, −
Blood pressure		
Systolic B.P.	+ + +	+ + +
Diastolic B.P.	+, 0, −	+ +
Peripheral vessels		
Total peripheral resistance	−	+ +
"Metabolic" effects		
Calorigenic effect	+ +	0, +
Hyperglycemia	+ + +	0, +
Blood lactic acid	+ + +	0, +

+ = increase, − = decrease and 0 = unchanged.
*Modified from Goldenberg, M.: Am. J. Med. 10:627, 1951.

effects of these substances on the fat depots we can fit the concept of FFA mobilization into the "fight-flight" syndrome very neatly. A detailed discussion of the hormonal regulation of adipose tissue metabolism will be presented in Chapter 10.

A summary of some of the effects of epinephrine and norepinephrine is given in Table 8-1.

Biochemical Mechanism of Action of Epinephrine (and Glucagon)

The broad outlines of the effects of epinephrine and norepinephrine at the physiological level have been sketched briefly. All of these results must follow some sort of transaction between epinephrine and the responsive cell at the molecular level. Even if we had very precise knowledge about the nature of the hypothetical receptor substances with which the catecholamine hormones interact we would still be left with the problem of describing the consequences of this interaction in biochemical terms. Therefore, we must examine the problem of the mechanism of action of epinephrine at a higher magnification.

In recent years, many important advances in our knowledge of the effects of epinephrine at the cellular level have been made by Cori, Sutherland and their colleagues. The elucidation of the biochemical events in the breakdown of glycogen was the point of departure for the series of experiments to be described. The sequence of events in glycogenolysis may be described as follows:

1. $\text{Glycogen} \longleftrightarrow \text{Glucose-1-PO}_4$
   (Phosphorylase)

2. $\text{Glucose-1-PO}_4 \longleftrightarrow \text{Glucose-6-PO}_4$
   (Phosphoglucomutase)

3. $\text{Glucose-6-PO}_4 \longrightarrow \text{Glucose} + \text{Pi}$
   (Phosphatase)

It was found that reaction 1 is the rate-limiting reaction in this sequence; i.e., the isomerase and phosphatase capability of the cell is present in excess, and the availability of active phosphorylase determines the rate of glycogenolysis. Under some circumstances phosphorylase can also be shown to facilitate glycogen synthesis, but (to anticipate the story) it is now widely believed that in the living cell conditions are such that glycogen is synthesized by one route (the Leloir-Cardini uridine diphosphoglucose pathway) and broken down by another route (the phosphorylase mechanism). We are slowly becoming accustomed to the fact that synthesis and breakdown of many substances can no longer be imagined as proceeding in a manner suggested by the traditional reversible arrows, for the processes are often quite separate. It is this very separateness, in fact, which offers so many opportunities for traffic control in the cell and makes possible the subtle direction or "steering" of metabolic processes. Other examples of anabolic and catabolic reactions which are quite distinct from the point of view of specific enzyme and coenzyme requirements can be found in lipogenesis, both in the formation of long chain fatty acids and in the formation and breakdown of triglycerides (see Chapter 10).

It was found that the enzyme phosphorylase exists in tissues (both muscle and liver) in two forms: an inactive (dephosphophosphorylase) and an active (phosphorylase). A specific enzyme (dephosphophosphorylase kinase) medi-

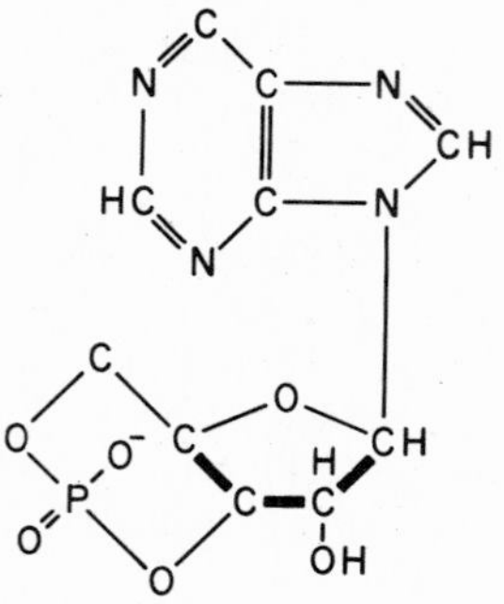

Fig. 8-7.—3′, 5′ AMP, or cyclic adenylic acid.

ates the activation of the inactive form to the active form by transferring a phosphate group to it from ATP. Cori and Illingworth showed that epinephrine increases the amount of active phosphorylase in muscle and increases the rate of resynthesis of the active enzyme in fatigued muscle. Sutherland and his colleagues demonstrated first that the hormone increases the formation of active phosphorylase in liver slices; later they

described a similar activation of the enzyme in cell-free homogenates of liver.

When various centrifugal fractions of homogenates were tested for phosphorylase activation by epinephrine addition it was found that a fairly heavy particulate fraction was essential for the activation reaction. Moreover, when the heavy particles (600 G) were separated from the rest of the homogenate and treated with ATP, magnesium, and other supplements, a substance was formed which, when added to the particle free supernatant, was capable of activating phosphorylase. This substance was shown to be 3′, 5′ AMP, or cyclic adenosine 3′, 5′ phosphate shown in Figure 8-7. This material is formed from ATP in a reaction catalyzed by a cyclase enzyme which has been found in every tissue studied except dog erythrocytes. Epinephrine-stimulated 3′, 5′ AMP production associated with phosphorylase activation has now been shown to occur in liver, heart, skeletal muscle, and other tissues. Parallel experiments have revealed that the pancreatic alpha cell hormone, glucagon (see Chapter 9), stimulates the activation of liver phosphorylase

Fig. 8-8.—The mechanism of phosphorylase activation by epinephrine, glucagon and ACTH. (EM, Embden-Meyerhoff pathway; PP, Pentose phosphate pathway.)

(Modified slightly from Sutherland, E. W., and Rall, T. W.: Pharmacol. Rev. 12:265-300, 1960.)

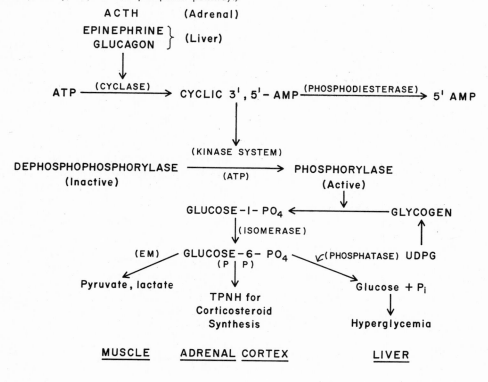

via 3′, 5′ AMP production in a manner precisely analogous to that described for epinephrine. A diagrammatic summary of the current hypothesis of the mechanism of activation of phosphorylase by these substances (and, in the adrenal, by ACTH, Chapter 7) is given in Figure 8-8. The exact mechanisms by which (1) the hormones stimulate the production of 3′, 5′ AMP, and (2) the cyclic adenylic acid participates in the conversion of dephosphophosphorylase to active phosphorylase are not yet known. The discovery of hormone-mediated phosphorylase activation, however, is generally regarded as an outstanding accomplishment in biochemical endocrinology and the present brief description of the logical sequence of experiments that led to this discovery is presented as a model of investigative imagination, energy, and industry.

THE "MOLECULAR DEPUTY" CONCEPT OF HORMONE ACTION

The discovery of 3′, 5′ cyclic adenylic acid (adenosine 3′, 5′ cyclophosphate) was followed by exciting repercussions in almost every area of metabolism and endocrinology. At first, most of the emphasis was on phosphorylase activation by the cyclic nucleotide, but as the realization dawned that many other catalytic and (possibly) structural proteins could be modified in some way by 3′, 5′ cyclic AMP, a new and fascinating general hypothesis of hormone action was formulated by Sutherland and his colleagues (1966). They refer to their idea as the "second messenger" concept, but, since the word "messenger" has unwanted connotations here, I am going to take the liberty of renaming Sutherland's "second messenger" the "deputy" molecule. The beauty of Sutherland's idea is in the concept that a hormone ("first messenger") can have a transaction in one part of the cell, either at or near the cell membrane. The effect of the hormone at this site is to produce many "deputy" molecules (cyclic 3′, 5′ AMP) from a readily available precursor (ATP). The "deputy" or "agent" molecule can then react with one or several of many strategically placed proteins in the cell. Some of these may be enzymes which catalyze rate-limiting reactions; others could be protein constituents of membranes. A co-ordinated response could be produced, since certain reactions could be accelerated at the same time that others were slowed.

The tissue specificity could be built into the cell at a number of places: (1) the recognition site where the primary action of the hormone takes place and (2) the cyclic nucleotide-recognizing proteins throughout the cell.

In the case of many cells which employ the "deputy" mechanism, the final result of the initial hormone stimulation is the production of another hormone (i.e., the adrenal cortices, the corpus luteum and the interstitial cells of the testis). In these cases, the initial "call" for more hormone may have been produced by a very small change in concentration of a steroid in the blood perfusing the hypothalamus. This may have triggered the release and production of a small amount of releasing factor which, in turn, was a signal for the release of a small amount of trophic hormone. Catalytic amounts of the trophic hormone, in turn, resulted in the production of enough 3′, 5′ cyclic AMP to bring about production of large amounts of steroid hormone. The sequence from releasing factor → trophic hormone → cyclic nucleotide ("deputy") → steroid hormone must represent an "amplification" of the original chemical message, since only a small fraction of the trophic hormone released from the pituitary actually stimulates the adrenals or the gonads while a large amount of steroid hormone is produced—as one can easily infer from the daily replacement doses of adrenal and gonadal steroids in deficiency states.

In this scheme, the primary recognition site for the hormone is either the adenyl cyclase enzyme itself or some other adjacent molecule which is able to activate the cyclase. The secondary recognition sites—i.e., those which are susceptible to the effects of the cyclic nucleotide —may be present in many different kinds of cells (see Fig. 8-9, from Sutherland) or, in the case of certain cells, there may be multiple reactive proteins. In the case of the liver, a beautifully co-

Fig. 8-9.—Some extra-hepatic effects of cyclic 3′, 5′ AMP.

Positive inotropic effect of epinephrine
Lipolysis in adipose tissue
Steroid hormone formation
  (Adrenal cortex, corpus luteum, testis)
Amylase release (rat parotid)
Water permeability (toad bladder, isolated renal tubule)
Glucose transport (TSH in thyroid)
HCl secretion (gastric mucosa)
Insulin secretion (Beta cell)

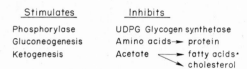

Stimulates	Inhibits
Phosphorylase	UDPG Glycogen synthetase
Gluconeogenesis	Amino acids → protein
Ketogenesis	Acetate ⇌ fatty acids· cholesterol

Fig. 8-10.—Some hepatic effects of cyclic 3′, 5′ AMP.

ordinated response occurs which appears to be designed to deliver glucose into the blood stream, promote fatty acid catabolism while inhibiting its synthesis, and produce new glucose from amino acids while inhibiting their incorporation into protein. These effects are shown diagrammatically in Figure 8-10. One can readily see that the effects of the cyclic nucleotides are to reproduce perfectly the characteristic features of hepatic metabolism in starvation. It is difficult to resist the conclusion that 3′, 5′ AMP is an important "deputy" through which the metabolic adaptation to starvation is accomplished. The mechanism by which 3′, 5′ cyclic AMP stimulates gluconeogenesis is not known. It may selectively and allosterically activate a rate-limiting enzyme in the metabolic pathway of gluconeogenesis immediately prior to the formation of phosphoenolpyruvate (PEP). Or it may (Ashmore, 1966) activate an hepatic lipase, thereby causing both a stimulation of gluconeogenesis somewhere below PEP by increasing the acetyl CoA concentration of the cell and, simultaneously, an inhibition of lipogenesis at the level of acetyl CoA carboxylase. Park is an articulate champion of the idea that 3′, 5′ cyclic AMP is the proximate stimulus for gluconeogenesis.

The recent discoveries by Butcher, Jungas, Exton, Park and their various colleagues that insulin can lower the 3′, 5′ cyclic AMP levels in both adipose tissue and liver when they had previously been elevated by epinephrine and caffeine add a new and fascinating dimension to the developing story. It now seems possible that at least some of the effects of insulin may be related to its 3′, 5′ cyclic AMP-lowering properties.

It is worth looking at one aspect of the hepatic response to 3′, 5′ cyclic AMP in more detail, for here, on the molecular level, is a precise analogue of Sherrington's idea of reciprocal innervation in a limb. You will recall Sherrington's description of muscle contraction as a coordinate response in which active contraction of one group of muscles (as, for example, in flexing an arm) is accompanied by inhibition of the opposing muscles (extensors).

Figure 8-11 illustrates the reciprocal effects of 3′, 5′ cyclic AMP on glycogen synthesis and degradation. These processes occur by different metabolic pathways: synthesis by way of UDPG transferase (or glycogen synthetase) and degradation by way of phosphorylase. Cyclic 3′, 5′ AMP stimulates phosphorylase (b) kinase, which results in the activation of phosphorylase (b) to phosphorylase (a). At the same time the cyclophosphate nucleotide stimulates UDPG transferase I kinase, which has the effect of diminishing the amount of physiologically effective transferase I (which stands for glucose-6-phosphate *I*ndependent) to the less effective form, UDPG transferase D (i.e., glucose-6-phosphate *D*ependent). This reciprocal stimulation and inhibition has the effect of promoting glycogenolysis. It so happens that, in the case of the phosphorylase *activation,* phosphate is acquired by the enzyme. In the case of UDPG *inactivation* phosphate is also combined with the enzyme protein. When these processes are understood in intimate molecular detail, it may turn out that the nucleotide is doing similar things to both enzymes, but there is now no doubt that they are different proteins.

While the developments that have followed

Fig. 8-11.—Reciprocal effects of cyclic 3′, 5′ AMP on glycogen synthesis and degradation. (See Huijing, Fr., and Larner, J.: Proc. Nat. Acad. Sc. 56:647, 1966.)

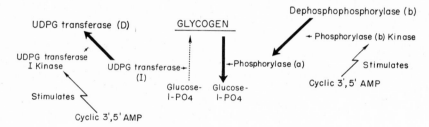

Sutherland's "deputy" hypothesis have aroused universal awe and admiration (tinged with the suspicion that any molecule which does so many things can be nothing more than the Devil's private artifact), we may have seen only the earliest stages of the applicability of this idea. Certainly, cyclic 3', 5' AMP will be found to participate in many other processes. (Most recently, it has been implicated in the mechanism by which insulin is released from the β cells of the pancreas.) But, beyond that, how about cyclic-IMP,-CMP,-UMP, etc.? Are there other "deputy" molecules that interact with other families of protein molecules? Are there other whole classes of compounds which function in this way? We have had vaguely formulated ideas about hormones causing a "propagated disturbance" in cells, or acting on a cell's "cytoskeleton" and thus changing the availability of intracompartmental cell constituents to one another. Now we can understand in a general way how one kind of "propagated disturbance" may work.

The connections between phosphorylase activation and the muscle effects of epinephrine are not easy to make. Glycogenolysis occurs in muscle, but since that tissue lacks the enzyme glucose-6-phosphatase, the glucose-6-PO_4 formed by glycogenolysis is broken down by way of the Embden-Heyerhof pathway. The capacity of the Krebs cycle to dispose of the acetyl CoA (formed by this massive charge of glucose) is exceeded and trioses, especially lactate, accumulate in sufficiently large amounts to diffuse into the blood.

The reason for the improved contractile performance of the epinephrine-stimulated muscle is not known. Phosphorylase activation in muscle is associated with the shift from a resting state to a working state, and a decline in active phosphorylase occurs characteristically in fatigued muscle. Epinephrine treatment delays this decline and at the same time increases the contractile force of fatigued muscle. Ellis and others have stressed the point that the beneficial effects of epinephrine on contractile ability of muscle is not due to the generation of energy by the breakdown of glycogen, for it occurs even when the energy-yielding reactions of glycolysis are blocked with inhibitors. He suggests the possibility that an increase in concentration of hexose phosphates intracellularly may influence the contractile machinery favorably in an unspecified way.

There is an important difference between phosphorylase activation in the epinephrine-treated muscle and that in the electrically stimulated one, as Posner, Stern and Krebs (1965) have shown. These investigators demonstrated that, in a muscle stimulated to contract electrically, phosphorylase activation occurs *without* 3', 5' cyclic AMP accumulation. Activation of the enzyme is readily demonstrable in vitro on the addition of Ca^{++} ions, and the suggestion was made that the release of Ca^{++} ions that occurs as a result of nerve stimulation may simultaneously play a role in initiating the contractile process and in triggering glycogenolysis by activating phosphorylase, thus providing a readily available energy source to power subsequent contractions. Consequently, Ca^{++} ions appear to elicit a coordinated biochemical response in the nerve-stimulated cell much as 3', 5' cyclic AMP does in the epinephrine-stimulated cell. In this instance, Ca^{++} fulfills the criteria for a "deputy" or "second messenger" which is produced intracellularly in response to an extracellular stimulus and affects functionally integrated mechanisms.

The connection, if any, between phosphorylation activation and the effects of epinephrine on nerve cells and smooth muscle cells has not been elucidated. The smooth muscle problem is especially difficult because of the variability in response of smooth muscle from species to species, from one vascular bed to another in the same animal and (in the case of uterus) from one time to another in the same animal of a given species. The solution of these problems must await improvement in our understanding of the cytophysiology of these tissues.

Hepatic phosphorylase activation precisely similar to that described for epinephrine has been seen with the pancreatic α cell hormone, glucagon (see Chapter 9). It is interesting to observe that, in addition to its glycogenolytic-hyperglycemic effect, glucagon has other effects which are similar to those of epinephrine. Farah has described a positive inotropic effect of glucagon in the dog heart-lung preparation and a smooth muscle inhibiting effect on rabbit intestine in vitro.

Genetics and Catecholamine Hormones

Although we cannot point to precisely localized inborn errors of metabolism in the adrenal medulla which result in readily identifiable pathophysiological syndromes, the suggestion has been made that genetically determined individual variations in catecholamine hormone production may be correlated with certain personality traits. Ferocious animals are said to have a high epinephrine/norepinephrine ratio, while meek ones are reputed to produce an adrenal medullary mixture with the reverse ratio. People apparently vary in catecholamine hormone ratio *and* degrees of ferocity (i.e., aggressiveness, hostility, etc.) in an analogous manner. Although one cannot accept the demonstrations of this point that have been described so far as incontrovertible proof of the existence of such correlations, it is an intriguing idea. Certainly the determinants of so complex an entity as personality structure are many, devious, and mysterious, but there is no reason to doubt that genetically determined internal communications systems resources in the form of the nervous system and endocrine system may be centrally involved in the construction of an identity or self.

An example of the manner in which epinephrine can be used in diagnosis is afforded by an inborn error of metabolism known as von Gierke's disease, or Type I glycogen storage disease of the liver and kidneys. This is a condition which is usually discovered during the first year of life and is characterized by hepatic enlargement, anorexia, weight loss, vomiting, and finally hypoglycemia, convulsions, and coma. Patients with this disease are very susceptible to hypoglycemia and ketosis on fasting. In 1952, Cori and Cori demonstrated that infants with this disease have a genetic deficiency of the enzyme glucose-6-phosphatase and therefore cannot break down glycogen and deliver glucose into the blood in response to the usual stimuli. One very suggestive diagnostic test for this condition is the absence of a glycogenolytic-hyperglycemic response to a test dose of epinephrine. The definitive diagnosis is made by the (biopsy or autopsy) finding of large concentrations of glycogen (12–16% of the wet weight) in the liver and the absence of glucose-6-phosphatase activity. This use of epinephrine is presented here for the purpose of emphasizing the point that, as more and more hereditary enzyme defects are discovered, the principle of attempting to bring the defect into relief by stimulating with an appropriate hormone is likely to have wide application.

Catecholamine-Producing Tumors

Just as tumors of the thyroid may produce thyroid hormone and tumors of the pancreatic β cells may produce insulin, tumors of chromaffin tissue secrete inappropriately large amounts of catecholamine hormones. Pheochromocytoma is a tumor that may arise in the adrenal medulla or in extramedullary sites. Most tumors in this category are well localized, encapsulated, and slow growing, although a few metastasize. Patients with such tumors secrete large amounts of catecholamine hormones either continuously or intermittently. If there is epinephrine in this excess secretion, it constitutes virtual proof that the tumor arose in the adrenal medulla; if the excess catecholamine is all norepinephrine an extramedullary site of origin is indicated. Norepinephrine usually is the predominant hormone involved.

Patients with this disorder exhibit a syndrome which recapitulates a textbook description of the effects of catecholamine hormones. They show hypertension, tachycardia and palpitations, constriction of the skin blood vessels, sweating, increased metabolic rate, hyperglycemia, and glycosuria. Loss of weight is often seen and emotional instability and headache may occur. The similarities between such a patient and one with thyrotoxicosis are often striking. The practical applicability of the sort of information contained in this chapter is readily seen in the diagnostic approach to patients with suspected pheochromocytoma. Patients with this disease excrete very large amounts of catecholamines in the urine: usually over 300 micrograms per day in contrast to the normal values of 20–100 micrograms per day. The newer methods of identifying the individual excretion products will no doubt lead to more and more elegant criteria for diagnosis and evaluation. The hypertension of pheochromocytoma can be readily distinguished from other types of hypertension by the administration of an adrenolytic agent such as benzodioxane (Goldenberg test). This causes a rapid return of the blood pressure to normal values if the hypertension is the result of overstimulation by catecholamines. Conversely, a paroxysm of hypertension can be induced by the (cautious!) administration of histamine or of an acetyl choline-like compound which stimulate chromaffin cells to release their stored hormones. Studies that have been done on patients with pheochromocytoma beautifully illustrate the point that the clinical scientist on the wards and the physiologist in the laboratory are studying the same phenomena from slightly different vantage points.

Recently, important advances have been made in our understanding of a group of tumors which appear in infants and children, the *neuroblastomata*. These tumors (known as ganglioneuromata, ganglioneuroblastomata and neuroblastomata) arise from primitive neural crest ectoderm and actively secrete norepinephrine in sufficient amounts to cause symptoms such as hypertension pallor, headache and so on. Several observers have commented on the presence of diarrhea in these children and its cessation following the operative removal of the tumor. Thus, the diarrhea appears to be dependent on the presence of the tumor but the mechanism by which it is caused is unknown, for one would ordinarily expect an excess of catecholamine to cause hypomotility of the gastrointestinal tract.

The availability of chromatographic and photofluorometric methods has enabled investigators (for example, Voorhess and Gardner) to follow the urinary excretion pattern of catecholamine hormone and its metabolites during the clinical course of the disease. In confirmation of previous findings, the main excretory amines were found to be metanephrine and VMA, which exceeded norepinephrine in concentration by 10–100-fold. The pattern was somewhat variable from patient to patient and, to some extent, reasonable correlations could be made between the urinary catecholamine excretion pattern on the one hand

and the histology of the tumor and the symptomatology on the other. In a number of instances, reduced norepinephrine and VMA excretion were seen to follow either surgical removal of a tumor, or (in one case) combined radiotherapy and chemotherapy of the tumor in situ. No doubt many advances in our understanding of patients with this disease (one of the most common malignant tumors of infancy and childhood) will accrue from the further application of new physiological knowledge to the clinical situation.

REFERENCES

Acheson, G. H. (ed.): *Second Symposium on Catecholamines* (Baltimore: Williams & Wilkins Co., 1966).

Krayer, O.: Symposium on catecholamines, Pharmacol. Rev. 11:241–566, 1959.

Posner, J. B., Stern, R., and Krebs, E. G.: Effects of electrical stimulation and epinephrine on muscle phosphorylase, phosphorylase B kinase and adenosine 3′, 5′ phosphate, J. Biol. Chem. 240:982-985, 1965.

Schildkraut, J. J., and Kety, S. S.: Biogenic amines and emotion, Science 156:21–30, 1967.

Sutherland, E. W., and Rall, T. W.: The relation of adenosine-3′, 5′-phosphate and phosphorylase to the actions of catecholamines and other hormones, Pharmacol. Rev. 12:265–300, 1960.

Vane, J. R., Wolstenholme, G. E. W., and O'Connor, M.: *Adrenergic Mechanisms,* Ciba Foundation Symposium (Boston: Little, Brown & Co., 1960).

Voorhess, M. L., and Gardner, L. I.: Urinary excretion of norepinephrine, epinephrine and 3-methoxy-4 hydroxymandelic acid by children with neuroblastoma, J. Clin. Endocrinol. 21:321–335, 1961.

Wurtman, R. J.: *Catecholamines* (Boston: Little, Brown & Co., 1966).

9

Endocrine Function of the Pancreas

SOME OF THE EARLIEST historical records of man, including the *Ebers Papyrus* (c. 1500 B.C.), contain accounts of a disease which was characterized by polyuria. The name "diabetes," which means "running through," goes back to the early part of the first century A.D. Avicenna (c. 1000 A.D.) gave a complete description of the disease we now call *diabetes mellitus,* and called attention not only to the characteristic polyuria and polydipsia but also to weight loss in spite of high food intake. He also described the susceptibility of diabetics to a variety of infections and to gangrene. A brief summary of some of the discoveries on which our knowledge of *diabetes mellitus* is based is given in the chronology (p. 146). Cursory inspection reveals that much of the impetus for the study of this aspect of metabolic physiology came originally from clinical observations and that laboratory investigations, stimulated by studies on sick people, yielded knowledge which was enormously helpful when it was taken back into the clinic. There are few stories which illustrate this bidirectional flow of ideas better than does the history of diabetes and insulin.

The Chemistry of Insulin

Within 5 years of the discovery of insulin by Banting and Best in 1921, Abel had prepared a highly purified insulin. By 1942, Chibnall and his colleagues had completed the amino acid analysis of the protein and had demonstrated that it consisted of comparatively short chains and that phenylalanine was at the end of one chain. This was the approximate state of development of the field of amino acid sequence analysis of proteins in 1945.

During the era following World War II the complete structure of the insulin molecule has been elucidated by Sanger, who worked with no more than one or two associates at a time over a 10-year period (1945–1955). First, he found that the molecule consisted of two chains joined by –S–S– bridges; then, he separated the chains; finally, using various kinds of chemical and enzymatic hydrolysis methods, and making extensive use of chromatographic separation of peptide fragments, he succeeded in describing the complete amino acid sequence of the two chains and in locating the three disulfide bridges in the molecule. This monumental achievement has significance which goes far beyond the field of insulin and diabetes, for other investigators have similarly analyzed many biologically important proteins and the possibility now exists of understanding structure-activity relationships of these substances.

The complete structure of insulin is shown in Figure 9-1. Of particular interest in the series of 6 amino acids in chain A included in the S–S rings and of these, the sequence Ala. Ser. Val. The biologically active peptides, oxytocin and vasopressin, also contain sequences of 6 amino acids enclosed by an S–S bridge, and this configuration has recently been found to be important in the interaction between these peptides and the hormone-sensitive cell. It has been suggested that insulin, which is known to be tightly

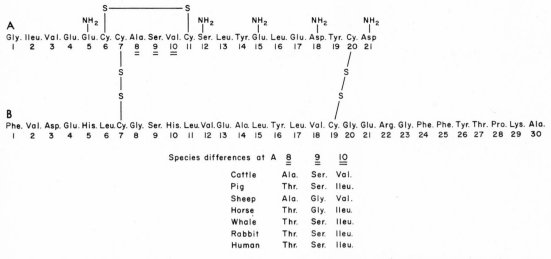

Fig. 9-1.—The structure of insulin in various species. (Sanger, F.: Brit. M. Bull. 16:183-188, 1960.)

bound to tissue such as muscle, may interact with a cell receptor site at this locus in the molecule.

The Ala. Ser. Val. sequence in the disulfide ring of the A chain is of something more than theoretical interest, for it is in this amino acid triplet that the most important species differences have been found, as shown in Figure 9-1.

Following the discovery that biologically inactive, separated A and B chains could be reunited into a biologically active insulin molecule, several groups of workers in Peking, Aachen and Brookhaven have succeeded in synthesizing insulin de novo from its constituent amino acids. They have constructed separate A and B chains and subsequently joined the sulfite derivatives into active insulin. At first, the yields were very small, but, more recently, yields of 16–50% have been reported. This remarkable achievement opens the possibility for making synthetic analogues of insulin which may help to elucidate its mechanism of action. It is even possible to imagine that complicated syntheses of this sort will one day be automated, and, therefore, commercially feasible.

It has been known for some time that a few diabetic patients become allergic to cattle and sheep insulin but that many can tolerate pig insulin. The similarity of human insulin to pig insulin, and the differences between both of these on the one hand and the protein obtained from cattle and sheep on the other, is clearly evident from the table in Figure 9-1. All of the insulins, however, cross species barriers in their physiological activity. This suggests that while the precise sequence of amino acids in the disulfide ring of the A chain may not play an important role in determining physiological activity, it may (at least in some individuals) have a marked effect on the antigenicity of the substance.

There is as yet little further information on the relation of insulin's structure to its biological activity. It is known that disulfide bridges must be intact for full activity and that esterification of carboxyl groups causes a loss of activity. Free amino groups can be acetylated without loss of activity.

Later work on insulin structure in many species (including some, like the coypu, which are known mainly to crossword puzzle workers) has revealed progressively larger numbers of sites in both the A and B chains where substitutions of amino acids can occur. Fish insulins are, not unexpectedly, quite different from mammalian insulins, but it is a little surprising to discover that guinea pig insulin differs from beef insulin at 17 different amino acid sites. Perhaps this is the explanation for the fact that the guinea pig is such an effective maker of insulin antibodies. The one constant feature of the insulins of all species is the location of the disulfide bridges. One can only conclude that there are certain permissible amino acid substitutions which do not distort the three-dimensional structure of the molecule. Also, the

SOME LANDMARKS IN DIABETES AND INSULIN CHRONOLOGY*

DATE		INVESTIGATOR
c. 10 A.D.	Clinical description	Celsus
c. 20 A.D.	Name "diabetes" introduced	Aretaeus
c. 1000	"Degenerative disease" complications	Avicenna
1679	Noted sweet taste of urine in "the pissing evil"	Thomas Willis
1788	Pathology of pancreas in association with diabetes	Cawley
c. 1850 et seq.	Dietary restriction in treatment of diabetes	Bouchardat; von Noorden; Naunyn; Allen and others
1869	Discovery of pancreatic islets	Langerhans
1870	Glycogenic function of liver (rabbit), hyperglycemia of diabetes	Bernard
1874	Hyperpnea of diabetic acetonemia	Kussmaul
1889	Experimental diabetes after pancreatectomy (dog)	Von Mering, Minkowski
1895	Hereditary nature of diabetes; distinction between juvenile and late-onset diabetes	Naunyn
1900	Islet lesions in diabetics	Opie, Weichselbaum, Stangle
1909	Hypothetical hormone of islets named "insuline"	deMeyer
1910–1920	Insulin "almost" discovered	Zuelzer, Scott, Knowlton, etc.
1921	Insulin discovered (dog)	Banting and Best
1923	Amelioration of pancreatic diabetes by hypophysectomy (toad)	Houssay
1925–	Elucidation of metabolic pathways	Embden, Meyerhof, Parnas, Cori, Lipman, Krebs, Dickens, Ochoa, Leloir, Lynen, etc.
1936	Amelioration of pancreatic diabetes by adrenalectomy (cat)	Long, Lukens
1937	Permanent diabetes by pituitary extract injection (dog)	Young
1955	Structure of insulin elucidated	Sanger

*Largely after Best, C. H., in *Diabetes,* Williams, R. H. (ed.) (New York: Paul B. Hoeber, Inc., 1960).

attachment of insulin to its receptor molecule may not involve individual amino acids in the chains as much as it does the S–S bridges.

Insulin Assay Methods

There are two circumstances in which it is desirable to test an unknown for its insulin content by comparing it with standards of known insulin activity: first, in the quality control of the product which is offered for sale to the diabetic; and second, in the estimation of the insulin content of blood plasma or pancreatic extracts. Most of the insulin assay methods have been biological methods; that is, they have been based upon a measurable physiological effect of the hormone. Chemical methods of assay have been developed recently but these are not yet in wide use.

The quality control methods (or those used in physiological experiments, such as the estimation of the insulin content of the pancreas) which involve comparatively large amounts of insulin are dependent on the blood glucose-lowering property of insulin. In the rabbit, test substances are compared with insulin of known potency for their ability to lower the blood glucose which is measured. In the mouse the blood glucose is lowered to the point at which convulsions appear, and the proportion of a suitable number of mice observed in convulsions is a measure of the insulin potency of the unknown. The 1926 League of Nations unit was defined as equivalent to one-third the amount of insulin required to produce a blood glucose concentration of 45 mg/100 ml of blood in 2–4 hours in a rabbit fasted for 24 hours. The First International Insulin Standard (1925) was set at 8 units per mg of activity.

Obviously, the crude rabbit hypoglycemia and mouse convulsion methods were not suitable for the detection of the minute amounts of insulin in blood plasma, which are of the order of $10^{-8}M$ and are measured in microunits. Intact rats and mice, the most readily available species, are comparatively insensitive to insulin. Therefore, the structures which are known to produce insulin antagonists were removed one at a time and in combination by various investigators, and the assay animals were designated by the extent of surgery and other treatment they had received: thus, AD = Alloxan Diabetic, H = Hypophysectomized, A = Adrenalectomized, and the animal ready for assay is referred to as ADHA. Insulin activity is measured by the blood glucose-lowering effect in such multiply operated animals. It must be apparent that these methods are not likely to be casually available in general hospitals, for the assay animals require immense skill for their preparation and equal devotion for their survival, and they cannot be mass produced. These methods, then, are used primarily by clinical scientists in their investigations.

In addition to the in vivo methods described above a number of in vitro micromethods have been developed and have proved useful. All of these involve the addition in vitro of known and unknown insulin samples to tissues and the measurement of some chemical indication of the magnitude of the insulin effect. For example, insulin stimulates the uptake of glucose by rat diaphragm and the incorporation of C^{14} glycine into the protein of the same structure. Also, when the rat epididymal fat pad is incubated with insulin, glucose uptake and CO_2 production are markedly stimulated.

Some attempts to estimate insulin by purely *chemical* means have been made, but the sensitivity of these methods is inadequate to permit their use on blood plasma. Recently, however, an *immunochemical* method has been developed (Yalow and Berson) in which extremely minute amounts of insulin can be detected by means of an ingenious combination of the formation of an insulin-antibody complex (the antibody having been obtained by immunizing guinea pigs with insulin of another species) and its separation from free insulin by paper electrophoresis. When insulin is labeled with radioactive iodine, conditions can be adjusted so that most of the radioactivity is bound by antibody. The addition of

---

TABLE 9-1.—SENSITIVITY OF INSULIN
ASSAY METHODS*

METHOD		SENSITIVITY (microunits/ml)
In vivo	Blood glucose in ADA mouse	1000
In vitro	Glucose uptake, rat diaphragm	10–100
	Glucose uptake, rat fat pad	10
	CO_2 output, rat fat pad	10
Immunochemical		1.25–5

*Adapted from Randle, P. J., and Taylor, K. W.: Brit. M. Bull. 16:210, 1960.

free insulin displaces radioactive insulin from the complex, and the extent of loss of radioactivity then becomes a measure of the unlabeled insulin added. All of the bio-assay methods have the disadvantage of indicating a net effect of insulin + insulin antagonist(s), but the new immunochemical method is capable of detecting insulin specifically, and thus offers great hope for the future (see Chapter 2).

A summary of the comparative sensitivity of some of the micromethods described above is given in Table 9-1.

Regulation of Blood Glucose Concentration

In one sense, Claude Bernard's famous remarks about the "constancy of the internal milieu" are somewhat misleading because they are often quoted out of context. Bernard was impressed by the fact that many chemical constituents of the blood and other body fluids tend to be maintained within more or less narrow limits. The fact that blood samples can readily be obtained for analysis from human subjects and animals sometimes results in overemphasis on the study of chemical anatomy of body fluids as an end in itself. It is true that a degree of chemical constancy is maintained in the body fluids, but *only because of the intervention of specific cells when the equilibrium is disturbed.* (Bernard himself was far more aware of this point than are many of his professional progeny.) Thus, the study of the chemistry of blood and other body fluids is most rewarding when we can make inferences about the metabolism of cells somewhere in the body from changes in the concentration of certain substances in these fluids.

The concentration of glucose (or of anything else) in the blood at any instant in time represents an equilibrium between the rate at which it is entering the blood stream and the rate at which it is leaving. If there are a number of routes of entry and a variety of routes of exit, it is convenient to think of the final equilibrium value as a vector of all of the forces which tend to raise the concentration of glucose in the blood (BG) balanced against all the forces that tend to lower it. As BG rises, events begin to occur in certain specific cells which modulate the rise and finally cause a fall in BG toward the equilibrium levels. Similarly, a falling of BG triggers responses in other cells which tend to raise the BG to its original level. We have some evidence obtained from observations of human subjects treated with short- and long-acting insulin that the *rate* of rise and fall of the BG rather than the absolute level of glucose at any instant is an impor-

Fig. 9-2.—An outline of the forces which tend to raise and lower blood glucose (BG). See text for detailed description.

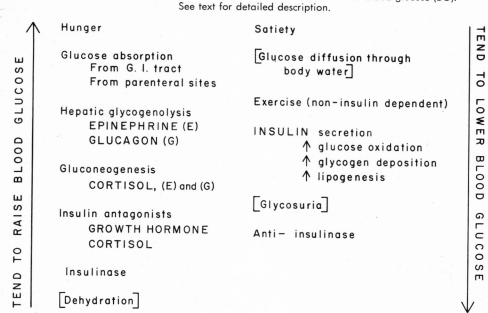

TEND TO RAISE BLOOD GLUCOSE	TEND TO LOWER BLOOD GLUCOSE
Hunger	Satiety

Glucose absorption
   From G. I. tract
   From parenteral sites
	[Glucose diffusion through
	   body water]

Hepatic glycogenolysis
   EPINEPHRINE (E)
   GLUCAGON (G)
	Exercise (non-insulin dependent)
	
	INSULIN secretion
	  ↑ glucose oxidation
	  ↑ glycogen deposition

Gluconeogenesis CORTISOL, (E) and (G)	↑ lipogenesis

Insulin antagonists
   GROWTH HORMONE
   CORTISOL
	[Glycosuria]
	
	Anti- insulinase

Insulinase	
[Dehydration]	

tant component of its signal strength to the "buffer" cells.

Thus, BG regulation appears to have many of the features of a servo system. It is analogous to the temperature in a house equipped with both an automatic furnace and an air conditioning system. (The analogy would be better if the thermostats responded to rate of change of temperature rather than absolute temperature.) The "information" that the BG is changing is delivered to certain cells which have a built-in capacity to respond appropriately to the physiologic need of the organism. Like other control systems, the complex machinery for BG regulation shows a certain amount of "hunting" when the equilibrium is greatly disturbed. For example, when glucose is injected intravenously and the blood sugar-lowering forces are brought sharply into play, the BG is likely to "overshoot" or dip down below the initial base line level, before the reverse buffer systems can operate successfully. This overshoot is of some importance to the clinician, especially when he is attempting to test the competence of the pituitary and adrenal glands which (as we shall see) are important components of the BG elevating complex of the body.

Some appreciation of the complexity of the BG maintenance system may be obtained by inspecting Figure 9-2 which lists some of the physiological processes and events which tend to elevate BG on the left and some which tend to lower BG on the right. A disturbance in any one of these functions may result in faulty BG maintenance and adjustment. But when the total BG regulating system is inspected in these terms, it is easy to see how a defect on the left and a defect on the right could cancel each other out and sum to maintain a "normal" BG.

Forces Which Tend To Elevate BG

HUNGER.—One of the symptoms of a rapidly falling BG level is hunger. Teleologically, this is an appropriate response, for hunger usually leads to food-seeking behavior and food ingestion. The inclusion of hunger among the forces which tend to elevate BG is an attempt to re-emphasize the point made by Richter and others; metabolic events often have behavioral expression, and the behavioral projection of a metabolic need which involves interaction of an animal with its environment is just as much a part of "homeostasis" as are the adjustments that take place within the body.

ROUTES OF ENTRY OF GLUCOSE INTO BLOOD.—There are only 3 ways by which glucose can enter the blood stream. The first (which is not the usual way) is by *injection,* either intravenously or by another parenteral route. This route may be especially important in the diagnosis and treatment of patients and in certain types of experimental analysis. The second (and customary) route is by *absorption* from the gastrointestinal tract. In ordinary circumstances men and animals have two main depots of ready calories on which to draw: the adipose tissue and the contents of the gastrointestinal tract. It is of some interest that the rate of absorption of sugar from the small intestine often parallels the total metabolic rate of the resting animal; i.e., glucose absorption is rapid in the hyperthyroid animal and slow in the hypothyroid one. It is easy to see how malabsorption of glucose or other carbohydrates could interfere with the proper maintenance of BG, and this, in fact, happens in certain human diseases.

The *third* route by which glucose enters the blood is that discovered by Bernard—the "internal secretion" of glucose into the blood by the liver. Some years ago it was demonstrated that even in the absence of obvious hormonal influence the liver has a certain degree of autonomous control over the amount of sugar it releases into the hepatic vein and the amount it retains. But this autonomous control is modulated by a number of hormonal forces. In time of need, and in response to appropriate hormonal signals, the liver can maintain an adequate level of BG even in the absence of absorption of glucose from the gastrointestinal tract. From an evolutionary point of view this must have been a crucial trick indeed, for the brain is just as dependent on a continuing supply of glucose as it is on oxygen, and on many occasions in the past our near and remote ancestors must have been forced to go without food for protracted periods.

There are two principal processes involved in the liver's ability to secrete glucose into the blood. The first, *glycogenolysis,* happens in minutes, and the second, *gluconeogenesis,* occurs over hours and days. Glycogenolysis is simply the breakdown of existing glycogen in the liver, ultimately to glucose-6-phosphate. This compound

$$NH_2 \qquad\qquad\qquad\qquad\qquad\qquad\qquad\qquad NH_2 \qquad\qquad NH_2$$

His. Ser. Glu. Gly. Thr. Phe. Thr. Ser. Asp. Tyr. Ser. Lys. Tyr. Leu. Asp. Ser. Arg. Arg. Ala. Glu. Asp. Phe. Val. Glu. Try. Leu. Met. Asp. Thr.

Fig. 9-3.—The structure of glucagon. (See review by Behrens, O. K., and Bromer, W. W.:
Vitamins and hormones 16:263-301, 1958.)

is split by a specific phosphatase which occurs in the liver, but not in muscle, with the liberation of free glucose into the circulation. As we have seen (Chapter 8), epinephrine stimulates the process of glycogenolysis by stimulating the formation of a substance called cyclic adenylic acid which, in turn, activates the enzyme phosphorylase, which in its turn catalyzes the rate-limiting step in glycogenolysis. Among the effects of either exogenous injection or endogenous release of epinephrine is an elevation of BG at the expense of liver glycogen. Obviously, if there is no glycogen in the liver, or if there are hereditary defects in certain of the enzymes which function in the reaction sequence glycogen → glucose-1-phosphate → glucose-6-phosphate → glucose + phosphate, epinephrine is without effect on the blood glucose.

GLUCAGON—A HORMONE IN GOOD STANDING.—Glucagon, originally only an annoying contaminant in early insulin preparations, is now a full-fledged hormone. It is a polypeptide with a MW of 3,450, and its amino acid sequence is known (Fig. 9-3). Glucagon is the most powerfully hepatic glycogenolytic agent known: the intraportal infusion of as little as 0.01 microgram of the hormone produces intense glycogenolysis in the isolated perfused liver (Sokal, 1966). In contrast, the concentration of epinephrine required to produce glycogenolysis in the same system is from 30 to 50 times that found in the blood after insulin-induced hypoglycemia.

In addition to its effect on glycogenolysis, glucagon also stimulates the production of new glucose from protein in the perfused liver, an effect first suggested by experiments of Miller (1960) and subsequently confirmed by others. Thus, glucagon raises BG on two different time scales: (1) acutely and (2) over a period of minutes and, perhaps, hours. It is believed that glucagon exerts both of these hepatic effects by increasing the concentration of cyclic 3', 5' AMP in the liver cell. The glycogenolysis is the result of a simultaneous activation of phosphorylase and inhibition of glycogen synthetase (see Chapter 8). but the mechanism of gluconeogenesis stimulation is still under discussion. It is possible that

some rate-limiting enzyme just before phosphoenol-pyruvate in the gluconeogenic pathway is activated by cyclic AMP. Alternatively (Ashmore, 1965) 3', 5' cyclic AMP may activate an hepatic lipase analogous to the hormone-sensitive lipase of the adipocyte. This, in turn, would cause an increase in acetyl CoA, which would then activate gluconeogenesis at some step between pyruvate and phosphoenol-pyruvate. Rather than insist on the primacy of one or another gluconeogenic stimulus, I prefer to emphasize the fact that gluconeogenesis characteristically occurs co-ordinately with fatty acid mobilization and catabolism.

The respectability of glucagon's hormonal status was markedly enhanced by studies of fluctuating glucagon concentrations in the blood of dogs and men by means of a highly sensitive radioimmunoassay (Unger et al., 1962). Glucagon concentrations in the pancreaticoduodenal vein blood of dogs was increased fourfold after the induction of acute insulin hypologlycemia. Rapid glucose infusion caused blood glucagon concentrations to drop quickly. Unger also found a threefold increase in glucagon concentration in the blood of men during the second and third days of starvation, with a slow decline following the injection of glucose. These findings suggest that our old conception of the primary role of glucocorticoids in the maintenance of gluconeogenesis during starvation should be modified to include a proper role for the glucagon mechanism as one of the important back-up systems in the protection of animals and men against food deprivation.

A number of biological effects of glucagon have been described following the administration of large doses of the hormone. Among these are: (1) activation of the hormone-sensitive lipase of adipose tissue (Hagen, 1961), (2) stimulation of epinephrine secretion (Sarcione et al., 1963) and (3) stimulation of insulin secretion (Samols et al., 1965). Too little has been done on these effects for mechanisms to be elucidated, but it is of some interest that Sussman (1966) has recently described stimulation of secretion of insulin by 3', 5' cyclic AMP, which suggests the possibility that the first and last of these effects may involve the mediation of the cyclophosphate "deputy."

The glycogenolytic release of glucose from the liver seems well adapted to acute emergencies, but a moment's reflection shows that the BG could not be maintained for long if the liver glycogen were quantitatively delivered to the blood stream as glucose. If a 1500 Gm human liver contained as much as 4% glycogen, only 60 Gm of glucose (or a paltry 240 calories) would be delivered to the blood as glucose on total glycogenolysis. In circumstances of prolonged glucose deprivation, as in starvation, or if there is a failure of renal reabsorption of glucose, as in phlorhizin diabetes, some other mechanism must come into play if the BG is to be effectively maintained. The other, or long range, hepatic maneuver for maintaining BG is called *gluconeogenesis* which, though defined variously, is used here to signify the transformation of deaminated residues of amino acids into glucose in the liver. Operationally, this process actually includes the delivery of the newly formed glucose to the blood stream at a very high rate, because those physiological conditions which are characterized by a high rate of gluconeogenesis are also characterized by an "hypertrophy" of the hepatic enzyme glucose-6-phosphatase, which is the equivalent of stamping a larger than usual number of glucose-6-phosphate molecules "for export only." The liver has an extraordinary capacity for absorbing amino acids from its incoming blood, as one can readily demonstrate by infusing large amounts of protein hydrolysate intravenously. It is difficult, in fact, to maintain an elevated blood concentration of amino acids, even with rapid infusion rates. The sources of the amino acids which are used for long-term maintenance of BG in starvation and in other conditions are the protein tissues of the body, principally the muscle mass which constitutes about 50% of the body's net weight. Adrenal cortical steroid hormones of the glucocorticoid type play an important role in the mobilization of peripheral tissue protein to the liver as amino acids, most of which are used for gluconeogenesis or (in the case of certain acids) for metabolism to acetyl CoA. Of course, some of the amino acids must be used to support protein synthetic activities going on in the liver and elsewhere. The precise mechanism by which the adrenal steroids

function in the process of gluconeogenesis remains obscure, but it is believed that they "permit" the anabolism-catabolism equilibrium in the muscle cell to be tipped in the direction of proteolysis. In addition, Exton and Park (1967) have shown that isolated, perfused livers obtained from adrenalectomized rats fail to respond to gluconeogenic stimuli such as epinephrine, glucagon or 3', 5' cyclic AMP.

If, under conditions of carbohydrate deprivation or chronic renal tubular loss, the glucose utilization rate of tissues other than the central nervous system remained as high as it is in the "fed" state, the problem of maintaining a continuing supply of glucose to the brain would be more demanding than it is. For in starvation, the peripheral tissues adapt in such a way that they use less glucose than before. This is partly due to the fact that adaptation to starvation includes a fall in total metabolism. A true tissue adaptation can also be demonstrated in the muscles of starved or fat-fed rats. Such muscles, incubated in vitro with glucose and a radioactively labeled fatty acid, burn less glucose and more fatty acid than do muscles taken from normal "fed" controls. There is, in fact, a demonstrable block in peripheral carbohydrate oxidation, and a tendency for the tissues to shift their "preference" to fatty acids. This, of course, makes the liver's job of supplying BG by way of gluconeogenesis far easier for, viewed in the light of the over-all economy of the animal, more of the newly formed glucose remains available for the critical central nervous system tissues which need it most.

The nature of the hormonal effects on the *blockade of peripheral glucose oxidation* in starvation is not known with certainty. We do know that both adrenal glucocorticoids and pituitary growth hormone have been alleged to have "braking" effects on glucose use by muscle. They are, in this sense, physiological antagonists to insulin, as we shall see. In starvation, the amount of insulin extractable from the pancreas diminishes sharply, and it is inferred that the rate of synthesis and delivery of the hormone to the blood stream also goes down. If the concentration of physiological insulin antagonists in the blood were maintained at prestarvation levels, it would require only a drop in insulin supply to permit the effects of the antagonists to come into relief. In disease states and in certain experimental circumstances there is no doubt that adrenal glucocorticoids or pituitary growth hormone can elevate the blood sugar. The former do so by a dual mechanism—increased gluconeogenesis and blockade of peripheral glucose oxidation. The latter, so far as we understand the mechanism, raises the blood sugar entirely by inhibiting the egress of glucose from the blood.

THE GLUCOSE FATTY ACID CYCLE.—It has long been known that starvation or feeding fat-rich, carbohydrate-poor diets results in impaired glucose tolerance and comparative insensitivity to insulin in intact animals and men. In fact, increased rates of oxidation of fatty acid and correspondingly decreased rates of glucose oxidation have been described in diaphragms obtained from either diabetic or fat-fed rats. It had been widely assumed that these effects were mainly attributable to the fact that the rate of insulin release from the pancreas is diminished in starvation and fat feeding.

More recently, Randle and his colleagues, among others, have emphasized the fact that fatty acids can modify the pattern of metabolism of carbohydrate in muscle in a striking way in a very short time. Such acute effects of fatty acids can even be seen in isolated tissues in vitro, particularly in the isolated perfused heart and the diaphragm. In such tissues, acute insulin insensitivity, impaired ability to oxidize glucose to lactic acid and a diminished rate of oxidation of pyruvic acid can all be elicited simply by perfusing the tissue with fatty acids or ketone bodies.

Garland and Randle (1964) have measured the acetyl CoA/CoA ratio in the tissues of diabetic animals, as well as in fatty acid-perfused tissues and have discovered a striking increase in this ratio in both circumstances. On the basis of this interesting finding and those of many other investigators, they have proposed the following mechanism to explain the inhibitory effect of fatty acid oxidation on glucose utilization in muscle:

1. Acetyl CoA concentration in the cell rises.
2. The reaction pyruvate → acetyl CoA is inhibited.
3. Citrate accumulates in the cell secondary to the stimulation of its synthesis by high levels of acetyl CoA.
4. Citrate inhibits phosphofructokinase, and thus inhibits glycolysis.
5. Fructose 6 PO_4 disposal is inhibited, but because the equilibrium G6P $\rightleftharpoons$ F6P is strongly in the direction of G6P, the former accumulates.
6. Hexokinase is inhibited by the accumulated G6P and thus causes a rise in free glucose.

7. The glucose transport mechanism is saturated and glucose entry into the cell is blocked.

It is still impossible to assess the importance of this mechanism compared with that of fluctuation in the rate of insulin secretion in the adaptation to starvation. Since the advent of immunoassay methods of measuring insulin in blood we have been impressed by the rapidity with which levels of circulating insulin can change. Now that we know that epinephrine can quickly inhibit insulin release from the β cell as well as stimulate release of FFA from the fat cell, one can imagine that fatty acid mobilization and inhibition of insulin release may be a co-ordinated response to carbohydrate deprivation. In the intact animal, it would be difficult to assign primacy to either decreasing insulin availability or an increased concentration of FFA as determinants of metabolic activity in peripheral tissues. The fact that FFA can have the effects described in vitro systems does not necessarily mean that other events in the intact animal (such as inhibition of insulin secretion) are not essential to an integrated metabolic response.

In any case, these ideas illustrate the concept that normally occurring intermediary metabolites participate in the "steering" of metabolic processes. In early discussions of metabolic control theory, Sir Hans Krebs emphasized that subtle and intricate metabolic control mechanisms exist in micro-organisms which function well without hormonal guidance or direction. Presumably, the control mechanisms of such primitive organisms importantly involve the concentrations of metabolites, the ratios of oxidized to reduced coenzymes, availability of ATP or ADP, availability of inorganic phosphorus, acetyl CoA/CoA ratios and similar signals. There is no reason to doubt the persistence of such control mechanisms, even in highly specialized mammalian cells which clearly contain autonomous, "microhomeostatic" regulatory machinery. The capacity to respond to hormones has been superimposed on these more primitive control mechanisms.

The carbohydrate-sparing action of fatty acids and their metabolic products also illustrates how an effect of hormone deprivation in one type of cell can powerfully influence events in a distant cell of another type. If too much FFA is released from the fat cells, it can function as a signal to inhibit carbohydrate metabolism in muscle cells in the manner described. In fact, there is evidence obtained from studies on maturity onset diabetic patients that carbohydrate and insulin intolerance may occur despite adequate or even super-normal amounts of insulin in the blood in response to a glucose challenge. While this subject is much too complex to discuss here in detail, it has been suggested that the insulin of these individuals is ineffective either because it may be bound by a protein in the blood or antagonized by a circulating anti-insulin substance called "synalbumin," by Vallance-Owen. Future studies will be necessary to clarify the role of insulin binding and insulin antagonism in the onset and persistence of diabetes. However, apart from these hypothetical mechanisms, Randle and his colleagues have mustered evidence to suggest that the serum FFA levels of these insulin-resistant diabetics is inappropriately high both in the fasting state and for some time after a glucose load. They suggest that some of the carbohydrate and insulin intolerance of this group of people may be attributed to the glucose-sparing effect of too much FFA in the blood.

Other investigators have postulated that FFA mobilized from fat cells and triglyceride hydrolysis in the liver cell during fasting may provide one of the major signals for the initiation of the process of gluconeogenesis. While, as we have seen, a high acetyl CoA/CoA ratio may *inhibit pyruvate* decarboxylation, it may *stimulate* the CO_2 fixation reaction through which oxalacetate is synthesized from pyruvate. This is the first step toward the reversal of the glycolytic reaction sequence which results in the production of new glucose (see Chapter 12). Thus, fluctuations in acetyl CoA concentration can determine the metabolic fate of pyruvate in a gluconeogenic organ. It is teleologically reasonable for a product of fatty acid oxidation to operate in this way, for fatty acid mobilization clearly takes place when glucose is in short supply. Therefore, it is eminently sensible for fatty acids to "instruct" the liver to begin to make new glucose out of deaminated residues of amino acids. This is not to assert that fatty acid mobilization from the fat depots and from intracellular triglyceride in the hepatic cell is the only signal for gluconeogenesis. Hormones, particularly glucagon, adrenal glucocorticoids and the lack of insulin serve as important control mechanisms for gluconeogenesis. One has to visualize all of these signals (and, perhaps, others as yet undiscovered) as acting smoothly in concert to initiate and sustain the process of gluconeogenesis. Fatty-acid-as-signal, which is the fundamental message of Randle's glucose-fatty acid cycle postulate, serves as an illustration that metabolic control occurs simultaneously at many levels and that concentrations of normally occurring metabolites constitute part of the information system of a cell and may determine substrate traffic patterns in the cell.

Insulin (see below) is a protein which is inactivated in certain tissues, especially the liver. The initial step in degrading insulin involves the reductive splitting of S–S bonds by a TPNH-requiring glutathione-insulin transhydrogenase. This enzyme is highly specific for insulin, but it also attacks other compounds, such as vasopressin and oxytocin. The insulin-destroying activity of liver homogenates has been shown to fluctuate in some experimental conditions, and it is certainly theoretically possible that the activity of this system could ultimately have an effect on the blood glucose level. For example, the liver appears to inactivate insulin most effectively when insulin secretion rates are presumed to be high. If this is so, the over-all adverse effect of chronic insulin overproduction in the organism would be partially compensated for by an increased rate of insulin destruction in this condition.

There are certain conditions and processes which have only an apparent effect on BG; a few of these are indicated on Figure 9-2 in brackets. Dehydration appears to elevate the BG only because the concentration of all blood solutes is increased by virtue of a diminution in the volume of the fluid in which they are dissolved. The very elevated blood glucose concentrations found in severely acidotic diabetics owe some of their height to coexisting hemoconcentration. These, then, are some of the influences that tend to raise the blood glucose concentration. With the possible exception of insulinase, all of these have been demonstrated to be important in the analysis of many diseases, in addition to their obvious importance in the adaptation of men and animals to changing nutritional conditions.

FORCES WHICH TEND TO LOWER BG

Just as hunger has the effect of raising the blood glucose the continued absorption of glucose from the intestine causes hunger to disappear. The resulting sensation of satiety causes a cessation of eating, and this limits the size of the glucose load that must be disposed of. Again, this is an illustration of a behavioral consequence of metabolic events, and it underscores the fact of environmental as well as organic homeostasis.

GLUCOSE DIFFUSION.—The apparent BG lowering effect of diffusion is significant only when large glucose loads are given intravenously, usually for diagnostic purposes. The initial very rapid fall, which usually takes only a few minutes, is related to the time it takes for equilibrium to be reached between the circulating blood and the total extracellular water. This point may have some practical significance in the analysis of glucose disposal patterns ("glucose tolerance curves") clinically because the coexistence of circulatory difficulties in a test patient may contribute to an apparently slowed rate of glucose removal from the blood.

INSULIN.—Insulin is synthesized in the β cells of the islets of Langerhans. Humbel (1965) presented evidence to support the view that the A and B chains of insulin are separately synthesized and, presumably, subsequently joined by what Lazarow has called a "zippase" enzyme. However, Steiner et al. (1967) have presented quite convincing evidence that radioactive amino acids, presented either to slices of human insulin-producing tumors or to islets of Langerhans isolated from rat pancreas, are incorporated into a larger protein ("proinsulin") before they appear in insulin. They also found that the label was transferred from proinsulin to insulin when protein synthesis was inhibited (cycloheximide) and suggest that the larger protein is a precursor in the biosynthesis of insulin. It is difficult to reconcile the idea of independently synthesized A and B chains with the proinsulin hypothesis at the present time. I suppose it is still conceivable that the large proinsulin molecule represents an instant aggregate of smaller subunits. In any case the proinsulin idea raises the possibility that the proteolytic step proinsulin → insulin may be a locus of an inborn error of metabolism that might result either in the production of inadequate supplies of insulin or an abnormal form of the hormone.

The hormone is presumably made in the region of the Golgi apparatus and stored in membrane-bound, electron-dense granules. When the β cell is stimulated to release insulin by a variety of stimuli, the insulin-containing granules migrate to the cell surface where their membranes fuse with the cell membrane as their contents are discharged into the extracellular space. Apparently, at this instant the material is solubilized, for it is no longer visible in discrete packets. It passes through several membranes, finally reaching the blood, and is discharged into the pancreatic vein which empties into the portal system. Thus, newly discharged insulin goes first to the liver, where it may (1) exert a physiologic effect (2) be broken down by a specific insulinase or (3) traverse the liver, appear in the systemic circulation and proceed to other insulin-sensitive cells of the body, mainly muscle and adipose tissue.

Not long ago, the main signal for insulin release was thought to be a rising blood glucose. Unquestionably, this is one of the signals, for insulin release can be demonstrated in the isolated, perfused pancreas if the glucose content of the perfusate is abruptly increased. However, recent work on whole animals, isolated, perfused pancreases and on pancreas slice systems in vitro has led to the view that the regulation of insulin release is an extremely complex process which involves a large number of signals and modulators.

For example, for many years Houssay has taught that there is a vagal component in insulin release, but this idea has not been widely appreciated in the United States. Now Krulich, in Prague, has done very convincing experiments which tend to confirm Houssay's teaching. This investigator has shown a small but consistent fall in blood glucose in the rabbit and dog when minute amounts of glucose are infused intra-arterially, either into the carotid or a peripheral artery. These amounts of glucose are too small to produce a perceptible change in the concentration of peripheral venous blood. Moreover, vagal section prevented the fall in glucose after intra-arterial glucose infusion. These and other experiments strongly suggest the possibility that a vagal reflex may be involved in the modulation of insulin release.

Glucagon certainly causes insulin release from the β cell, as do amino acid mixtures or certain individual amino acids. Tolbutamide and its congeners (see below) also trigger release of insulin and β cell degranulation. It is of great interest that secretin and pancreozymin stimulate insulin release in vivo, for, as McIntyre et al. have shown (1965), the rise in immunoassayable insulin in the blood is much greater when glucose is given directly into the jejunum than it is when glucose is given intravenously, despite the fact that the blood glucose levels attained by IV injection are 2½ times as high as they are after intrajejunal administration. Whether or not secretin or pancreozymin or some intestinally derived form of glucagon is the means by which this remarkable effect is accomplished, the presence of glucose in the intestine is enough to elicit a powerful insulin-releasing signal which can cause a great outpouring of insulin.

Not much is known about the events in the β cell which are associated with insulin release. Recently, Kipnis has found that glucagon-induced insulin release is potentiated by caffeine. This, along with the fact that 3′, 5′ cyclic adenylic acid can induce insulin release from pancreas slices in vitro suggests the possibility that Sutherland's ubiquitous "deputy" molecule may be at work in this cell as it appears to be in so many others. The release of insulin from the β cell can be inhibited by a number of experimental maneuvers, including vagotomy. Perhaps the most interesting insulin release inhibitors are epinephrine and norepinephrine, which have been shown to decrease insulin output by the pancreas both in vivo and in vitro. From the point of view of integrative physiology, this is a most interesting finding, for the epinephrine appears to be causing a glycogenolytic hyperglycemia and, at the same time, prolonging the hyperglycemia by inhibiting the release of the hormone that would quickly end it.

Other inhibitors of insulin release are of great interest because they can be used as experimental tools to produce an acute insulin deficiency. One such is the sugar d-mannoheptulose, which is abundantly present in avocados. The mechanism of inhibition of glucose release by mannoheptulose is unknown.

Insulin facilitates the removal of glucose from the blood by way of three main routes—*lipogenesis* (in adipose tissue and liver), *glycogen deposition* (mainly in muscle), and *glucose oxidation* (probably in all insulin-sensitive tissues). Insulin lack is characterized by a greater or lesser degree of failure of these processes. A discussion of current knowledge and speculation about these effects of insulin will be given in a later section of this chapter.

Some of the factors which have been found to influence insulin release can be summarized as follows:

INSULIN RELEASE	
STIMULATED	INHIBITED
Glucose	Epinephrine
Fructose	Norepinephrine
Amino acids	d-Mannoheptulose
Glucagon	2 Deoxyglucose
Sulfonylureas	Diazoxide
3′, 5′ Cyclic AMP	Vagotomy
Secretin	
Pancreozymin	
Vagus stimulation	

The reader should understand that working muscle does not require insulin in order to oxidize glucose and that muscular activity has the effect of lowering the blood glucose level in diabetics and in normal people. A well-regulated diabetic can precipitate an attack of hypoglycemia by a sudden burst of heavy work. Many of them understand this and "cover" unforeseen work with a bit of chocolate without increasing their insulin requirement. Diabetic children in summer camps often show a paradoxical increase in food intake and a decrease in insulin requirement when they shift from their sedentary city lives to an active life at camp.

When the blood glucose concentration exceeds the renal threshold for glucose reabsorption (generally about 180 mg%), glucose appears in the urine. This has the effect of diminishing blood glucose, and therefore re-establishing the equilibrium blood level.

Certain drugs have been described which apparently lower the blood glucose by interfering with the destruction of insulin by "insulinase," thus permitting whatever insulin is present to have a more prolonged and extensive effect. While this development is of no great practical importance as yet, it illustrates an interesting mechanism by which an effect on blood glucose can be obtained.

The *Houssay phenomenon* is the name given to the amelioration of pancreatic diabetes that occurs when the hypophysis is removed. This observation was first made on toads, but it has been seen repeatedly in many species of animal, including man. This is an example of balanced defects on the BG raising and BG lowering sides of the ledger. The pancreatectomized animal or the diabetic human shows marked elevation of the BG and profuse glycosuria. When the hypophysis is removed, BG returns to normal levels and glycosuria disappears. Moreover, there is fairly good regulation of the blood glucose as long as the animal or man continues to have a readily available supply of food. The insulin deficiency in this instance is compensated for by the removal of prominent insulin antagonists, · pituitary growth hormone, and adrenal glucocorticoids. In fact, a similar decrease in the severity of diabetes may be seen when pancreatectomized or alloxan-diabetic animals are bilaterally adrenalectomized (the Long-Lukens phenomenon). The reader is referred to Chapter 3 for a more complete discussion of the role of the adenohypophysis in metabolism.

The Panmetabolic Nature of Insulin Lack

There is no better way to appreciate what insulin means to the economy of the body than to study the effect of acute insulin deprivation. When insulin is withdrawn acutely from a severely diabetic animal or man, a remarkable sequence of intricately interconnected events is begun and, if there is no intervention, the inevitable outcome is coma and death. These events involve not merely carbohydrate metabolism but fat, protein, electrolyte, and water metabolism as well. The repercussions of insulin lack appear in the central nervous system, the respiratory system, the cardiovascular system, the renal excretory system, and the gastrointestinal system. As an exercise in the correlation and integration of biochemical and physiological information, and as an example of the rational basis of the treatment of patients, thoughtful contemplation of the pathophysiology of diabetic acidosis cannot be surpassed.

In order to understand diabetic acidosis, the student should recall that the body adapts to starvation in a certain characteristic way. First, there is a decrease in the use of glucose by peripheral tissues, accompanied by a mobilization of depot fat in the form of free fatty acids (FFA, also known as "NEFA," that is, nonesterified fatty acids, or "UFA," unesterified fatty acids). There is also an increase in breakdown of peripheral tissue proteins, with the delivery of amino acids to the liver for gluconeogenesis. There is some ketonemia, and often ketonuria. A test dose

of glucose ("glucose tolerance curve") often reveals an upward displacement of the curve, i.e., a diabetic type of response. These adaptations have obvious survival value, for when carbohydrate is unavailable, the "wisdom of the body" negotiates a shift to a fat metabolic mixture and arranges to have the BG sustained by gluconeogenesis. All of this, no doubt, took a long segment of evolutionary time to develop.

What happens in the insulin-deprived diabetic is a ghastly caricature of the normal adaptation to starvation. Many of the same kinds of changes occur, but the responses are inappropriately violent, so to speak, and get out of hand. Moreover, it is often difficult for the beginning student to understand the interrelations of many things that are happening more or less simultaneously. For this reason we have elected to make an arbitrary division of our description into three fragments, and then to show how all of these processes are related. This discussion is concerned with the level of organization of the whole animal or man. It will be followed by an attempt to consider the biochemical effect of insulin lack on certain tissues—an examination of the same events at a higher power of biochemical magnification.

"CARBOHYDRATE" METABOLISM

The primary event is relative insulin withdrawal. In diabetic patients, this may not necessarily mean an absolute decrease in the amount of insulin the patient takes but rather a sudden and unexpected increase in his requirement. An attack of acidosis may be precipitated by an infection, by physical trauma, by emotional stress, all of which tend to increase the need for insulin. Or it may be initiated by the omission of insulin. Often, there is nausea and vomiting, which are associated with failure of food and water intake.

With insulin lack, there is decrease in glucose use by the peripheral tissues, mainly muscle and adipose tissue. This contributes to the developing hyperglycemia, and liver and muscle glycogenolysis contribute more. (Gluconeogenesis, to be described below, makes an additional contribution to the increase in blood sugar.) When the BG rises above the renal threshold for glucose, glycosuria appears and an osmotic diuresis is instituted. Glucose cannot be excreted as a dry powder by the kidneys; inevitably, it takes water and electrolytes with it into the urine. This is the

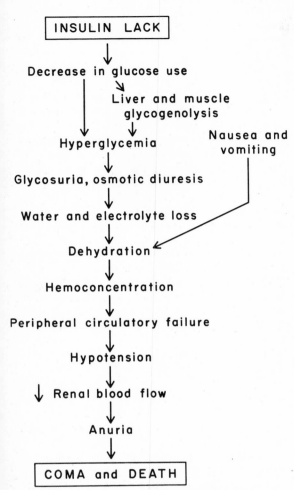

Fig. 9-4.—The effect of insulin lack on carbohydrate metabolism.

Generalized tissue anoxia, with a consequent shift to anaerobic metabolism, results in increasing concentrations of lactic acid in the blood. Coma appears some time after the appearance of peripheral circulatory failure. Death is inevitable in the untreated individual. Figure 9-4 is a diagrammatic summary of this sequence of events.

"Fat" Metabolism

The relative insulin lack and decrease in glucose use by the adipose tissue of the body result in a large-scale mobilization of depot fat into the blood. This may result in a secondary hypertriglyceridemia as the FFA are synthesized into low density lipoproteins by the liver.

The liver is flooded with fat, much of which, for reasons to be discussed, it can oxidize only as far as the acetyl CoA stage. The two-carbon fragments aggregate into acetoacetic acid and beta hydroxybutyric acid in which form they appear in hepatic venous blood in increasing concentrations. The developing ketonemia has two prominent effects: first, it leads to a progressive metabolic acidosis which in turn initiates the characteristic deep and rapid (Kussmaul) breathing which is one of the diagnostic signs of diabetic acidosis. Second, as ketonemia exceeds the

basis of the polyuria of diabetes, which was the first symptom of the disease to be recognized in antiquity.

The loss of water and electrolytes in the urine, especially in view of the fact that intake by mouth has usually ceased, leads to dehydration and hemoconcentration. This is turn leads to peripheral circulatory failure because of the marked reduction in circulating blood volume— a situation that has been nicknamed "medical shock" to distinguish it from the peripheral circulatory failure associated with trauma, which had previously been called "surgical shock." One of the characteristic features of shock is hypotension followed by diminished renal blood flow which may progress to the point of anuria.

Fig. 9-5.—The effect of insulin lack on fat metabolism.

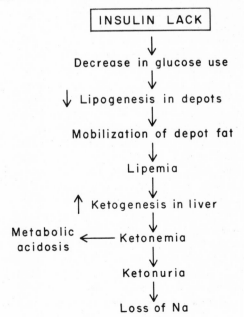

renal threshold for ketone body reabsorption, ketone bodies appear in the urine. In the process of being excreted by the kidneys, they deplete the body of fixed base. This contributes to the net sodium loss which means, in effect, that the ionic "skeleton" of extracellular water is diminished and can therefore "support" progressively smaller volumes of fluid. These developments are summarized in Figure 9-5.

"PROTEIN" METABOLISM

Withdrawal of insulin and impaired use of glucose causes a decrease in protein synthesis and therefore has the effect of promoting net protein catabolism, at first in insulin-sensitive tissues and especially in muscle. The products of tissue proteolysis, amino acids, diffuse into the blood and are delivered to the liver. There they are oxidatively deaminated, their carbon residues contribute either to new glucose formation or to the already too large pool of ketone bodies and the NH_2 appears as urea which is excreted. This process is accompanied by a net loss of nitrogen from the body. It is also accompanied by the release of K and other intracellular ions into the blood.

Fig. 9-6.—The effect of insulin lack on protein metabolism.

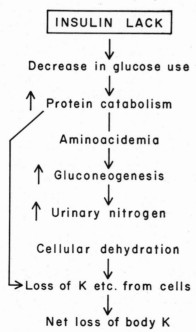

In addition to the impairment in protein metabolism that is secondary to deficient use of glucose by cells (and to nonglucose transport-linked effects as well), some of the other effects of insulin lack also interfere with cell function and cause further breakdown of the biochemical machinery of cells. For example, progressive water loss eventually causes intracellular dehydration, which favors catabolic processes and adds to the diffusion of intracellular electrolytes into extracellular water. As long as urine flow continues there is an opportunity for K to be lost to the body in cumulatively dangerous amounts. A summary of these developments is given in Figure 9-6.

When all of these sequential events are united into a single diagram (Fig. 9-7) certain important points become obvious. In the first place, the common starting place for the disturbance can be seen clearly. All of this began because there was an inadequate supply of the material shown in Figure 9-1. Second, the intricate interrelations of carbohydrate, fat, protein, electrolyte and water metabolism are well shown. Finally, this chart shows the cause and effect relationships that have been discussed; it gives some idea of the complexity of the disturbance, and it suggests that many of these interrelated events are occurring at the same time.

The summary diagram also affords an opportunity to point out that the metabolic acidosis is complicated by lacticacidemia which arises as a result of peripheral circulatory failure. The extreme insulin resistance often encountered in diabetic acidosis is not entirely understood, but it is believed to be due, at least in part, to an increase in production of adrenal glucocorticoids that occurs regularly in this condition, and to the fact that insulin antagonists may contribute to the insulin resistance, but this is merely a speculation. The presence of large amounts of FFA in the blood and tissues may contribute to insulin resistance, as we have already seen in our discussion of Randle's glucose fatty acid cycle (p. 160).

The profound disturbance in central nervous system function that progresses to coma is probably not explicable on the basis of any single factor. The infusion of acetoacetate into experimental animals at very rapid rates may produce coma, but acetone and beta hydroxybutyric acid are not highly toxic in the concentrations in

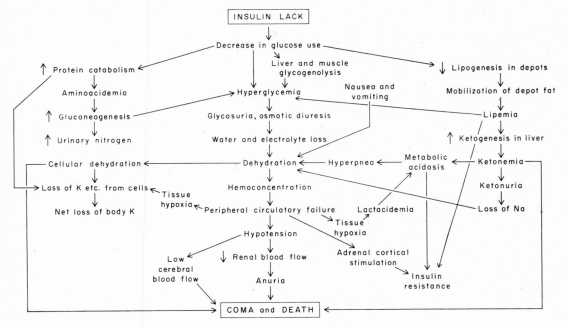

Fig. 9-7.——Composite summary of the pathophysiology of diabetic acidosis. Note, particularly, connections among the three general areas of metabolism.

which they are often found in acidotic animals. At present, it is perhaps best to attribute the coma to a complex of factors, including cellular dehydration, low cerebral blood flow, ketonemia, and possibly impairment of renal function. The oxygen consumption of the brain of a severely acidotic individual is markedly depressed.

The one thing that distinguishes the modern physician from some of his enthusiastic empiricist ancestors, who purged, cupped, and bled patients with an abandon that frightens us in retrospect, is the ability to analyze a disease process in dynamic terms and to institute treatment which is rationally designed to correct the defect. Progress in the treatment of diabetic acidosis reflects the improved understanding of the pathophysiology of the condition. Proper management of the acidotic patient is almost obvious from the outline given above. If shock is present, measures to increase the effective circulating blood volume should be instituted. This involves the administration of fluid and electrolytes (plus whole blood, plasma, or plasma expanders when indicated). Acidosis can be combated by the administration of a sodium salt with a combustible anion, such as sodium lactate. Since insulin

lack triggered the whole disturbance, insulin must be given—by vein, if shock is profound and the likelihood of its being picked up from a subcutaneous depot is small. In spite of the fact that the BG may be very high, the depletion of muscle and liver glycogen stores has usually been so extensive that carbohydrate must be infused soon after the beginning of treatment. In recent years, more and more attention has been paid to the net K deficit that develops in some people, and K-containing infusion mixtures are used (with caution) in repairing the electrolyte disturbance. After the acute phase of the treatment, when the patient begins to take fluids by mouth, K-containing substances, such as fruit juices, are often given. As treatment proceeds, the general condition of the patient is carefully observed, and blood pressure records are kept. The efficacy of the management can be assessed by means of blood glucose, blood CO_2-combining power, serum K, and NPN. Electrocardiographic tracings are often made for the purpose of guiding K administration. As the quantitative data come from the laboratory, the physician's therapeutic plan may be modified. Before this condition was as well understood as it is now, the results of treatment were disappointing and mortality was high. Now, at one representative teaching hospital, the mortality rate is given as 1.5%. Understanding of the physiology involved is not merely intellectually satisfying, it is life-saving.

The Cellular Significance of Insulin and Its Lack

We have analyzed certain features of the pathophysiology of insulin lack at the level of organization of the intact animal or man. How far into the cell does our understanding go, and where are the gaps in our knowledge about insulin? For convenience, we propose to divide the discussion into three parts: "carbohydrate," "fat," and "protein" metabolism, but it should be obvious by this time that such a division has no real meaning. This lack of meaning, in fact, will be the *leit motif* of this section.

"CARBOHYDRATE" METABOLISM

Insulin promotes the utilization of glucose by many tissues, principally muscle and adipose tissues, but there are certain tissues, such as brain, retina (and very likely the germinal epithelium of the testis and ovary) which do not require the hormone although they are obligatory glucose users. The effect of insulin on the carbohydrate metabolism of the liver is an unresolved problem at present, but I am inclined to the view that insulin does indeed have the effect of making glucose available to the pool of intermediary metabolites in the liver cell by an effect on the enzyme glucokinase.

Most authorities now agree that insulin affects the carbohydrate metabolism of muscle by facilitating the transfer of glucose from the extracellular fluid to the interior of the cell, a view first advocated by Levine and his colleagues. It is inappropriate here to go into the experimental evidence that has been advanced in support of this view, and the interested student is invited to consult review articles for details. It should be emphasized that most of the work on which this statement is based was done on muscle, and may or may not be transferable to adipose tissue cells or to liver.

The intracellular transfer or glucose transport hypothesis should be examined in the light of the total glucose economy of the animal. The extracellular concentration of free glucose is far in excess of the intracellular level of free glucose, for when glucose gains entry to the cell interior it is immediately phosphorylated. If the transfer of glucose across the cell membrane were entirely by diffusion, there would be a steady abstraction of glucose from the extracellular fluid. In fasting, this would constitute a great drain on the net glucose supply, and the obligatory glucose-burning tissues could be compromised thereby. It is useful to imagine that, in the absence of insulin, there is a barrier to the entry of glucose into insulin-sensitive cells. Recently, the idea of a glucose barrier in muscle has received experimental support from the work of Randle and others, who have demonstrated that oxygen lack and various poisons which interfere with the production of high energy phosphorus compounds by cells duplicate, in some measure, the action of insulin on cells. That is to say, the entry of glucose into cells is enhanced by various maneuvers which embarrass the ATP-producing machinery of cells. From these studies the hypothesis has been suggested that the glucose barrier at the cell surface is maintained by the constant application of energy to it in the form of ATP, just as a swinging door may be kept shut by the application of pressure to one side of it. Insulin is then presumed to act by interfering with the application of energy to the glucose barrier (see Fig. 9-8 for a graphic model of this hypothesis). It should be emphasized that there is no detailed knowledge as yet about the nature of the hypothetical barrier or the intimate mechanism of insulin's interaction with it, but this is an area of active exploration at the present time, and one which will bear watching in the future.

Once glucose enters the cell, it is phosphorylated to glucose-6-phosphate, which can be metabolized by a number of routes, depending on the biochemical versatility of the cell entered. In liver, glucose carbon can appear as glycogen, CO_2, pentose, acetyl CoA, ketone bodies, fatty acids, cholesterol, Krebs cycle intermediates, and amino acids. In muscle, it can appear principally as glycogen, CO_2, Embden-Meyerhoff intermediates, and Krebs cycle intermediates, although many of the latter can ultimately appear in protein. In adipose tissue, it can appear as glycogen, CO_2, or fat, and both Embden-Meyerhoff and the direct oxidative pathway are present. The UDPG glycogen synthetic pathway of Leloir is present

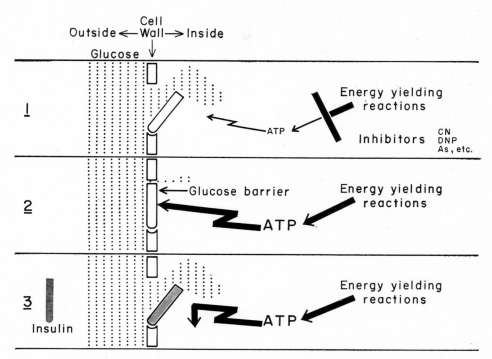

Fig. 9-8.—A diagrammatic model of Randle and Smith's theory of the mechanism of insulin's action on glucose transport. (Suggested by Randle, P. J., and Smith, G. H.: Biochem. J. 70:490-500; 501-508, 1958.)

(Note: The swinging doors are not to be construed as indicating the precise nature of the glucose transport system!)

in the three tissues, and its physiological significance is now beginning to be stressed by a number of investigators. The important point to grasp is the fact that *all of the enzymes involved in the myriad of reactions outlined above are present in amounts which permit the disposal of large amounts of glucose.* Therefore, the rate of glucose metabolism by the cell, no matter what its ultimate disposal route, may be largely determined by the rate at which it is transported from the outside of the cell into the cell interior.

Glucose is far more than a cell fuel, and the continuing metabolism of at least small amounts of glucose furnish the cell with much more than a ready source of energy. During the metabolism of glucose, many chemical substances arise which play important roles in the vital chemical reactions of the cell and, indeed, may actually serve as substrate traffic control signals. For example, oxalacetic acid is formed from pyruvic acid, and the rate of its formation may influence the total size of the pool of Krebs cycle intermediates and thus help to set the level of opera-

tion of the cycle. If glucose oxidation is proceeding at a low rate, the supply of oxalacetate may be low and the capacity of the Krebs cycle to deal with acetyl CoA may be diminished. This, in fact, is the state of affairs in the diabetic liver, although some authorities suggest that deficient oxalacetate synthesis is not the primary reason for it.

Other examples of critical intermediates of glucose oxidation will be discussed. It should be emphasized that some of these materials may be effective in only catalytic concentrations, and that lavish supplies of glucose may not be necessary in order to supply the cell interior with "operational" or "machine tool" intermediates in sufficient supply to keep the machinery in good order. This may well be a clue to the current controversy about the role of insulin in the liver. Some investigators find it difficult to demonstrate retention of glucose by the liver when they use arteriovenous difference techniques in insulin-treated animals, and therefore question whether or not insulin has an effect on the liver.

There is no difficulty, however, in demonstrating effects of insulin in liver slices to which insulin is added, especially if one uses an indirect measure of the effect, such as stimulation of fat formation or protein synthesis. This may mean simply that the total *amount* of glucose involved in the insulin effect may be extremely small when it is related to the total energy expenditure of the liver, but that this small amount has very great *operational* significance for the liver cell because it furnishes critical materials required for synthetic reactions.

"FAT" METABOLISM

One of the most striking effects seen as a result of insulin deprivation is extensive mobilization of depot fat. The liver is called upon to oxidize far more fat than it can conveniently handle, especially in view of the inadequacy of its Krebs cycle described above. Moreover, synthesis of fatty acids from two-carbon units virtually stops both in the liver cell and in the adipose tissue. The result is a piling up of acetoacetic acid by the deacetylation of the 6-carbon intermediate β hydroxy-β methyl glutaryl CoA.

Until recently, the adipose tissue storage cell was largely ignored by physiologists as a dull and glamourless repository of fat globules. But the studies of Wertheimer and his colleagues and of many others have taught us that the adipose tissue cell is one of the principal end-organs upon which insulin acts and that its metabolism is as interesting as that of any other cell. In fact, the lipemia and its sequelae (hepatic ketogenesis, ketonemia, metabolic acidosis, and so on) may be initiated by the effect of insulin lack on the adipose tissue cell. Neutral fat is constantly being synthesized and degraded in the adipose tissue cell. When synthesis of new fat from glucose is occurring, the balance is in favor of synthesis and there is no significant release of FFA. When the cell is deprived of carbohydrate, as in starvation or diabetes, the stored triglycerides are attacked by a lipase which frees fatty acids for release into the circulation. All of the details of these events are by no means clearly understood, but these problems are among those being pursued most actively in research laboratories around the world. A more complete discussion of the physiology of adipose tissue will be found in Chapter 10.

At present, we believe it is safe to attribute fatty acid mobilization from the adipose tissue in diabetes to failure of fatty acid synthesis, a defect which is present both in the liver and adipose tissue of insulin-deprived animals and men. What is the nature of this defect? We can summarize the work of many investigators in the following way: When glucose is available to the interior of the lipogenic cell in large amounts it furnishes (1) substrate for conversion to fatty acids, i.e., acetyl CoA; (2) α glycerophosphate, which is the specific precursor of glycerol with which fatty acids are esterified for storage (essential because adipose tissue does not have a glycerol kinase, and all the glycerol necessary for triglyceride synthesis must be generated by the

Fig. 9-9.—Some secondary effects of insulin on lipogenesis. Note that an action of insulin at **A** could accomplish all of these results.

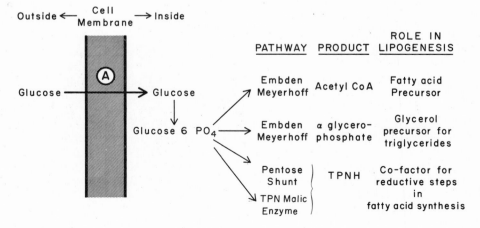

metabolism of glucose by way of the Embden-Meyerhoff pathway); and (3) DPNH (generated by the Embden-Meyerhoff pathway) and TPNH (generated by the direct oxidative, or pentose shunt pathway). The former is specifically required for the synthesis of fatty acids by one of two postulated pathways. The latter is specifically required for fatty acid synthesis by both pathways that have been described. It is used specifically at recurring ethylene reductase steps (double bond saturation) in the synthesis of long chain acids. When all of these materials are present in adequate supply, the glucose-derived acetyl CoA fragments are swept up into fatty acids in the reducing environment provided by the appropriate coenzymes. The fatty acids are promptly esterified with α glycerophosphate and stored. In the absence of glucose, the élan is in the opposite direction. A summary of these events is given in Figure 9-9.

A similar state of affairs obtains in the liver, but in that tissue it has been shown to be complicated by the fact that insulin deprivation results in an "atrophy" of certain crucial enzymes, specifically those involved in lipogenesis. Thus, even when glucose is returned to the interior of the cell, it takes some time before the full lipogenic capacity of the cell is restored. Also, the liver is an important site of cholesterol synthesis, and the lipogenesis failure, excessive fatty acid catabolism, and Krebs cycle insufficiency somehow result in an increased rate of synthesis of cholesterol. This may be of importance in some of the long range complications of the disease diabetes mellitus.

"Protein" Metabolism

The literature on the subject of insulin and protein metabolism is extensive, but it is difficult to do more than describe a few of the well-established facts. The mechanisms of the participation of insulin in protein synthesis are not yet known.

Insulin causes a lowering of the blood amino acid nitrogen and a disappearance of amino acids from the circulating blood in exactly the proportion in which they are represented in muscle. Radioactively labeled amino acids appear in tissue protein in greater amounts in insulin-treated animals and tissues. A discussion of the mechanism of insulin effect on protein metabolism will

be found in Chapter 12. Effects of insulin on promoting protein synthesis are obtainable in the absence of growth hormone, but they only reach their full expression when the tissue is under the influence of both hormones. Possibly these effects of insulin on protein synthesis and the historic "protein-sparing action of glucose" are not achieved by the same mechanisms. Whatever the mechanism, insulin lack causes a shift in the protein anabolism-catabolism equilibrium in the direction of protein breakdown, and this is the starting point for the physiologically inappropriate overproduction of new glucose from protein described above.

The effect of insulin on protein metabolism is of far greater interest than this for the reason that the enzymes of the cell are themselves specific proteins, presumably in dynamic equilibrium like other proteins. That is to say, they are being synthesized and destroyed constantly, and are maintained at an equilibrium level. Not long ago the impression was widespread that a cell receives a fixed complement of enzymes which remains immutable for the duration of its life. We now realize that the profile of enzyme activities of many cells may be altered very radically with changes in physiological circumstances. A discussion of coordinated adaptive changes in enzymes will be found in Chapter 12.

The Long-Range Effects of Insulin Lack

The effects of acute deprivation of insulin, or of pancreatectomy, have been described. These effects become manifest in hours and if no substitution hormone treatment is given death occurs within 1 to several days. The effects of incomplete insulin substitution treatment occur over a very much longer time scale which is measured in years and decades. Among these effects are: atherosclerosis, particularly of the coronary, cerebral and renal arteries, and arteries of the lower extremities; lesions of the retina and lens of the eye; intercapillary glomerulosclerosis; neuropathies; various disorders of the skin. Many of these are recognizable as a group of so-called degenerative disorders of unknown etiology which are highly prevalent in the nondiabetic elderly population. The disease diabetes, even when patient and physician collaborate conscientiously to substitute for the relative insulin lack as carefully as they can, is associated with a high incidence of these diseases and a kind of telescoping of their time scale, so that extensive lesions appear at an earlier age in diabetics than they do in nondiabetics.

It is extraordinarily difficult to make meaningful observations in this field and authorities have not reached anything like a consensus about it. Subscribers to one school of thought hold that even if the diabetic is as perfectly controlled as he can be he will exhibit early degenerative disease of the arteries or capillaries and that less compulsive control does not much increase the risk of such complications. Others take the view that rigid control diminishes the number and severity of, but does not abolish, these lesions. Some feel that predisposition to diabetes and to these vascular "complications" may simply represent a coincident genetic circumstance, while others point to the early and severe vascular lesions seen in pancreatectomized humans with negative family history as evidence that the vascular degeneration is, in fact, a true complication of the diabetes.

Hyperlipemia and hypercholesterolemia are seen in association with certain vascular diseases both in nondiabetics and in diabetics, and they are widely believed to contribute to the etiology of these multifactorial diseases. It is possible that, even with the most skilled administration of exogenous insulin, the smoothness of control that is provided by the normally functioning β cells which deliver insulin on demand cannot be duplicated and that patches of comparatively hyperlipemic time occur each day. This sort of thing, possibly in association with an increased local vulnerability of the vessels to the deposition of lipid, may have a cumulative effect over a period of years. There is some basis for speculating that such an increase in local vascular vulnerability may occur, for an elevation of serum mucoproteins has been found in human diabetics, and a marked decrease in the concentration of acid mucopolysaccharides has been described in the skin of the alloxan diabetic rat. It is entirely possible that a defective metabolism of mucopolysaccharides with a consequent modification of the ground substance of blood vessel walls may play a role in the vascular degeneration so characteristic of diabetes. It should be emphasized that this is conjectural, and that an ordered and lucid description of the relation between diabetes and vascular disease must await more information than we now have about both conditions.

Very recently Siperstein and his colleagues (1966) have reported on a careful study of the width of capillary basement membranes in normal, diabetic and prediabetic patients. Their measurements were made on electron micrographs of muscle biopsy specimens. It is not surprising that the capillary basement membranes of diabetics were highly significantly thicker than were those of nondiabetics. However, it is a distinct surprise to discover that 50% of prediabetic patients destined to become diabetic showed significant basement membrane hypertrophy *in the absence of any measurable defect in carbohydrate metabolism*. The authors suggest that this form of vascular disease may be the primary lesion in diabetes and that metabolic disturbances may arise only secondarily. Alternatively, both the basement membrane thickening and the carbohydrate-fat-protein metabolism defect may be due to a common biochemical lesion—for example, one associated with insulin release—but the full expression of this lesion may be more readily apparent in the vascular abnormality than in the metabolic one.

The Hereditary Factor in Diabetes

There is no doubt that genetic predisposition to the disease *diabetes mellitus* occurs in the human. The disease is clearly familial in character, and it appears much more frequently in monozygotic twins than in heterozygotic ones. Most authorities now accept the view that overt diabetics and potential diabetics are homozygous for a recessive gene "d," that is, "dd." The normal allele of this gene is "D," and the individual *without the diabetic trait* is designated "DD." The *carrier* of the trait is, of course, "Dd."

Using these designations, we can tabulate the results of mating the possible combinations in the following way: (*dd* = diabetic).

1.	dd + dd = dd	dd	dd	dd
2.	Dd + dd = dd	dd	Dd	Dd
3.	Dd + Dd = dd	Dd	Dd	DD
4.	Dd + DD = Dd	Dd	DD	DD

One would predict from these reflections that 100% of the offspring of two diabetic parents would become diabetic. In practice (according to J. V. Neel), the figure may be closer to 75%. This and other similar data suggest that the inheritance pattern of the disease is more complicated than that which one would expect if a single recessive gene were involved. There may be modifier genes, or the expression of a single (or multiple) gene(s) may be influenced by environmental factors. In any case, from the point of view of genetic counseling, 75% is not substantially different from 100%, and, at the present stage of our ignorance of the details of the genetics of diabetes, it is permissible to use the single recessive gene hypothesis in advising people who contemplate marriage.

From a known diabetic population of about 1.0%, it has been calculated that "the" diabetic gene is present in from 20 to 25% of the total population. Doubtless this figure must have increased since the beginning of the insulin era, for many juvenile diabetics who formerly would have died of the disease are now surviving to childbearing age, and improved methods of management have resulted in the salvaging of many babies of diabetic mothers. This means more and more responsibility for the understanding and care of diabetics by physicians in the future.

Most diabetics do not exhibit overt disease until after the age of 40. Thus, since the genetic predisposition must have existed in these people from the time of their conception, we must conclude that there is a condition which has been termed "prediabetes." There are certain environmental circumstances which bring such hereditary predisposition into clear relief, and the most prominent of these is *obesity*. In fact, certain obese, middle-aged diabetics who have all of the classical symptoms and signs of the disease can become aglycosuric and show a normal glucose tolerance curve simply by reducing their body weight and maintaining it at a lower level. This suggests that these individuals have marginally compensated insulin-producing cells which, while they are not equal to the task of coping with an excessively large glucose-disposal problem, can deal successfully with a less demanding glucose load (see Chapter 10).

At present, much clinical investigation is being done on the prediabetes problem for the reason that, if people with a tendency to develop the disease can be identified before it becomes manifest, measures may be taken which will prevent "beta cell decompensation" from occurring. (This does not differ, in principle, from identifying a man with a weak heart and then restricting his work load.) Several types of tests have been suggested, including the ACTH, or cortisone-glucose tolerance test, the rapid intravenous glucose tolerance test, and the tolbutamide response test (see p. 174). In the cortisone-glucose test, for example, aglycosuric people with normal glucose tolerance who do not have a family history of diabetes (3%) rarely show upward displacement of the curve in the direction of a diabetic response, while 25% of similar individuals with a positive family history of diabetes show a diabetic response under these conditions. The tolbutamide test (blood sugar lowering in response to a test dose of the drug) is based on the hypothesis that tolbutamide stimulates the β cells to release insulin, and that the hypoglycemia is a sort of built-in insulin assay which measures the competence of the insulin-producing cells to deliver the hormone to the blood on signal. Prediabetics are said to have a slower fall in blood glucose following the drug than do normal individuals.

These and other tests for prediabetes have not been validated against one another, but all of them show a much higher percentage of abnormalities among relatives of diabetics than among people with a negative diabetes family history. They are stressed here because, in my view, a discriminating and practical method of identifying prediabetics will enable physicians of the future to prevent much overt diabetes, even if they use no preventive technique other than rigid body weight control in their patients. The development of objective criteria for detecting the diabetes trait will also be of great importance in future studies of the genetics of the disease.

There are now many genetic models of diabetes in various kinds of experimental animals, including the Chinese hamster, several strains of mice, the desert rat (see Chapter 10) and others. It is of some interest that, in the mouse and desert rat models especially, diabetes is always associated with obesity—as it often is in adult onset human diabetics. There is no assurance in the case of any of these models that we are dealing with a disease which is identical with human diabetes mellitus. But, by working with rapidly breeding populations of animals, one can pose many interesting questions about diabetes, particularly about the relation between vascular disease (such as Siperstein's capillary basement membrane hypertrophy) and the metabolic derangements. Thoughtful study of genetic diabetes in animals cannot fail to illuminate problems of human diabetes.

Use of Chemical Agents in Study of Islet Cell Function

Pharmacology is defined as the study of the effect of chemical agents on living systems. Some people think that pharmacology is an entirely derivative subdiscipline and that the understanding of the effects of drugs on living tissue simply represents an application of basic biochemical and physiological knowledge to a study of drug effects. Actually, the debt has often been in the opposite direction, for certain drugs have played extremely important roles in the development of our understanding of biochemistry and physiology. Langley's use of the drug nicotine in his analysis of the organization of the autonomic nervous system is a case in point. Similarly, several chemical agents have been widely used as tools in the study of pancreatic islet function.

ALLOXAN.—Certain chemical compounds, such as *alloxan*, uric acid, dialuric acid and others seek out the β cells of the pancreatic islets and destroy them, as if the molecules are equipped with some sort of guidance system which directs them to the vulnerable cells. In fact, alloxan is not as selective in its effect as it seems to be, for it is not difficult to demonstrate acute effects of alloxan intoxication in other tissues, such as liver and kidney for example. But the effects in these tissues are generally transitory, while the chemical blow dealt to the β cells is a mortal one. This may be simply a reflection of the fact that the insulin-producing cell is a highly specialized one, and the biochemical machinery that is destroyed by the alloxan monkey wrench represents a more vital part of the cell's total equipment than it does in a more versatile cell.

When alloxan is injected into a suitably prepared animal, a serial response occurs: (1) hyperglycemia, which is believed to be due to epinephrinemia, and also (possibly) to a direct effect of alloxan on the liver; (2) hypoglycemia, which probably represents a response to the sudden release of stored insulin into the blood from damaged β cells; and (3) chronic hyperglycemia, presumably due to irreversible β cell damage.

The advantage of such a chemical tool is obvious. Indeed, countless animals of many species have been rendered diabetic in this way as investigators have studied many of the problems of diabetes and insulin deficiency. There is some reason to believe that an alloxan diabetic animal is not the physiological equivalent of a depancreatized one, for it has been found that the insulin requirement of the alloxan diabetic is decreased by subsequent pancreatectomy. This result could be due either to the removal of a blood sugar raising material with the alloxan-treated pancreas (i.e., glucagon) or to a diminished spontaneous food intake postoperatively.

Since alloxan is chemically related to uric acid, a naturally occurring metabolite, it has been suggested that diabetogenic substances may be produced in the body and may be of some importance in the etiology of human diabetes, but there is no proof that such is the case. It is interesting to note that glutathione, cysteine, British Anti-Lewisite (dimercaptopropanol, a dithiol) and other –SH containing substances, protect the β cell from damage by alloxan. This suggests that alloxan exerts its toxic effect by combining with –SH groups of vital β cell proteins and that –SH enzymes may be centrally important in the highly specialized function of β cells, which is to synthesize and release insulin.

COBALT.—Degranulation and vacuolization of the α cells of the islets occur after the injection of $CoCl_2$ in the guinea pig, rabbit, and dog. It has been claimed by some investigators that the extent of α cell damage is correlated with a diminished glucagon content of the pancreas in the guinea pig, but other investigators working with other species deny that this is so. The histological evidence of cytotoxicity suggests a highly specific affinity of $CoCl_2$ for α cells, since there is neither histological nor functional evidence of impairment or stimulation of β cell function in cobalt-treated animals.

ORAL INSULIN SUBSTITUTES.—Shortly after the sulfonamide drugs were introduced (c. 1935) the observation was made that certain patients with typhoid fever exhibited hypoglycemia after one of these drugs had been given. Between 1942 and 1946 the hypoglycemic effects of sulfonamides was studied by Loubatiéres, and in 1955 it was demonstrated that a sulfonamide drug could function as an "insulin substitute" in certain diabetic patients when it was given orally. This finding stimulated a vast amount of research in this field, both experimental and clinical. The original drug used in the German clinical trials in

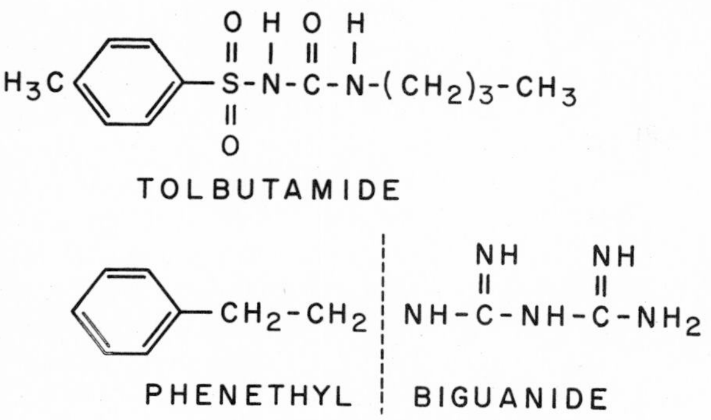

$$H_3C - \bigcirc - \overset{\overset{O}{\|}}{\underset{\underset{O}{\|}}{S}} - \overset{\overset{H}{|}}{N} - \overset{\overset{O}{\|}}{C} - \overset{\overset{H}{|}}{N} - (CH_2)_3 - CH_3$$

TOLBUTAMIDE

$$\bigcirc - CH_2 - CH_2 \quad NH - \overset{\overset{NH}{\|}}{C} - NH - \overset{\overset{NH}{\|}}{C} - NH_2$$

PHENETHYL   BIGUANIDE

Fig. 9-10.—Oral insulin substitutes.

1955 was called *carbutamide,* but this compound (although it is still extensively used in Europe) was largely replaced in the United States by a closely related substance, *tolbutamide* (Fig. 9-10).

The mechanism of action of tolbutamide in controlling the symptoms of diabetes is not yet entirely clear, but it is definitely known that the substance is effective only in those diabetics who have some remaining β cell function. In juvenile diabetics, who may be virtually without functioning β cells, tolbutamide is ineffective. The action of tolbutamide is to cause a release of insulin into the blood from the β cell. The precise mechanism by which this occurs is not known. Either the substance itself functions as a signal for the release of insulin or it combines with some cell constituent in such a way as to render the insulin-releasing mechanism more responsive to existing physiological stimuli than it was. If something like the latter mechanism is operative, the result would be much more comparable to the normal control of blood glucose than periodically spaced insulin injections could possibly be. It is much too early to say anything about the comparative susceptibility of tolbutamide and insulin-treated diabetics to degenerative diseases.

There are other oral insulin substitutes in addition to tolbutamide, but their mechanism of action is still not clear. Tolbutamide was included in this discussion not only because it is a proved therapeutic agent in diabetes, but because its introduction underlined our ignorance of the fundamental interaction of the β cell with its physiological stimulus, glucose. Future work with tolbutamide may bring us a better understanding of this interaction.

Among other types of orally effective hypoglycemic agents are the *biguanides,* of which phenethylbiguanide (Fig. 9-10) is a prototype. These compounds do indeed lower the blood glucose of diabetic patients, but they do so by a mechanism which is quite different from that of tolbutamide. Their primary effect is exerted on the peripheral tissues and not on the β cells, for they can be used in juvenile diabetics. Clinicians feel that this compound is a useful adjunct in the management of some diabetic patients, particularly in certain difficult-to-manage juvenile diabetics who shuttle rapidly from brink to brink, that is, who always seem on the verge of going either into a hypoglycemic attack or into diabetic acidosis. It has been suggested that the biguanides may make the control of selected mercurial diabetics more smooth even if these drugs do not entirely replace insulin but are given in conjunction with it. Unfortunately, many patients cannot tolerate biguanides because they tend to cause gastrointestinal disturbances such as anorexia, nausea, and vomiting. These symptoms occasionally are transitory, and the agent can be given successfully after an initial period of difficulty.

The mechanism of action of the biguanides is still only dimly understood, although much is known about their metabolic effects. Apparently, they cause a sort of histotoxic hypoxia of the cells of the body, with an increased lactic acid production, an increased glucose uptake, diminished gluconeogenesis and diminished hepatic output of glucose. This catalogue sounds not unlike a recital of the sort of thing sublethal doses of cyanide might do, and it is therefore difficult to understand why the biguanides are in fact effective therapeutic agents. It is possible that the tissue effects of the biguanides outlined here are demonstrable with larger-than-therapeutic concentrations of the compound and that when the agent is used in ordinary doses it may have a selective effect on either the glucose barrier itself or on the way in which energy is applied to it to keep it closed. This, of course, is a speculation.

REFERENCES

Berthet, J.: Some aspects of the glucagon problem, Am. J. Med. 26:703–714, 1959.

Brookhaven Symposium on Insulin, Am. J. Med. 40: 651–772, 1966.

Foa, P. P., Galansino, G., and Pozza, G.: Glucagon, a second pancreatic hormone, Recent Hormone Res. 13:473–510, 1957.

Krahl, M. E.: *The Action of Insulin on Cells* (New York: Academic Press, Inc., 1961).

Leibel, B. S., and Wrenshall, G. A.: *On the Nature and Treatment of Diabetes* (New York: Excerpta Medica Foundation, 1965).

Levine, R.: Symposium on diabetes, Am. J. Med. 31:837–930, 1961.

Levine, R., and Mahler, R.: Production, secretion and availability of insulin, Ann. Rev. Med. 15:413–432, 1964.

Siperstein, M. D., Norton, W., Unger, R. H., and Madison, L. L.: Muscle capillary basement membrane width in normal, diabetic and prediabetic patients, Tr. A. Am. Physicians 79:330-347, 1966.

Steiner, D. F., Cunningham, D., Spigelman, L., and Aten, B.: Insulin biosynthesis: Evidence for a precursor, Science 157:697-700, 1967.

Williams, R. H.: *Diabetes* (New York: Paul B. Hoeber, Inc., 1960).

Williams, R. H., and Ensinck, W.: Secretion, fates and actions of insulin and related products, Diabetes 15:623-654, 1966.

Young, F. G.: Insulin, Brit. M. Bull. 16:175–260, 1960.

10

Energy Balance

SOME LANDMARKS IN ENERGY BALANCE CHRONOLOGY

DATE		INVESTIGATOR
1776	"Hunger nerves" in gastric mucosa postulated	Haller
1826	Hunger center in brain postulated	Magendie
1840	Obesity associated with brain-compressing pituitary tumor described	Mohr
1900	Persistence of hunger and food intake regulation after gastric denervation and gastrectomy	Sherrington
1901	Adiposity and genital underdevelopment due to a pituitary tumor. Pituitary etiology of obesity stressed	Fröhlich
1912	Obesity in dogs after hypophysectomy seen only when base of brain was damaged	Aschner
1916	Association of gastric hunger contractions and level of blood glucose	Carlson
1921	Experimental obesity in dogs with intact pituitaries	Bailey, Bremer
1940	Hypothalamic obesity in rats; hypoactivity emphasized	Hetherington, Ranson
1943	Hypothalamic obesity in rats; hyperphagia emphasized	Brobeck *et al.*
1947	Animals adapt to dilution of food with inert materials by increasing food intake	Adolph
1951	Studies on genetically determined obesity in mice	Mayer *et al.*
1951	Aphagia produced in rats by destructive lesions in lateral hypothalamus	Anand, Brobeck

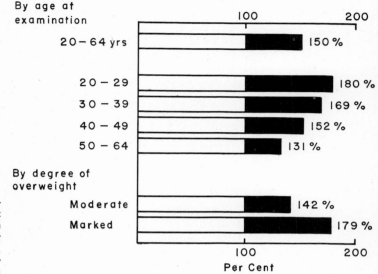

Per cent actual of expected deaths

By age at examination

20 – 64 yrs	150%
20 – 29	180%
30 – 39	169%
40 – 49	152%
50 – 64	131%

By degree of overweight

Moderate	142%
Marked	179%

Per Cent

(Death rates of men accepted for standard insurance)

Fig. 10-1.—Effect of over-weight on life expectancy. Black bars represent excess mortality in individuals who were overweight at the time insurance was issued. (After Marks, H. H.: Bull. New York Acad. Med. 36:15-31, 1960.)

ANIMALS ARE GOVERNED by the same thermo-dynamic laws that apply to the rest of the physical universe. If the energy content of the food ingested by a man is exactly equal to his total energy expenditure he is said to be in energy balance. A state of positive energy balance can be produced either by an increase in food intake over energy output or by a diminished output or by a combination of these. Similarly, a decrease in food intake or an increased energy requirement results in negative energy or caloric balance. These facts are so starkly obvious it hardly seems necessary to state them. Yet some of the physiological mechanisms involved in the maintenance of energy balance in men and animals are only now beginning to be explored.

The physiological, medical, and public health importance of the problem of energy balance cannot be overestimated. In many countries of the world, insufficient food is available to large numbers of people who are therefore forced to become adapted to a chronic state of undernutrition. This may not be merely a quantitative caloric deficit. In many instances, the quality of the food is poor and the accompanying accessory food factors are in short supply. At the other extreme, affluent societies provide a plethora of food and every conceivable chance to avoid physical activity, both of which contribute to a high incidence of obesity. This condition has been called one of our most important public health problems because it predisposes people to a large number of vascular and metabolic diseases. The life expectancy of the overweight individual is substantially less than that of people of average weight, a fact which the life insurance companies are not likely to let us forget (Fig. 10-1).

Men and women are variably successful in maintaining energy balance. For some, the equation input-outgo is achieved readily and with no conscious effort, whereas others who are successful in maintaining energy equilibrium can do so only by consciously monitoring body weight over a long time. When one considers the extraordinary complexity and variety of the biochemical and physiological mechanisms which are operative in man and other animals the precision with which energy balance is maintained in many individuals is remarkable. It is less remarkable that, with so many forces at work which tend to upset the equilibrium, there is a high incidence of obesity in economically favored countries.

In Figure 10-2, a graphic outline of this chap-

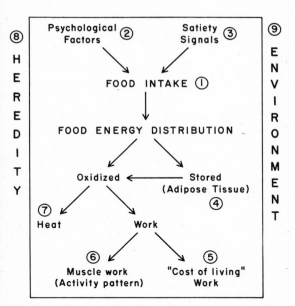

Fig. 10-2.—Some factors which influence energy balance.

ter is given. It was designed to suggest the fact that caloric balance represents a vector of many forces which operate to displace it in either direction. If these forces tend to cancel one another (for example, high food intake and high rate of muscle work), balance may still be maintained. The following subjects will be discussed:

① The central nervous regulation of food intake.

② Psychological factors in food intake behavior.

③ Satiety signals.

④ The physiology of adipose tissue.

⑤ The operational cost of metabolism.

⑥ Activity pattern and energy balance.

⑦ Heat production.

⑧ Heredity.

⑨ Environment.

The long-term repercussions of obesity.

① The Central Nervous Regulation of Food Intake

The study of food intake regulation has been somewhat inhibited by a certain amount of semantic confusion; the following lexicon is therefore in order. *Hunger* is the awareness of the need to ingest food, and it may be accompanied by a complex set of phenomena, including hunger pangs, anticipatory salivation, increased food-searching behavior, and others. In sum, hunger is a malaise, a disagreeable combination of sensations which, as it progresses, acquires a frantic character. *Appetite* is the desire to ingest food. Unlike hunger, which occurs when the body's store of nutrients becomes depleted below a certain preset maintenance level, appetite may persist even when hunger has been appeased. Appetite is strongly influenced by emotion, by the presence or absence of conditioning or distracting stimuli, and by discriminatory choices of various kinds. *Satiety* is the lack of desire to eat which occurs after the ingestion of food. *Anorexia* describes a situation in which the physiological state which would ordinarily produce a sensation of hunger is present, but all available signals call in vain for the resumption of eating behavior.

Cannon's demonstration of the association between the sensation of hunger and the appearance of vigorous, rhythmic gastric contractions led Carlson to the view that the stomach was the organ which communicated the essential hunger and satiety information to the nervous system. Further, he anticipated a widely held modern view that the level of blood glucose has something to do with hunger and satiety, for he was able to amplify hunger contractions by producing insulin hypoglycemia and cause them to disappear by injecting glucose intravenously.

Antecedent observations on the successful maintenance of caloric balance in gastrectomized animals and later ones on vagotomized (and therefore stomach-denervated) patients failed to sustain Carlson's gastric contraction hypothesis of regulation. Adolph's demonstration that the dilution of the diet with inert bulk materials caused rats to increase their food intake to the point at which they were consuming as many calories as in the control period also pointed to extragastrointestinal factors in the regulation of food intake.

SURGICAL HYPOTHALAMIC OBESITY

Many of the clinical and experimental observations referred to in the chronology above had suggested some sort of relationship between structures at the base of the brain and food intake, but recent exploration of the subject began with Hetherington's and Ranson's successful induction of experimental obesity in the rat by the stereotaxic placement of symmetrical, bilateral hypothalamic lesions which involved the ventromedial nuclei. Hetherington's lesions were rather large and his animals were young—circumstances which would tend to obscure changes in food intake and favor the interpretation that the lesions produced obesity by diminishing spontaneous motor activity. Brobeck and his colleagues used smaller lesions and older rats, and were impressed by the marked increase in food intake that occurred in their lesioned animals. Occasionally some of their animals began to eat voraciously even before they had recovered completely from the state of anesthesia. It was found that most of the obesity in this group of ventromedial nucleus-lesioned animals could be accounted for on the basis of increased food intake, or hyperphagia. Only 3 of 12 animals outgained their controls slightly on the pair-feeding regimen, and we can assume that decreased activity was a minor contributory factor to the obesity that occurred in these animals when feeding was permitted ad libitum.

It is now generally agreed that effective ventromedial nuclear lesions in young animals at first produce obesity mainly by decreasing spontaneous activity and not by increasing food intake but that, as the young animal matures, the usual fall in food intake does not occur and the excessive food intake then becomes an important determinant of the obesity (G. C. Kennedy). In the adult animal, the major cause of the obesity is an increase in food intake which Brobeck has called "hyperphagia," although there may be a component of hypoactivity in the development of obesity in some animals.

There is a curiously paradoxical aspect of the syndrome of hypothalamic obesity, for, although animals with ventromedial lesions overeat when food is readily available in their cages, they will not exert themselves unduly to secure it if they are maintained in circumstances in which they must push a lever or negotiate a maze in order to eat. Very recently, Hashim and Van Itallie (1965) have described very similar behavior in two massively obese human subjects who were fed by a device which delivered a measured quantum of a balanced liquid diet into their mouths when they pressed a lever—a sort of Skinner Box for people. Subjects of normal weight tended to take

their full quota of calories spaced into three meals when they were fed in this way, but the two obese subjects took as little as 200 calories per day and did not complain of hunger. The precise neurophysiologic interpretation of this behavior is, of course, not known, but the similarity between the results of this experiment and those on rats with hypothalamic obesity is very striking.

In addition to its disinclination to press levers in order to obtain food, the hypothalamic obese animal exhibits what has been called "finickiness" when he is offered unpleasantly flavored food. The normal animal tolerates a very much higher concentration of quinine sulfate in the diet than does the animal with an effective ventromedial nuclear lesion. This fact reminds us that there are perceptible effects of many stimuli on food intake in the hypothalamic obese animal and, in fact, such an animal appears to be hypersensitive to some of them. Certain anorexigenic drugs (see below) are actually more effective in reducing food intake in the obese animal than in the lean. In addition, diets very high in protein and those containing unbalanced amino acid mixtures appear to be more anorexigenic in hypothalamic-lesioned animals than in controls (Krauss and Mayer, 1965). The hyperphagic rat, like the normal one, will not eat a dry diet if it does not have access to water.

All of these responses indicate the great complexity of the process of food intake regulation and support the view of Morgane that, although the hypothalamic structures are obviously crucial in regulating food intake behavior, many other parts of the brain are doubtless involved in the process. A number of observers have seen hyperphagia in experimental animals after placing lesions in the frontal or temporal lobes, while others have observed decreases in food intake after injuring similar parts of the brain. It is difficult for a reviewer to assess the significance of such experiments since the lesions are never exactly the same, and often observations are made in different species. Both aphagia and hyperphagia have been observed following destructive lesions in the amygdalar complex. Clearly, the hypothalamic food intake regulatory structures are only the best studied part of what must be an extraordinarily complex set of interconnected circuits in the brain which, together, constitute what we tend to think of as *the* "appestat."

Anand and Morgane agree that the modulation of food intake by the limbic structures and by cortical lobes is more concerned with discriminatory food-seeking behavior than with the primitive urge to eat.

After the establishment of the significance of the ventromedial nuclei, Anand and Brobeck discovered other hypothalamic structures which are of enormous importance in the regulation of feeding behavior. They found that small lesions in the outer part of the lateral hypothalamus, at the same rostrocaudal plane as the ventromedial nucleus, produced a complete absence of food intake behavior. Some of their animals were kept alive by tube feeding. Others would swallow food placed in the mouth, which signified that some eating reflexes were still operative in them although they did not themselves initiate the eating process even when food was readily available to them. Animals which had been made hyperphagic by lesions placed in the ventromedial nuclei became aphagic when lateral lesions were made.

Later Teitelbaum and Stellar (1954) and, independently, Montemurro and Stevenson (1957) showed that drinking behavior was also affected by lateral hypothalamic lesions. The latter group was able to show that some lateral lesions produced adipsia without aphagia. These observations suggest that, in the intact animal, the expression of primitive urges to eat and to drink may involve certain common neuronal equipment. The complexity of the interrelations of eating, drinking and taste is beautifully illustrated in Teitelbaum's (1961) analysis of the sequence of events that occurs during recovery from effective aphagia-adipsia-producing lesions of the lateral hypothalamus. This investigator found that if animals were kept alive by tube-feeding a certain number showed a staged sequence of recovery to a state of essentially normal food and water regulation according to the following: stage I (aphagia, adipsia) no spontaneous intake of either food or water; stage II, adipsia with intake of only wet, agreeably flavored food but not moistened dry food; stage III, persistent adipsia, intake of moistened dry food; and stage IV, normal eating and drinking behavior. The last function to return is normal water-drinking behavior, though, prior to this stage, the animal can be tricked into drinking water if it is flavored with saccharin! The infer-

ence is that the rat categorizes a fluid as food or drink on the basis of how it tastes.

Morgane (1961) has suggested that there are distinct "feeding" and "hunger motivating" systems in the lateral hypothalamus, for stimulation in the midlateral area produces feeding responses in sated animals, but animals will not cross an electrified grill to press a lever for food. Far lateral stimulation, however, produces both eating behavior and the motivation to seek food even in an uncomfortable situation. The latter response depends on the integrity of the median forebrain bundle.

In another study (Baillie and Morrison, 1963), the imaginative use of the technique of operant conditioning in the analysis of the behavior of rats with lateral lesions is illustrated. These investigators showed that rats preconditioned to feed themselves a liquid diet continued their lever-pressing behavior after the placement of lateral lesions, although they did not eat the food delivered. Similarly, animals operated on with their stomachs intubated by way of a gastric fistula and preconditioned to feed themselves by way of the fistula continued to do so, but when they were placed in a free-feeding situation, they showed aphagia. The authors believe that their lesions did not interfere with the motivational control of eating but represented rather a failure of the coordinative, motor aspects of feeding behavior. Rodgers, Epstein and Teitelbaum (1965), who came to precisely the opposite conclusion on the basis of similar experiments, provide a critique of Baillie and Morrison's work for the interested reader.

There can be no definitive statement about the question of motivation versus motor aphagia, since the experts are still working energetically on this problem. This brief account is included to illustrate the fact that the behavioral component of the maintenance of energy balance is an extremely important part of the problem and that resourceful people are attempting to analyze it in these terms.

Many experiments have been done in which the ventromedial and lateral hypothalamic areas have been stimulated in unanesthetized animals and the effects of such stimulation on food intake behavior has been noted. In general, the results have conformed to a kind of mirror image of the lesion observations. For example, stimulation of the lateral hypothalamic center has been ob-

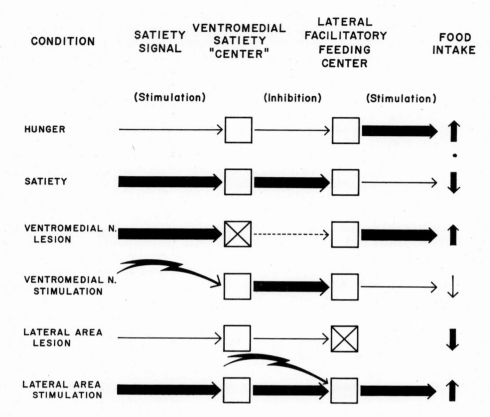

Fig. 10-3.—Diagram of current hypothesis of the role of the hypothalamus in the determination of feeding behavior. These are symmetrical, bilateral structures, but only one side is shown in the diagram. (See review by Anand, B. K.: Physiol. Rev. 41:677-708, 1961, for documentation.)

served to increase food intake in several species, and also to cause such effects as licking, chewing, swallowing, and salivating. Stimulation of the region of the ventromedial nucleus resulted in a small decrease in daily food intake. In the self-stimulation experiments of Olds, rats with electrodes in the medial hypothalamus pushed the stimulating button more when they were hungry than when they were satiated, a result which can be interpreted loosely as the substitution by the rat of an electrical satiety signal for the physiological one(s).

Out of these and other experiments there has grown a tentative conception of the role of the hypothalamic regions in the regulation of food intake. The ventromedial nuclei represent a satiety "center," or more properly an integrating relay station for satiety information. The destruction of this region results in failure to receive satiety signals, which results in inappropriate overeating and, finally, obesity. The lateral hypo-

thalamic area contains a "facilitatory feeding center" which functions as an integrative communications center for all of the complex visual, auditory, olfactory, tactile, gustatory, and enteroceptive reflexes associated with food intake behavior. These, as Brobeck has suggested, go far beyond simply chewing and swallowing reflexes, and involve food-seeking, examination of food—in fact, the whole complex enterprise of food-getting. According to current theory, satiety information reaches the ventromedial nucleus component of the regulating machinery and this structure, in turn, acts to inhibit the lateral facilitatory feeding centers. A diagrammatic representation of this hypothesis is given in Figure 10-3.

CHEMICAL AGENTS AND FOOD INTAKE REGULATION

AUROTHIOGLUCOSE.—Brecher and Waxler (1949), while doing routine toxicity tests on a potential arthritis remedy called *aurothioglu-cose* (ATG, or gold thioglucose), discovered that a certain percentage of mice which survived an I.D. 50 of the compound (i.e., a dose which is lethal for 50% of the animals) showed very striking obesity (Fig. 10-4). The original discoverers of the phenomenon demonstrated that the eating behavior of mice with obesity-producing doses of ATG resembled that of rats with ventromedial lesions of the hypothalamus. Mayer and his colleagues showed that ATG produces destructive lesions of the ventromedial nuclei in the hypothalamus, and it is now generally accepted that ATG obesity represents a chemical form of hypothalamic obesity. Although the ventromedial nuclear lesion is the most prominent one observed, other small lesions, which have no known relation to the process of food intake regulation, are also seen (Perry and Liebelt, 1961). Radioautographic studies with Au[198]-labeled ATG have revealed increased concentrations of gold in areas of the brain damaged by the compound. Studies on the distribution of Au[198] and S[35] suggest that there the gold can be split from the parent molecule and the cytotoxicity of the compound is therefore believed to be due primarily to the heavy metal. It is possible that one of the reasons for the increased vulnerability of certain cells to ATG is the presence in them of a higher activity of a metallic gold-releasing enzyme.

Recent studies on ATG obesity contain implications for biology that go far beyond the energy balance problem. For Luse and her colleagues (1961) have advanced electron micrographic evidence that pathologic changes produced by ATG

appear first in the oligodendroglial elements interposed between blood vessels and the neurones of the ventromedial nucleus. P. M. Edelman *et al.* (1965) have recently reviewed their important experiments on the concentration of gold in the hypothalami of ATG-injected animals. Suitably prepared mouse hypothalami were bombarded with neutrons in the Brookhaven National Laboratory Graphite reactor—heavy artillery for a mouse hypothalamus! In this way, very high specific activity radioactive gold was produced, and this, in turn, permitted analysis of the factors which influence the concentration of the metal in the hypothalamus. The amount of gold concentrated in the hypothalamus was, in general, proportional to the blood level during the few minutes following injection. It is currently believed that the destruction of the cellular elements of the ventromedial nuclei is secondary to the destruction of the glial elements that surround them. No more convincing demonstration has been made of the dependence of neurons on the integrity of their associated glial elements. It has been suggested that the selective concentration of ATG in the glia of the ventromedial nucleus indicates that these cells have a specific glucoreceptor function related to food intake regulation. Since there is a similar concentration of ATG at sites remote from these, the precise location of the hypothetical glucoreceptors cannot be stated with certainty. (See discussion of the "glucostatic" theory, p. 186).

Quite apart from the question of the precise nature of the central nervous system lesion produced by ATG, the widespread availability of a

AUROTHIOGLUCOSE ("ATG") OBESITY

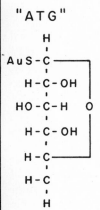

"ATG"

Fig. 10-4. — Aurothioglucose obesity in the mouse. Author's photograph. (See Brecher, G., and Waxler, S.: Proc. Soc. Exper. Biol. & Med. 70:498-501, 1949.)

method of mass-producing obese animals at will has made it possible to study many of the metabolic effects of a sustained high level of food intake on the organism. Many adaptive changes have been reported in the gastrointestinal tract, including hypertrophy of the stomach and increased intestinal absorption rate of glucose. There is not merely obesity, but also a splanchnomegaly, for there is increase in the size of the liver, kidneys and heart in obese mice. Pancreatic islet cell hypertrophy and hyperplasia have been reported in ATG obese animals, as has an increase in the rate of lipogenesis from glucose or acetate in the fed animal. Increased excretion of 17-OH corticosteroids has been reported, and various signs suggestive of modified gonadotrophin secretion have been seen. It is difficult to state whether the latter are secondary to obesity or to the lesion itself, but, in the case of the gonadotrophins, evidence of dysfunction has been observed in the gold-injected nonobese mouse (Browning and Kwan, 1964). An extensive review of the use of gold thioglucose as an experimental tool was written by Deter and Liebelt (1964).

SYMPATHOMIMETIC AMINES.—Certain drugs have profound effects on food intake. Sympathomimetic amines and related compounds are widely used in the clinic as a sort of pharmacological crutch for patients who have great difficulty in restricting their caloric intake voluntarily. These compounds (of which amphetamine is a prototype) are powerful central nervous system stimulants, and there is no doubt that they accelerate weight loss for a time. They do so in several ways (1) by inhibiting food intake, (2) by increasing spontaneous activity, and (3) (possibly) by facilitating the mobilization of fatty acids from adipose tissue stores (see p. 192). The mechanism by which they decrease food intake is not known, but it is certainly true that intact ventromedial satiety "centers" are not necessary for the hypophagic effect to occur. In fact, aurothioglucose obese mice and animals with ventromedial nucleus lesions are more sensitive to the anorexigenic effect of amphetamine than are intact controls.

GLUCAGON.—This substance has epinephrine-like effects in the liver and is a powerful inhibitor of food intake. It will be recalled that glucagon causes hepatic glycogenolysis and hyperglycemia, and some observers have suggested that its effect on food intake is secondary to its blood sugar-raising action. Other investigators, however, have pointed out that human subjects who receive glucagon may experience anorexia when blood glucose changes are minimal.

OTHER AGENTS.—There are suggestions that depressant drugs and certain tranquilizers (e.g., chlorpromazine, meprobamate) have the effect of increasing spontaneous food intake. There is some evidence in experimental animals that barbiturates may do this. Patients who receive tranquilizers often gain considerable amounts of weight, and sometimes even become obese. It is difficult to analyze this situation in terms of physiological mechanism, for the change in food habit might just as well be related to the alleviation of anxiety as to an effect on the central nervous system structures involved in food intake regulation. Moreover, a reduction in motor activity may contribute to the weight gain in some of these individuals.

Very recently, enterogastrone has been found to inhibit food intake for 4–8 hrs in mice. This raises the very interesting possibility that humoral chemical satiety signals may be generated simply by introducing food into the gastrointestinal tract.

② Psychological Factors

In most human societies the eating of food, or abstention from it, is associated with ceremonial, emotional, hedonistic, and even religious overtones. The symbolic character of the act of eating is well illustrated by the institutionalization of hyperphagia in the form of Thanksgiving dinner. The mother-child relationship is focused on the giving and receiving of food. It is not surprising, then, that emotional disturbances can upset the energy balance equation in either direction. At one end of the scale, one sees patients with the disease anorexia nervosa, which can progress through extreme inanition to death. This condition may be described as slow suicide by self-starvation. It always occurs in extremely disturbed people and occasionally in compulsive dieters who were once desperately worried about obesity. At the other extreme is psychogenic bulimia or hyperphagia, a disorder which can be imagined best as a sort of chronic addiction similar to alcohol addiction in which food substitutes for ethanol. These people are truly compulsive eaters and may become enormously obese. Not rarely, they are unhappy children.

The mechanisms involved in the establishment of either of these conditions are certainly not known. However, it is easy to imagine that profound emotional difficulties may somehow affect the function of the hypothalamic food intake-regulating complex in either direction. The circuitry is doubtless present for cortical input into this area, and, depending on the nature of the functional disturbance caused by the incoming volleys, the functional equivalent of either a ventromedial lesion or a lateral facilitatory area lesion may be induced. It is not possible to detect any morphological changes in the hypothalamus in these people at this time, but this is no reason to doubt the possibility of a functional disturbance.

There is fairly wide agreement on the existence of psychogenically derived anorexia and hyperphagia and also of transitory effects of anxiety on the desire for food. Most medical students have experienced anorexia in association with the anxiety attendant on examination taking, and a few have reported hyperphagia under similar circumstances. Nevertheless, the role of psychological factors in the etiology of obesity is still dimly understood. A number of psychiatrists who have studied the problem are inclined to the view that overeating is *always* caused primarily by an emotional disturbance. To put it crudely, the obese individual is said to compensate for unmet needs by seeking solace in the infantile pleasure of eating. In my view, this represents an oversimplification of the problem. While it is true that fat people have troubles, lean people have them too. At the present time, it is best to accept the view that anxiety and other emotional difficulties can certainly be a contributory cause of obesity, but that it is only one variable in a complex set which includes many other hereditary and environmental factors, some of which are outlined in Figure 10-2.

Studies on psychological factors in obesity, together with those on genetics which will be reviewed later in this chapter, have led to a modification of the rigid, almost punitive attitude of many physicians toward obese patients. For certain patients have been seen who, on being deprived of food, began to have serious and incapacitating emotional disturbances of other kinds, including the threat of self-destruction. Although weight reduction is no doubt a desirable objective on statistical grounds, the results of caloric restriction in certain individuals may be such that the physician is willing to compromise for a reduced weight somewhat above the average. It is beyond the scope of this essay to discuss weight reduction regimens in detail, but it is not out of order to point out that crash programs which yield dramatic results for the first 2 weeks are rarely successful in the long run. A more lasting effect can be achieved only in a highly motivated individual who takes the trouble to "re-educate" his food intake-regulating equipment and, hopefully, change his activity pattern.

③ Satiety Signals

We have examined some of the structures in the central nervous system which are concerned with processing of information related to the metering of food intake. It is pertinent to inquire into the possible nature of the signals that are set up by the ingestion of food and how (or whether) these signals can participate in the long-term regulation of energy balance. A growing and perplexing literature on the subject of satiety signals reveals that most experts in this field keep the peace by conceding that no single signal can account for all of the experimentally observed facts. Most of them tentatively conclude that food intake regulation by the central nervous system must represent the results of the processing of many kinds of data. Among the interesting hypotheses the following have been advanced.

METERING OF FOOD INTAKE IN THE MOUTH, PHARYNX AND GASTROINTESTINAL TRACT

Although the presence or absence of gastric hunger contractions does not appear to affect the quantity of food eaten, Janowitz and Grossman have demonstrated that prefed dogs ate less than did animals fed the same amount of food by gastric fistula, and have suggested that gastric distention may constitute a satiety message. The fact that denervation of the upper gastrointestinal tract does not interfere with long-term regulation certainly does not mean that signals arising in the mouth, pharynx, and stomach are not somehow factored into the information received in the central nervous system and interpreted as satiety.

THERMOSTATIC REGULATION

Brobeck and his colleagues have advanced the interesting suggestion that the heat generated by the ingestion of food—the specific dynamic action, or SDA—is one variable that is metered in the central nervous system and functions as a satiety signal. This theory has the great virtue of including the major foodstuffs—protein, fat and carbohydrate—as potential contributors to the satiety message. Other authors point out, however, that muscular exercise (which results in far greater heat production than does eating) does not have great thermostatic satiety value, and that the hyperphagia of hyperthyroidism (in which the SDA of food is markedly increased) does not fit the hypothesis. Although it is not universally accepted, the thermostatic theory is a useful one and the studies on which it is based are well worth the contemplation of the student as elegant model energy balance experiments.

THE "GLUCOSTATIC" THEORY

Mayer has suggested that the cells in the region of the ventromedial hypothalamic nuclei are chemoreceptors. There is a good deal of circumstantial evidence to support the view that these cells are somehow capable of reflecting the rate of glucose utilization by peripheral tissues and that when the peripheral arteriovenous blood glucose difference is small (i.e., when glucose utilization is low) hunger is experienced. Conversely, when the peripheral arteriovenous glucose difference is high (i.e., when glucose oxidation is high) a subjective feeling of satiety supervenes. Recently, the glucostatic theory received apparent support from the report by Anand et al. who studied the electrical activity of the medial and lateral feeding centers in monkeys and cats in which blood glucose was changed either by glucose infusion or insulin injection. They found increased electrical activity in satiety "centers" with elevation of the blood glucose, but not after infusing protein hydrolysate or fat emulsions. Forssberg and Larsson found that the P^{32} uptake of a part of the hypothalamus containing the feeding complex was higher in hungry rats than in fed ones, which suggests a specialized type of metabolism in this part of the brain. It should be pointed out that neither of these experiments constitutes proof of the glucoreceptor function of the ventromedial nuclei, for these results could have been obtained as a result of signals converging on the satiety areas from other parts of the brain.

Attractive as it appears to be there are two reasons for questioning the physiological importance of the glucostatic hypothesis. In the first place, Janowitz and Grossman found that prior glucose infusion did not appreciably decrease spontaneous food intake in rats, dogs, or human subjects. Second, Van Itallie has demonstrated cycles of hunger and satiety in a subject on a high fat, low carbohydrate diet who showed no fluctuations in arteriovenous glucose difference. In his subjects, the feeling of hunger correlated best with a high level of circulating free fatty acids (FFA, NEFA), signifying that mobilization of depot fat had occurred. It is clearly gratuitous to suggest still another hypothesis to add to the existing plethora, but Van Itallie's experiments open the possibility that satiety may normally be correlated with fatty acid uptake by the depots and hunger with fatty acid release. Information about transactions in adipose tissue could reach the central nervous system either by afferent nerves or by way of the blood stream.

A variant of this hypothesis has been advanced as the "lipostatic" theory by Kennedy et al., who visualize communication between the aggregate fat depot and the central nervous-regulating structures by way of the blood stream. Since the quantity of fat mobilized per day may be roughly proportional to the total amount in all the depots, a running inventory of the size of the total fat deposit could be kept by the brain if a critical metabolite were released in association with mobilized free fatty acids (FFA). This theory has the great virtue of suggesting how long-range regulation of energy exchange might be achieved in contrast with the acute, single meal regulations possibly accomplished by local gastrointestinal tract metering, or postprandial heat or blood glucose fluctuations (see p. 156).

One interesting feature of the lipostatic hypothesis is pointed out by Teitelbaum, i.e., the hypothalamic obese animal does, in fact, regulate its body weight. In the earliest studies on the effect of producing ventromedial nuclear lesions on food intake, Brobeck noticed that the animals ate very large amounts of food in the immediate postoperative period (dynamic phase), but, as excess fat accumulated, they ate progressively less (static phase). However, if food was withheld and the animal lost a large amount of the excess weight, the level of food intake when feeding was resumed was approximately that of the immediate postoperative period, although a considerable amount of time may have elapsed since the operation. Weight is quickly regained to the level attained just before weight reduction; then, food intake diminishes. Teitelbaum suggests that this is, indeed, regulation of food intake and that this kind of food intake regulation is accomplished in spite of an imperfectly functioning hypothalamic satiety mechanism.

The lipostatic hypothesis is sufficiently elastic to account for another interesting experimental observation, this one on parabiotic (or surgically produced siamese twin) rats. Hervey has placed obesity-inducing hypothalamic lesions in one member of a pair of such parabiotic twins and has been able to measure food intake by each. The lesioned animal became very obese, while the "normal" twin decreased its food intake and lost weight. The greater the obesity in the one, the more striking was the inanition in the other. Hervey suggests that the lean twin was responding to a humorally carried satiety signal transported across the shared circulation, and that this signal is proportional in strength to the mass of fat stored in the depots of the lesioned rat. The signal must have been noncaloric in nature and its nature is unspecified.

Both excess protein and imbalanced amino acid mixtures cause anorexia by mechanisms which are presently unknown, but which do not require an intact ventromedial nucleus for their expression (Krauss and Mayer, 1965). Anorexia is also often associated with clinical liver disease, such as hepatitis, but the mechanism of this relationship is also obscure. Possibly, these two causes of anorexia may be related, for a sick liver, unable to metabolize amino acids at a sufficiently rapid rate, may lead to accumulation of anorexigenic quantities of amino acids in the body fluids.

In summary, the regulation of food intake represents a kind of rhythmic, recurrent physiological adjustment such as one sees in respiration, water balance, sleeping and waking and in many other life transactions. The acute or meal-to-meal regulation may be accomplished by a battery of signals, including SDA of ingested food, rate of glucose utilization, metabolic events in the adipose tissue, local metering in the gastrointestinal tract, and others still unsuspected. The long-range balance may be achieved by a complicated central nervous system integration and analysis of many of these processes into which is factored a kind of cumulative work log, for, as we shall see, delayed effects of heavy work on food intake are readily demonstrable in careful studies on humans.

④ Physiology of Adipose Tissue

Adipose tissue is a sort of Cinderella among the specialized cell clusters of the body. Long scorned by the physiologist because it looked so unprepossessing under the microscope, it was widely regarded as nothing but an inert repository for grease until 1937 when Schoenheimer and Rittenberg, working with deuterium-labeled fatty acids, demonstrated that the fat in the depots of a mouse fed a high carbohydrate diet had a half life of only 7 days. Now adipose tissue is being studied by squads of enthusiastic investigators, and countless rats daily sacrifice their epididymal fat pads in the interest of elucidating the physiology of this glamorous tissue.

The first review article on adipose tissue was published in 1948 by Wertheimer and Shapiro whose prescient interest in the subject anticipated current developments by decades. The reviewers wrote the following:

Adipose tissue is a tissue with a special structure and a special type of cell. It is supplied by a comparatively dense capillary net and innervated by sympathetic nerve fibers. Deposition and mobilization of fat in adipose tissue is an active process, involving the metabolism of the tissue. Under conditions favoring fat deposition, adipose tissue accumulates glycogen, which is presumably built in the tissue cells themselves. Synthesis of new fatty acids from carbohydrates as well as transformation of one fatty acid into another proceed continuously in this tissue. All of these metabolic activities are regulated by nervous and endocrine factors.

It is unfortunate that fat and adipose tissue are so closely associated with the subject of obesity and are therefore considered to be vaguely pathological. Actually, in order to exist without the convenience afforded by adipose tissue, it would be necessary to be able to adjust the rate of absorption of food from the gastrointestinal tract to accommodate different rates of energy expenditure. Moreover, fasts of even short duration would be impossible because the total store of tissue and fluid carbohydrate in an adult male is rarely more than 75 Gm, or 300 calories, the equivalent of a modest piece of pie. The maneuver of storing both fat and carbohydrate (as fat) in the fat depots postprandially affords a degree of metabolic resiliency and adaptability that must have contributed to the survival advantage of our remote evolutionary ancestors. For the adipose tissue is a sort of energy bank; deposits are made at meal time and demand notes in the form of fat mobilization signals may be presented any time thereafter. Thus, the fat depots are enormously important in the day-to-day vital economy of men and animals in energy balance. If the deposits exceed withdrawals over a sufficiently long time, obesity occurs. The extent of fat deposition can be unbelievably large—the depot organ appears to be almost infinitely distensible. For example, it is by no means unusual to see a rat with hypothalamic obesity whose carcass contains 50% fat, or 250 Gm. This represents 2150 calories, which would last 43 days at a rate of expenditure of 50 calories per day. Obesity of comparable extent is not rare in the human.

While Wertheimer and his colleagues (1960) have demonstrated that the various individual fat depots of the body are not metabolically identical either in their biosynthetic activities or in their responses to hormonal stimulation, it is sometimes convenient to think of the sum of all the depots of the body as one large depot organ. Liebelt (1965) has demonstrated that when the gonadal fat bodies are amputated in a gold thioglucose obese mouse there is a compensatory hypertrophy of the remainder so that the final content of adipose tissue is the same as it is in animals with an intact depot organ. Peckham *et al.* (1962) made rats obese by feeding a high fat diet, then reduced their weight by feeding a stock diet and subsequently re-fed the high fat diet. Rats which had once been obese gained weight more rapidly than did others transferred directly from chow to the obesity-producing diet. DNA analyses of the epididymal fat pad indicated that the rats first fed the fat diet had a larger number of adipose tissue cells and their more rapid weight gain during the second period of fat feeding was attributed to this fact. Experiments of this type have important implications in the study of human obesity.

Interesting new experiments of Knittle and Hirsch (1967) suggest that the demands placed on the adipose tissue during the immediate postnatal period may have important repercussions throughout the life of the animal. These investigators (confirming earlier observations of G. Kennedy) discovered that when 4 rat pups were nursed by a single mother and compared with littermates nursed 22 per mother they were not only larger and heavier at the time of weaning but remained larger and more obese as adults. In addition, Knittle and Hirsch were able to estimate mean cell size and cell number in the fat pads of both weanling and adult rats in both groups after they had unlimited access to food for several weeks after weaning. The "privileged" rats had larger fat pads at weaning and the difference in size was accounted for entirely by an *increase in cell number*. At 20 weeks, the adult rats with a history of neonatal hyperphagia also had strikingly larger epididymal fat pads, but the adipose tissue at this time had both an increased *number of cells* and *larger individual cells*. The implications of these experiments for human obesity are arresting, for they suggest that an adaptive increase in adipose tissue cell number during the immediate postnatal period can have consequences for energy balance that persist throughout the life of the individual. It is even possible that neonatal feeding habits could be more important than genetic factors in predisposing to obesity.

Early observations on the oxygen consumption and vascularity of adipose tissue were misleading because experimenters failed to refer metabolic activity and the size of the capillary bed to the active metabolic mass of the tissue, which represents only a small proportion of its total weight. The stored triglycerides in the cell vacuoles are, indeed, metabolically inert, but the thin zone of cytoplasm surrounding the vacuoles is extremely active. Inspection of electronmicrographs of adipose tissue cells reveals that the cytoplasm surrounding the stored fat globules is full of mitochondria, endoplasmic reticulum and other standard cytologic equipment. Metabolic and enzymatic analysis reveals a whole spectrum of activities from which we can infer the presence of at least the following metabolic apparatus in the adipose tissue cell: (1) Embden-Meyerhoff pathway (DPNH producing); (2) pentose phosphate pathway (TPNH producing); (3) Krebs cycle; (4) oxidative enzymes of the electron transport system; (5) fatty acid and phospholipid synthetic pathways; (6) fatty acid degradation pathway; (7) specialized lipases; (8) many enzymes involved in phospholipid metabolism; (9) Leloir uridine diphosphoglucose pathway for glycogen synthesis; (10) protein synthetic machinery, and so on. This biochemical potential represents a considerable repertory of reactions, but the outstanding characteristic of the cell is its tendency to store fat when foodstuffs are present in abundance and to dole it out in the form of free fatty acids (FFA) on demand.

It is now becoming increasingly evident that the comparative role of adipose tissue as a primary site of fatty acid synthesis varies strikingly from species to species. Goodridge and Ball (1966) found that, in the pigeon, lipogenesis from nonfat precursors was very limited and that the activities of the enzymes of lipogenesis and of lipogenesis-supporting pathways (see Chapter 12) were low. In contrast, hepatic lipogenesis was much more active than in the rat. The reader, who, perhaps, has no more than a passing interest in pigeons, may find this observation only mildly interesting. It is, perhaps, more interesting that Shrago and Edgar Gordon (personal communication) have found a situation in man similar to that described by Goodridge and Ball in the pigeon, i.e., low lipogenesis in adipose tissue and active lipogenesis in liver. One gets the impression that the importance of the liver as a major lipogenic organ—which had been questioned in the first flush of enthusiasm for the metabolic capabilities of adipose tissue—is now being reasserted. The major storage function of the adipose tissue in those species which show an inherently low lipogenic activity of adipose tissue may be to form triglycerides from fatty acids previously synthesized or processed by the liver and exported as lipoproteins. In abstracting these fatty acids from the circulating blood, the enzyme lipoprotein lipase plays a central role (see below).

The processes of fat deposition and fatty acid mobilization are under nervous and endocrine control. They may be studied either in the intact animal with the use of radioactively labeled metabolites or, in the case of mobilization, by observing the rise and fall of FFA in the blood under various physiological circumstances. Samples of mesenteric fat body or the conveniently paired, symmetrical epididymal fat pads of the rat

or mouse can be incubated in vitro and the effects of hormones on fatty acid synthesis and mobilization can be observed outside the body. This approach has been extremely popular in recent years and much valuable information has been obtained in this way, but results of such in vitro studies may not necessarily reflect the true situation in vivo because the neural component of adipose tissue physiology is eliminated by this method.

If a rat is unilaterally sympathectomized, accumulation of lipid occurs in the depots of the denervated side. Conversely, stimulation of sympathetic nerve results in fat mobilization. These experiments strongly suggest that the prominent nerve net demonstrable in adipose tissue is of great functional importance, particularly for the process of FFA mobilization.

Fat is stored in adipose tissue cells in the form of triglycerides which are synthesized from long-chain fatty acids and α glycerophosphate, which is "active" glycerol, or glycerol precursor. The tissue contains no glycerol kinase, so the glycerol moiety of the triglyceride must come from the metabolism of glucose. Fatty acids may be either synthesized in the cell from glucose or other precursors or they may be obtained by the cell from the circulating triglycerides (in the form of chylomicrons) which release their constituent fatty acids in close proximity to the cell when they are acted upon by a lipoprotein lipase. Adipose tissue has a very active lipase which fluctuates in activity with the state of nutrition of the animal. Immediately after a meal, when the chylomicron count is most likely to be high, adipose tissue lipoprotein lipase activity is also conveniently high. During starvation, when fat is being actively mobilized from the depots, the lipoprotein lipase activity is low.

ROLE OF INSULIN IN TRIGLYCERIDE SYNTHESIS

The traffic of calories into or out of the depots depends on the balance between the rates of triglyceride synthesis and breakdown. It should be emphasized that this is not a true chemical equilibrium, for synthesis and breakdown are accomplished by different routes. When food is in abundant supply, triglyceride synthesis is favored over FFA release; during fasting, synthesis is inhibited and FFA release is stimulated. Synthesis of long-chain fatty acids and of triglycerides is possible only when a certain amount of glucose oxidation is proceeding concurrently. Therefore, the rate of glucose utilization by the cell may determine the rate of triglyceride synthesis. There are at least three ways in which an increase in glucose utilization rate can promote triglyceride synthesis (1) by furnishing acetyl CoA precursors for the long-chain acids, (2) by supplying α glycerophosphate, or active glycerol for esterification and (3) by generating TPNH by way of the hexose monophosphate shunt and the TPN malic enzyme, and thereby furnishing the specific coenzyme required for the frequent ethylene bond saturation that must take place as fatty acid chain length is progressively lengthened by two-carbon fragments. All of these events collaborate in triglyceride synthesis not only by contributing to the synthetic élan (by furnishing building blocks and coenzymes) but also by removing fatty acids as they are formed and thus preventing product inhibition of the reaction sequence. These events are summarized in Figure 9-9, page 170.

Since carbohydrate utilization is so prominently featured in the process of fat storage, the regulation of its rate affords a likely locus for the operation of a fat storage signal. The absorption of a carbohydrate meal represents a call for insulin from the β cells of the pancreatic islets. The insulin secreted in response to this call probably acts to facilitate the entry of glucose into adipose tissue cells. The increased intracellular accumulation of glucose intermediates results in increased lipogenesis rates and triglyceride formation, and fat is stored. The release of FFA from the depots is inhibited.

It is now generally conceded that the adipose tissue is one of the major sites of action of insulin, for it has been shown that this tissue is exquisitely sensitive to the action of the hormone (see section on insulin assay, p. 155). Barrnett and Ball have given a vivid demonstration of the action of insulin added in vitro on adipose tissue. In a system in which they were able to monitor continuously the metabolic effects of the hormone, they examined samples of the tissue periodically with the electron microscope and were able to show a striking stimulation of the formation of pinocytotic vesicles at the cell membrane and the appearance of new endoplasmic reticular structure in the cytoplasm. Pinocytosis is a proc-

ess which is characterized by the sending out of many miniature pseudopods from the surface of the cell and the coalescence of adjacent projections to include tiny droplets of the surrounding medium. It has been referred to as "cell-drinking" and, since the transport of glucose into cells is markedly accelerated, Barrnett and Ball have suggested that glucose transport rate may depend in part on pinocytotic activity of the adipose tissue cell membrane. This is an interesting hypothesis, but it is unlikely (as Barrnett and Ball's calculations indicate) that sufficient volumes of fluid could be moved into the cell to account for the magnitude of the increase in glucose utilization induced by insulin. One of the Barrnett-Ball experiments is illustrated in Figure 10-5.

The rate of lipogenesis is markedly slowed in the liver of fasted animals, and the process virtually stops in both liver and adipose tissue in the diabetic. The failure of the process evidently is secondary to a decreased intracellular availability of glucose, but the hepatic defect cannot be repaired instantly by glucose feeding. This is due to the fact that a sort of "disuse atrophy" occurs of certain enzymes which participate in the synthesis of fatty acids from acetyl CoA. It is likely that a time-consuming resynthesis of these enzymes must occur before the tissues can perform at the prestarvation rate.

The lipogenic machinery shows a remarkable capacity to adapt not only to circumstances in which it is of no great use (such as starvation) but also in situations in which great demands are made on the carbohydrate storage capacity of the body. In chronic overfeeding, as in experimental hypothalamic obesity (surgical or chemical) and in experimental genetic obesity, the capacity of both liver and adipose tissue to transform carbohydrate to fat is greatly increased. The increase is both a unit change (i.e., increased lipogenesis per unit of tissue) and an aggregate change (increase in total tissue weight). This adaptation to overfeeding may be one of the reasons for frequently observed difficulty in achieving lasting weight reduction in individuals who have permitted themselves to become markedly obese. For, in the process of gaining weight, they have progressively increased their total lipogenic capacity and have thus drastically altered their glucose disposal pattern.

Apart from obesity, other adaptive changes occur in lipogenesis in liver and adipose tissue.

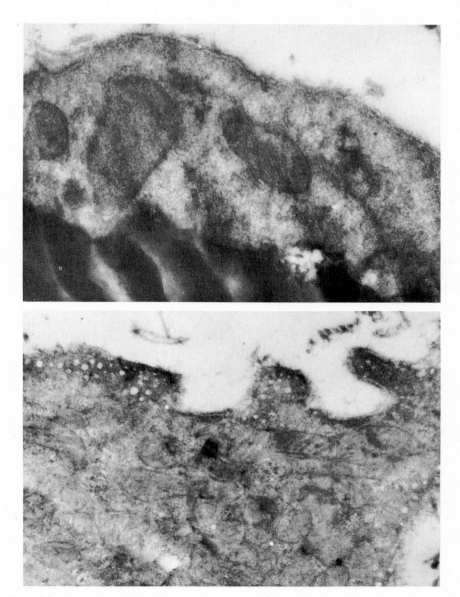

Fig. 10-5.—Effect of insulin added in vitro on morphology of an adipose tissue cell. Comparably thick sections of adipose tissue cells incubated for 20 min in basic medium. The control tissue *(upper)* was incubated without insulin; the experimental *(lower)* was exposed to 10^3 microunits of insulin. The numerous vesicles that give the insulin-treated cell a vacuolated appearance just below the plasma membrane are seen in thinner sections to have been formed by the fusion of many finger-like projections of the membrane which pinch off droplets of the surrounding medium. Electronmicrographs ($\times 42,000$) courtesy of R. Barrnett. (See Barrnett, R. J., and Ball, E. G.: J. Biophys. & Biochem. Cytol. 8:83-101, 1960.)

The body normally uses two large calorie depots; the gastrointestinal tract and the adipose tissue. If an animal is periodically overfed and the gastrointestinal tract is empty for a considerable part of the day, the lipogenic tissues become "trained" to store carbohydrate calories very quickly as fat, and the depots therefore compensate for the loss of a considerable amount of gastrointestinal tract calorie storage function. Both liver and fat tissue show strikingly "supernormal" capacities to incorporate glucose or acetate into fatty acids, and they also exhibit increases in certain enzymes believed to be functionally related to the process of lipogenesis. If animals are tube-fed, for example, they show much more fat in their bodies on carcass analysis than do animals eating the same amount of the same ration in the normal way, although their total weight does not differ from that of controls. Cohn refers to this phenomenon as "nonobese obesity" and has described many interesting derivative effects of periodic overfeeding on metabolism, and even on susceptibility to disease. Experiments of this type indicate that metabolic events can be influenced not only by the character of the diet and its total amount but also by the time pattern of food intake. They also illustrate the remarkable elasticity of the adipose tissue as it participates in integrative adjustments to new dietary situations.

Recently attempts have been made to assess the factor of periodicity of food intake in man. Fabry and his colleagues (1964), who explored the relationship between food intake pattern and metabolism in a long series of publications, have estimated food intake and measured body weight, glucose tolerance, serum cholesterol and blood lipids and skin fold thickness in apparently normal men who ate three meals per day or less and in others who ate five meals per day or more. Those who ate fewer meals ate absolutely less per day, but they weighed significantly more than did the high meal frequency group. Moreover, the men in the latter group showed significantly fewer diabetic glucose tolerance curves, lower serum cholesterol and blood lipid values and thinner skin folds. The results of this careful study are of great interest in view of Stunkard's finding that many obese patients give a history of consuming practically all of their food within a very restricted period of the day, usually between the evening meal and bed time (the "night-eating syndrome"). Gordon et al. (1965) have attempted to apply these findings in the management of obese patients by using frequent small feedings in their weight reduction regimens. It is difficult to assess the contribution of the altered food intake pattern to the total program in their experiments because frequency of feeding is only one of many maneuvers used by these investigators in their management program. The concept of adaptive hyperlipogenesis has been reviewed in two recent essays by Tepperman and Tepperman (1964, 1965). A discussion of specific enzyme changes in hyperlipogenesis will be found in Chapter 12.

MOBILIZATION OF FREE FATTY ACIDS FROM ADIPOSE TISSUE

When triglycerides break down, the concentration of FFA and glycerol in the adipose tissue cell increases and these substances diffuse out of the cell and eventually into the circulating blood in sufficiently high concentration to be readily detectable. The FFA, which have also been called unesterified fatty acids (UFA) and nonesterified fatty acids (NEFA), are now generally accepted to be the form in which adipose tissue supplies its stored lipid. Their half-life in the circulating blood (where they travel loosely attached to albumin) is only a few minutes, and they are readily utilizable by most nonnervous tissues of the body. They are released on starvation or in circumstances (emotional tension, fright, fear) that are associated with a sympathoadrenomedullary discharge. Carbohydrate ingestion or injection or insulin injection lowers their concentration in the blood. In diabetes, the FFA concentration is high (see Chapter 9).

Epinephrine and *norepinephrine* appear to be the most important physiological signals for instant calories in the form of FFA. The functional importance of the sympathetic innervation of adipose tissue has already been mentioned in connection with older experiments on the effects of denervation and nerve stimulation on the fat content of specific depots. Bogdanoff has found that the FFA in the blood of human subjects increases markedly when topics emotionally disturbing to them are discussed in an interview. A rise in plasma FFA regularly accompanies the myriad of other responses that are classified in the category "alarm reaction" (see p. 121). That the central nervous system plays a prominent role in the transmission of the FFA demand signal to the adipose tissue is suggested by the finding of Mallov and Witt that the FFA rise usually seen following the application of electric shock to rats was inhibited by pretreatment with a tranquilizer drug. Inhibition of FFA mobilization has also been observed in animals treated with ganglionic blocking agents or with sympatholytic drugs (example: dibenzyline), which act locally in the hormone-sensitive tissue to prevent the effects of epinephrine.

Our present knowledge of the biochemical locus of action of epinephrine in the adipose tissue cell is incomplete. It now appears probable, however, that the hormone activates a specific adipose tissue cell lipase which is distinguishable from other lipases by a number of criteria and that this enzyme is specifically responsible for the hydrolysis of tissue triglyceride and the release of FFA and glycerol into the body fluids. At the same time, it increases the utilization of glucose by the cell, but *not* by way of the hexosemonophosphate shunt, or pentose phosphate pathway. Thus, TPNH is not generated at an increased rate, but increased amounts of labeled carbohydrate appear in trioses and CO_2. There may be some re-esterification of the accumulated FFA in the cell because the production of α glycerophosphate is stimulated by epinephrine, but the action of the stimulated lipase far overpowers the resynthesis of triglyceride and the FFA is exported.

The formation of 3′, 5′ cyclic AMP is an essential part of the response, not only to catecholamine hormones but also to other peptides such as ACTH, TSH, glucagon, etc. Butcher and his colleagues (1965) have convincingly demonstrated accumulation of the cyclic nucleotide in adipose tissue stimulated by epinephrine, particularly when the phosphodiesterase which destroys 3′, 5′ cyclic AMP is inhibited by caffeine. Nucleotide accumulation correlates well with lipolysis. In addition, Rizack (1964) has demon-

Fig. 10-6.—Effects of insulin (I) and epinephrine (E) on the metabolism of the adipose tissue cell. (Modified from Jeanrenaud, B.: Metabolism 10:535–581, 1961, from Wertheimer, E., and Shafrir, E.: Recent Prog. Hormone Res. 16:467-495, 1960, and from the work of others cited in these reviews.)

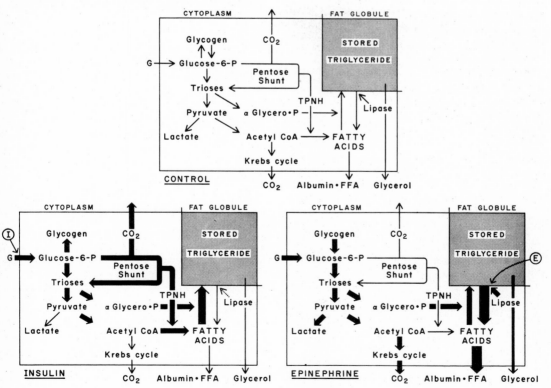

strated activation of the hormone-sensitive lipase by 3', 5' cyclic AMP added to cell-free systems prepared from adipose tissue. Phosphorylase activation occurs in epinephrine-stimulated adipose tissue, but what, if anything, this has to do with lipolysis is quite unknown. The mechanism of the increased glucose utilization and the reason for the preferential increase in glucose utilization by way of the Embden-Meyerhoff pathway are unknown. The demonstration by Cahill and his colleagues that the epinephrine pattern of response can be simulated to some extent by increasing the FFA concentration of the medium surrounding an isolated fat pad suggests that the primary effect of epinephrine may be lipolysis, and that other events (such as increased glucose utilization and relative suppression of glucose oxidation via the pentose shunt) may be secondary to the large increase in intracellular FFA concentration.

Recently, a distinct anti-lipolytic effect of insulin in adipose tissue has been described by Ball (1964) and by Fain (1965). The presence of very small concentrations of insulin apparently inhibits the lipolytic effect of epinephrine. One of the most interesting aspects of this insulin effect on the adipocyte is the fact that it occurs in the absence of glucose from in vitro systems. When one remembers that the membrane activity stimulated by insulin in the experiments of Barrnett and Ball also occurred in the absence of added glucose, one must leave open the possibility that in the adipocyte as well as in the muscle cell and liver cell insulin may have profound effects which are not related to its capacity to facilitate the ingress of glucose into the cell.

The anti-lipolytic effect of insulin has recently been correlated with an apparent 3', 5' cyclic AMP-lowering effect of insulin in adipose tissue by Jungas (1966). This investigator inferred a decrease in cyclic AMP in insulin-stimulated adipose tissue and demonstrated a decrease in adenyl cyclase activity in adipose tissue under the influence of insulin.

A comparison of the effects of insulin and epinephrine on the adipose tissue cell is given diagrammatically in Figure 10-6. The absolute thickness of the lines is not intended to communicate quantitative information about the amounts of intermediates that are metabolized by way of the various pathways shown. One wishes only to emphasize the point that the pattern of metabolism in the adipose tissue cell is markedly different under circumstances in which fat is being deposited as compared with those in which it is being mobilized. Moreover, the biochemical events described in these diagrams are beautifully consistent with observations at the level of organization of the whole animal.

EFFECTS OF OTHER HORMONES ON FAT MOBILIZATION

A number of substances in addition to epinephrine have been observed to cause a rise in FFA in the blood, a rise in blood ketone level and an increase in liver fat concentration. Among these are ACTH, GH, certain preparations of TSH, a fat-mobilizing peptide isolated from human urine, a posterior pituitary lipid mobilizing material and peptides from the anterior pituitary which are distinguishable from other, well-characterized pituitary materials. Our information about these substances and their possible physiological role in the regulation of adipose tissue metabolism is too meager to permit us to attempt anything more than a superficial evaluation.

It seems unlikely that ACTH or TSH is normally secreted in sufficiently large quantities to affect adipose tissue except in extraordinary circumstances. There is increasing reason to believe that the anterior pituitary secretes exceedingly potent fat-mobilizing peptides which are distinct from any of the six well-characterized pituitary hormones (Chalmers, Astwood, Rudman, Seifter —see review by Jeanrenaud for references). Future studies in this field will be watched with interest, for it is possible that if any of these is shown to participate in fat-mobilization to a significant degree, human deficiency states with respect to such substances may be described.

Other hormones may participate in the metabolism of adipose tissue, not as signals but as conditioning influences on the tissue's capacity to respond to signals, that is, in a so-called permissive way. The adrenal glucocorticoids and thyroxin fall into this category, for many investigators have described impaired ability of many recognized fat-mobilizing substances to cause release of FFA in the absence of either adrenal cortical hormones or thyroxin. In the adrenalectomized animal, fat-mobilization which is normally seen following the administration of ethyl alcohol does not occur, and the response can be restored by pretreatment with an adrenal glucocorticoid. In the hypophysectomized animal, there is no rise in FFA following epinephrine, and the correction of all known hormonal deficiencies *except* hypothyroidism fails to restore the ability of the fat depots to respond to the stimulus. Treatment with TSH or thyroid hormone restores the FFA epinephrine response. The hyperthyroid state, on the other hand, markedly accentuates the response of adipose tissue both to the FFA-mobilizing effect of epinephrine and to the lipogenesis-stimulating effect of insulin.

There has been considerable confusion about the fat-mobilizing effect of growth hormone, for while serum FFA and ketone bodies and liver fat content increase after growth hormone administration, it was not possible to demonstrate FFA release when purified growth hormone was added directly to the epididymal fat pad in vitro. In fact, it had been proposed that the fat-mobilizing effects of growth hormone seen in the intact animal were artifacts due to the contamination of the preparations with TSH, a known FFA mobilizer. A considerable clarification of this point has resulted from the work of Fain *et al.* (1965). These investigators found that neither purified bovine growth hormone nor dexamethasone (a synthetic glucocorticoid) had a perceptible fatty acid-releasing effect on isolated fat cells prepared by the collagenase method of Rodbell (1964). However, in dexamethasone-primed cells, minute concentrations of growth hormone (as little as 0.001 microgram per ml) definitely increased fatty acid release. Insulin showed an anti-lipolytic effect in this system. Moreover, lipolysis with epinephrine was immediate, whereas that due to the growth hormone-dexamethasone combination showed a 1-hr lag period. Also, the latter was blocked by both puromycin and actinomycin D. Fain *et al.* suggest that all of the biochemical machinery necessary for lipolysis are present and acutely activated by epinephrine and the lipolytic peptides but that the FFA-mobilizing effect of the growth hormone-dexamethasone combination requires the synthesis of new protein. Whether this new protein is the hormone-sensitive lipase is not as yet known, but whatever it is, DNA-mediated RNA synthesis is necessary for the response.

There are no better illustrations of the point that hormone-sensitive tissues are under extraordinarily complex directive influences which may include those of many hormones as well as neural ones. Some of these (insulin and epinephrine in the case of fat cells) may be primary regulatory signals, while others (glucocorticoids, thyroxin) may function to maintain the capacity of the cell to respond to its controlling influences.

Energy Expenditure

We have examined the problem of food intake and its regulation and we have reviewed briefly the development of modern views concerning the physiology of adipose tissue and the convenient storage of energy in the form of triglycerides. It is now appropriate to turn our interest to the other side of the energy balance equation, energy expenditure. Energy derived from the oxidation of foodstuffs appears as work or heat; the chemical energy derived from the stepwise oxidative cascade of metabolic intermediates is neatly packaged in "quanta" of phosphate bond energy which are available to operate all sorts of life machinery or are dissipated as heat. Bond energy can be transduced into contractile work, osmotic work, electrical energy, biosynthetic work or, in the firefly, into light. In the case of biosynthetic work, the oxidation of substrates must provide a continuing supply of reduced coenzymes for reductive syntheses.

⑤ THE METABOLIC "COST OF LIVING"

The basal metabolic rate (BMR) of an adult male approximately 40 years of age is about 35–40 calories per square meter of body surface per hour (or $0.6 \ Cal/m^2/min$); for a woman of the same age the value is from 6 to 10% lower. These figures tend to be higher in children and adolescents, and lower with increasing age. Also, with increasing age, the sex difference tends to disappear. As the test is usually performed in the postabsorptive state and after a satisfactory night's rest, it can be fairly said to measure the metabolic cost of living in the waking state. The energy cost during sleep is about 10% less than the BMR; the difference between the two probably represents a difference in skeletal muscle tone.

The energy expenditure estimated by the BMR includes that required to operate the heart, lungs and other vital organs. Since the body constituents are in a dynamic steady state, even in the nongrowing individual, and since anabolic processes balance catabolic ones, there must be a continuous supply of energy for anabolism. In special physiological circumstances, such as periods of rapid growth in young animals, pregnancy and lactation, energy is stored and at the same time energy is spent during the storage process.

When food is eaten, a rise in oxygen consumption occurs—the so-called specific dynamic action or SDA of foodstuffs. Of the three major foodstuffs, protein produces the highest SDA which, in some individuals, may be as much of an increment over the BMR as 10–30%. The SDA represents energy which is spent in the metabolic "processing" of food—in driving synthetic reactions, in oxidative deamination of amino acids, and so on. Before fats, carbohydrates and amino acids can be used for any metabolic purpose, they must be "activated" by an energy-requiring reaction. The synthesis of protein, glycogen and fatty acids all require energy expenditure.

Quantitatively, the aggregate "cost of living" metabolism is extremely small in comparison with the total metabolism of a man doing hard physical work. Differences in efficiency of "cost of living" metabolic transactions would seem, then, to be rather unimportant in the determination of over-all energy balance. Yet, energy balance occurs over a very long period of time, and it is possible for extremely minor, and scarcely measurable, differences in operative metabolism to have a perceptible cumulative effect on energy balance. For example, Forbes and Swift have shown that rats fed a high fat, low carbohydrate diet outgain control rats fed an isocaloric high carbohydrate, low fat diet. Moreover, on carcass analysis, the composition of the excess gain is a mixture of fat and protein. All of the reasons for this are not clear, but it appears to be energetically less wasteful to store absorbed fat calories in the depots and mobilize them for use than it does to convert the same number of calories of carbohydrate into fat, store them and subsequently mobilize them. If a process costs less in energy, more energy is therefore available for surplus storage.

There have been other demonstrations of the effect of small differences in metabolic efficiency on the disposition of calories. For example, animals pair-fed isocaloric amounts of sucrose deposit more fat in their depots than do glucose-fed controls. The metabolism of fructose is such that fatty acid synthesis is favored when this monosaccharide is fed. The mechanisms involved in this operational difference is the metabolism of these sugars are now being studied.

It is obviously impossible here to begin to explore the many conceivable ways in which apparently minor metabolic differences could contribute, over a long period of time, to disturbances in energy balance. There is no reason to doubt that such differences could influence the efficiency of utilization of food for muscle work as well as for maintenance energy needs. Many physiologists and clinicians scorn the idea that differences of this sort could contribute materially to the etiology of obesity. I take the view that this scorn is inappropriate in the light of our still inadequate knowledge of this subject.

⑥ ACTIVITY PATTERN

Skeletal muscle constitutes about 50% of the weight of the body. It is the one tissue which can vary its energy requirement by a factor of 20 or more. In an exercising man, work is performed not only by the muscles which are active but also by the heart and respiratory muscles which must collaborate to deliver sufficient oxygenated blood to meet the increased requirement of the working muscle.

TABLE 10-1.—PHYSIOLOGIC EFFECTS OF EXERCISE*

PHYSIOLOGIC EFFECTS	RESTING	DURING EXERCISE	
		AVERAGE	MAXIMAL
Oxygen consumption cc/min	250	2500–3500	5000
Oxygen debt, L	. . . .	4–8	16–19
Lactacidemia, mg/%	10–15	50–100	200
Respiration			
Rate	12–16	30	60
Inspiratory vol, cc	350	2000	2200
Minute-volume, L	4.5–6	50–70	120
Circulation			
Pulse rate, min	70	120–150	200
Systolic output, cc	60–70	90–110	150
Minute-volume, L	4–5	10–20	35
Systolic B.P., mm Hg	120	160	180
Temperature °C	. . . .	0.5–1	2

*From Houssay, B. A.: *Human Physiology* (New York: McGraw-Hill Book Co., 1955).

Table 10-1 illustrates some of the changes produced in oxygen consumption and other physiological parameters by exercise. Many of these changes can be shown to be related to the state of athletic training of the individual under study. Two generalizations can be made about highly trained athletes as compared with sedentary people (1) athletic people show a smaller deviation from the resting level than do the nonathletic in all parameters measured while they are working at similar, moderate work loads and (2) the more highly trained an athlete is the more nearly can he approach the maximal levels of oxygen consumption expenditure, blood lactate accumulation, ventilation rate, cardiac output and all the rest. In a word, the athlete can work more efficiently (i.e., at a smaller energy cost) at low and moderate work loads, and he can do more work before he is overcome by exhaustion.

Until recently, there was a widespread tendency to belittle the importance of activity pattern as a contributory factor to the maintenance of energy balance. The emphasis was mainly on food intake, and there appeared to be a tacit assumption that the 2000–3000 calorie differences in energy expenditure per day that may occur between a sedentary individual and one who is doing heavy manual labor really were not very significant. Many students of human energy balance problems are now emphasizing the importance of considering inactivity as an important contributory factor to the etiology of obesity in some individuals.

Mayer and his colleagues have made careful studies on obese high school girls and have classified them into two groups (1) girls who clearly ate too much and (2) extremely inactive girls who did not eat more than did their normally active siblings of average weight. There is experimental evidence to support the view that the food intake-regulating equipment in the central nervous system was not designed, in a manner of speaking, to cope with the extremely low activity levels that are possible in modern industrial societies. Contrary to a widely held superstition, a change in activity pattern from very low to moderately high does not necessarily stimulate the appetite and therefore cancel out the benefit of the added energy expenditure associated with exercise.

Stunkard and his colleagues have also studied the possibility that activity pattern may contribute to the etiology of obesity. Even with their crude method of estimating activity by means of the pedometer, an instrument which keeps a cumulative record of distance walked, they were able to show that many obese women (but not obese men) were significantly less active than were their controls of average weight. The food intake of these women was not especially high.

Edholm *et al.* have explored a most interesting facet of the relation of energy expenditure to caloric balance. These workers studied a group of cadets in training under circumstances that permitted careful estimation of caloric intake and energy expenditure. When they made a correlation plot of many individual daily food intake measurements against daily energy expenditure on any given day, there was an almost perfect *lack* of correlation. But when they plotted energy expenditure on day 0 *versus* food intake 2 days later, there was an excellent correlation, suggesting that today's level of activity is somehow factored into the spontaneous food intake the day after tomorrow. It is difficult to imagine how this type of long-term regulation could be accomplished through the operation of any of the satiety signals that have been suggested so far.

Another aspect of the contribution of muscle work to energy balance deserves comment. If a man overeats and becomes progressively more obese, the energy cost of moving his body from place to place becomes greater and greater. Obviously, a 300-pound man does a considerable amount of work when he merely moves across a room. Thus, the increased effort involved in supporting and moving a fat body tends to put limits on the degree of obesity that can be achieved. The absolute oxygen consumption of the obese individual at rest is higher than that of his lean control, but in addition to this the energy expenditure involved in working may be extremely large. Many obese individuals must overeat in order to remain fat. The sad fact is that, just as progressively increasing weight tends to limit weight gain by increasing work load, weight loss tends to limit itself in the opposite way. For as weight is lost, less work is required to support and move the body, and, therefore, the more closely does the diminished food intake approach the actual requirement for maintenance. This may be one of the contributory reasons for the deplorable results that are often seen clinically when people who have permitted themselves to become markedly obese are treated with low calorie diets.

When we think of activity and energy balance, we tend to imagine such activities as tennis, walking, manual labor and so on. There is another kind of activity which may exert a subtle, long-range influence on energy balance, namely, the activity of inactivity or the muscular activity associated with sitting or lying. Recent studies have shown that there is a very striking individual variation in the energy cost of the "inactivities" and that some people who are simply sitting down have energy expenditures which approximate those of others doing light work. The fact that oxygen consumption during sleep is about 10% below the BMR suggests that muscle tone contributes substantially to the energy cost of being merely awake. Even excluding the compulsive pencil-tappers and foot-twitchers, there must be a normal distribution curve of intensity of muscle tone in people who pass for "normal." If 2 individuals (precisely similar in all other respects) at either extreme of such a curve were pair-fed, thermodynamic necessity requires that the "low-tone" subject would outgain the "high-tone" one. I am unaware of any clinical application of this idea but believe firmly that an expert in electromyography could contribute substantially to our knowledge of human obesity.

⑦ HEAT EXCHANGE AND ENERGY BALANCE

Warm-blooded animals characteristically maintain their internal temperature environment within narrow limits. Temperature regulation involves the bringing into play of heat production and heat conservation mechanisms when temperature begins to fall and of heat dissipating mechanisms when the environmental temperature rises. Temperature regulation is accomplished in a staged progression of responses: first, acute reflex changes (vasodilation or vasoconstriction, shivering, panting, sweating, etc.) and second, longer range adaptive changes (for example, thyroid hypertrophy, increased food intake, and change in the character of peripheral depot fat on cold exposure). Clearly, the problems of temperature regulation and of energy balance are intricately related, and it was this relationship which originally suggested to Brobeck the idea of thermostatic regulation of food

intake. In his energy balance studies, in which he measured food intake, spontaneous activity and body weight in the rat over a wide range of ambient air temperatures, he found that high temperatures were associated with decreases in both food intake and locomotor activity, while exposure to low temperatures produced hyperphagia and increased activity. Certainly, the animal in the cold must "eat to keep warm" (in Brobeck's phrase), for if he did not increase his food intake he would soon go into negative energy balance because of the necessity of stoking his heat production furnace with his own substance.

No energy-converting engine, whether steam engine, diesel engine, or man, operates at 100% efficiency levels. Man, in fact, is between the other two, for the efficiencies of the three kinds of engines mentioned are 15%, 35% and 25%, respectively. This should not be regarded as a rigidly set figure, for the efficiencies of all kinds of engines vary with the rate at which they are operated. In man, for example, efficiency tends to be low when the rate of work is either very low or extremely high, with the most efficient range at the top of a parabolic curve. Moreover, as we have seen, efficiency in man is in part a function of training and skill.

The stimulation of TSH production by the pituitary that occurs on cold exposure is of considerable adaptive significance from the point of view of energy balance. The increased amounts of thyroid hormone which are secreted cause an uncoupling of oxidation and phosphorylation in the mitochondria, so that for each mole of fuel oxidized, a smaller proportion is trapped as utilizable phosphate bond energy and a larger proportion contributes to heat production. The food intake goes up to such an extent that the *net* high energy phosphate bond production may be even higher than it was during the control period although the efficiency of the process of phosphorylation may have gone down. The mitochondria then become so many miniature intracellular furnaces, and, in fact, in animals exposed to cold for several weeks their number can be seen to increase.

Impatient with long-continued dietary weight reduction regimens, a certain number of physicians in the past have prescribed thyroid hormone to promote weight loss. This is not regarded as good practice in individuals who show no sign of thyroid deficiency, for the hormone is usually given in doses too small to accomplish much in a euthyroid patient or, if it is given in effective doses, iatrogenic or factitious hyperthyroidism may be produced.

That other chemical agents can cause weight loss or failure of weight gain by rendering the metabolic processes less than normally efficient is suggested by the unfortunate story of the use of dinitrophenol as an adjuvant to weight reducing regimens. This drug does indeed cause a very striking increase in oxygen consumption and an uncoupling of oxidation and phosphorylation (though the mechanism by which it does this differs from that of thyroxin). Obese patients were able to lose weight while they were being poisoned with dinitrophenol. But it was found that the drug produced cataracts in some patients and it was therefore withdrawn. There is no doubt in my mind that many toxic substances can decrease the efficiency of utilization of food and thereby induce weight loss, but this is not now considered to be a potentially fruitful field for the development of new therapeutic approaches to the problem of clinical obesity.

⑧ Heredity

Everyone agrees that the development of effective chemotherapeutic agents in the treatment of infectious diseases was one of medicine's greatest achievements. It is not as widely recognized as it should be that this development was made possible by the use of experimental animal models of human infections. The susceptibility of the mouse to human pathogens was exploited in the development of sulfonamides, penicillin and many other effective anti-infectious agents.

In the field of metabolic disorders, which are often of obscure and complicated etiology, animal models serve the extremely important function of stimulating thought about related human diseases and guiding the clinical investigator to ask pointed questions in his experimental study of sick people. Rats, mice, guinea pigs, dogs, cats and monkeys deprived of one or another endocrine gland, or treated with various hormones, have played central roles in the development of many of the concepts developed in this series of essays. Of course, species differences exist, and all ideas developed from observation of non-

human forms must be validated or invalidated in the human. But in many ways the physiological and biochemical mechanisms which man shares with other species are much more impressive than are the differences. This fact in no way diminishes the stature of man, who still belongs to the only species which is capable of contemplating these problems and discussing them.

Experimental Hereditary Obesities

Recent studies of hereditary and nonhereditary forms of obesity in mice and other animals have captured the imagination of many clinicians and have led to a reconsideration of the role of heredity as a contributory factor to the development of obesity in man. It has not yet been possible to apply many of the theoretical aspects of the animal work in the clinic, but I confidently predict that in not too many years *obesity* will be regarded as a symptom, like *dyspnea* or *hypertension* or *polyuria* or *fever,* and that it will be possible to classify obese patients into various pathophysiological categories. The most impressive single fact about the experimental obesities is their variety, i.e., the fact that animals get fat for quite different reasons.

Long before the physiologist became interested in obesity, the stock breeder had demonstrated convincingly that it was possible to breed selectively for many traits, among them, obesity (in hogs). There is, in fact, a vast literature on artificial selection of genetic traits in farm animals that now becomes of great interest to physicians who are in the midst of a widespread renascence of interest in the whole subject of genetics.

The background studies which helped to guide recent work on the genetic obesities were done on animals made obese either by surgical or chemical (aurothioglucose, or ATG) lesions of the medial hypothalamic area. This kind of obesity is primarily a disorder of food intake regulation, for immediately after the placement of effective hypothalamic lesions, such animals may eat two to three times their preoperative food intake. Mayer has referred to this type of obesity as the "regulatory" type in contrast to many genetic obesities in which the primary disturbance appears to be a biochemical defect and which he designates as "metabolic." This is a useful classification, but it may sometimes be

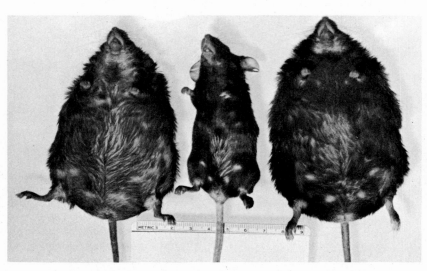

Fig. 10-7.—Hereditary obesity-diabetes syndrome in the mouse. These animals have quite different metabolic characteristics from the obese mice shown in Figure 10-4. Author's photograph. (See Mayer, J.: Am. J. Clin. Nutrition 8:712-718, 1960.)

misleading, for animals with hypothalamic lesions quickly develop metabolic characteristics which are quite different from those of control animals, and which are believed to be adaptive changes in response to the demand to store and process very large amounts of absorbed foodstuffs. Among the most prominent adaptive changes seen in such animals are (1) an increased capacity of the liver and adipose tissue to synthesize fatty acids from either glucose or acetate when the tissues are obtained from an animal in the fed state and (2) a generalized splanchnomegaly, or enlargement of the viscera, including the gastrointestinal tract, the liver, the heart and the kidneys. The hypothalamic-lesioned animal, then, became a standard preparation with which genetically obese mice could be conveniently compared.

The most widely known form of genetic obesity occurs in the obese-hyperglycemic strain which has been studied imaginatively and extensively by Mayer and his collaborators (Fig. 10-7). Mice of this strain carry a recessive gene which manifests itself as extreme obesity in 1 out of 4 animals. The obesity does not appear until after the fourth week of life. Since the fat animals do not mate, a continuing supply is provided by matings of nonobese siblings. When the food intake of an obese mouse is restricted to 3–4 Gm/day and the animals achieve weights in the control range of 26–30 Gm, their carcasses still contain three times as much fat as do those of nonobese siblings.

Although these animals have a very large number of metabolic peculiarities, the obesity is certainly due in part to excessive food intake, for while they do not show the same degree of hyperphagia seen in hypothalamic-obese animals, they do eat from 20 to 50% more than do their nonobese siblings. Since their total oxygen consumption is extremely low and since they are strikingly hypoactive as compared with their controls, this represents a considerable excess of food. In connection with the sluggishness most workers have observed in these animals, it has been found that their total body protein is not increased but that they do show enlargement of the liver, gastrointestinal tract, heart, and kidneys, just as ATG mice do. This can mean only that their skeletal muscle mass must be *smaller* than that of their nonobese siblings. The same inference can be drawn from the "nonobese obesity" of the animals fed a restricted diet.

These mice have been shown to exhibit many other abnormal responses. They are extremely resistant to insulin; they are hyperglycemic, and exquisitely sensitive to the hyperglycemic effect of growth hormone; the pancreatic islets are hypertrophic; they are extremely sensitive to cold and are unable to maintain their body temperature in a cold environment. Renold and his colleagues have found that the adipose tissue of such mice is comparatively insensitive to the lipogenesis-stimulating effects of insulin or glucose, but that in spite of this, it shows hyperactive lipogenesis from acetate. In other words, this tissue does not show the usual close correlation between fat formation and carbohydrate utilization. Marshall and Engel have reported that the FFA concentration of the blood does not rise when the obese mice are starved; nor do their fat pads respond to epinephrine with the release of FFA as normal fat pads do.

In this type of obesity, a biochemical abnormality in the adipose tissue cell itself was suggested by the fact that when adipose tissue from an hereditary-obese mouse was transplanted to one ear lobe of a lean mouse and a similar piece of tissue from a lean mouse was transplanted to the other ear lobe of the same recipient, "obesity" developed in the transplant from the fat mouse (Liebelt). Recently, Treble and Mayer have suggested a possible biochemical explanation for the fact that the adipocytes of these mice appear to be so reluctant to surrender their fatty acids when the usual signals for fat mobilization are presented to them. As we have seen, adipose tissue normally lacks the enzyme *glycerokinase* which has the function of phosphorylating glycerol to α glycerophosphate. Since the latter compound is the obligatory precursor of triglyceride glycerol, triglyceride formation can only occur if there is a continuing supply of α glycerophosphate from the breakdown of carbohydrate. Glycerol derived from the breakdown of triglycerides is not normally recycled; in fact, it appears in the blood with FFA when fat is mobilized and the level of free glycerol in the blood can be used as an estimate of lipolysis in the adipose tissue. In the obese hyperglycemic mouse, however, the enzyme glycerokinase is inappropriately *present* in the adipose tissue. This makes it possible for triglyceride-derived glycerol to be reused for the esterification of fatty acids. Whatever the fat-mobilizing signal, at any given strength it becomes less effective because the size of the α glycerophosphate pool continues to favor resynthesis of triglycerides. Notice that, unlike normal adipose tissue cells, these abnormal cells do not require a concurrent oxidation of glucose to promote fat storage, a fact suggested by the work of Renold (cited above). This may not be the complete story of the biochemical lesion in the hereditary obesity-diabetes syndrome, but the finding of one enzyme too many in the fat cells of these mice is certainly an important one and should lead to a search for similar abnormalities in the obese human.

Other types of experimental obesity have been described. One (widely known in the United States as Danforth's obesity although it was described more than 50 years ago by Cuenot) is of particular interest because it always appears in association with a readily visible hereditary trait, namely, yellow fur. While yellow-linked obesity has not been studied as exhaustively as has the hereditary obese-diabetes type described previously, it appears to resemble it in some respects. There is a combination of hyperphagia and inactivity, together with insulin resistance and sensitivity to insulin antagonists.

Several new experimental animal models of obesity have been described recently. One of these, hereditary obesity and hyperlipemia in the rat, was originally studied by Zucker and Zucker (see Brodoff, 1965). The syndrome consists of massive obesity accompanied by a striking panhyperlipemia, i.e., highly elevated serum concentrations of cholesterol, triglycerides, fatty acids and phospholipids. The lipemia persists even in the fasted state. Although the precise biochemical locus of the genetic defect in these animals is not yet known, they are being studied energetically and will no doubt help in the conceptualization of the nature of the biochemical lesions in the hyperlipemias of man.

Another interesting study which illustrates the interplay of heredity and environment in the etiology of obesity is that of Hackel *et al.* (see Brodoff, 1965) on the occurrence of obesity and diabetes in the desert rat. In its native desert, this animal eats succulent plants and never becomes either obese or diabetic. If it is maintained in the laboratory on a similar diet it remains normal. However, if it is fed a laboratory chow ration in the laboratory, it quickly becomes both obese and diabetic. Apparently, the desert rat has inherited food intake-regulating equipment and a metabolic constitution which are appropriate to its natural habitat, but both appestat and metabolic machinery fail to function adequately when a concentrated pellet type of ration is fed in the laboratory. The desert rat and his story represent a miniaturized version of what happens to certain human populations when they change their mode of living drastically. In South Africa, certain Bantu tribesmen show a low incidence of obesity and diabetes in villages, but when they migrate to urban centers and experience striking changes in dietary habits and activity pattern, they exhibit both in appreciable numbers.

Following Fröhlich's description of the adiposogenital syndrome at the turn of the century, there was a dialogue that lasted 40 years about whether the pituitary or the hypothalamus was concerned with the etiology of obesity. With the successful demonstration of experimental obesity in animals with hypothalamic lesions and intact pituitaries, the controversy was presumed to be settled, and it was (and is) widely taught that the endocrine system has little or nothing to do with the etiology of obesity—this in spite of the manifest obesity of many patients with Cushing's syndrome. Now, the possible etiological significance of the hypophysis is widely acknowledged in at least one species, the mouse. Recently, Furth *et al.* have described a strain of mice which shows a very high incidence of obesity and, concurrently, tumors of the pituitary which secrete an excess of ACTH. A characteristic finding in these animals is enormous hypertrophy of the islets of Langerhans. A similar effect can be reproduced in mice by implanting corticosterone pellets subcutaneously. Hausberger has suggested that hyperadrenocorticism, whether induced by hormone pellet implantation or by spontaneously occurring ACTH-producing tumor, produces a secondary hyperinsulinism and that the obesity results because the adrenal steroid does not antagonize the lipogenesis-stimulating effect of insulin in the adipose tissue. Furthermore, he has shown that adrenalectomy prevents the development of obesity in the yellow-linked strain. A secondary hyperphagia is associated with periods of rapid weight gain in induced or naturally occurring hyperadrenocorticism in mice. Hausberger also makes the interesting suggestion that the obesity that is seen in some strains of some species following castration may also belong to the hyperadrenocorticism with secondary hyperinsulinism category of obesity. The extent to which these interesting ideas can be extrapolated to man remains to be determined.

Another interesting form of genetic predisposition to obesity has been described by Fenton, who found that in certain strains of mice a shift from a high carbohydrate to a high-fat diet resulted in obesity. Mice of other genetic composition were able to make this shift without becoming obese. This experiment suggests that the mechanisms for the long range regulation of energy balance may vary with the composition of the diet, for the mice which became obese on fat feeding were able to regulate body weight successfully on the high carbohydrate diet.

HEREDITY IN MAN

There is as yet no absolute proof that hereditary predisposition to obesity exists in such a genetically heterogeneous species as man. It is extremely difficult to evaluate the comparative contribution of the genes on the one hand and a large number of potentially important cultural and environmental factors on the other in the etiology of this condition. Many clinical teachers believe that hereditary factors in most individuals are negligible and that, in any case, it is not good practice to admit even the possibility of the existence of such factors to patients for fear that their motivation to lose weight will be destroyed. There is, in fact, a large body of suggestive evidence which supports the view that hereditary factors are at least contributory causes of obesity in man. The finding of a high correlation between the incidence of fatness in parents and children may not be very convincing, for children learn food habits from parents very early and may adhere to these habits for many years. But studies on identical twins have revealed a very close correspondence of body weight, much closer than that found in fraternal twins or in other siblings. Moreover, when identical twins have been separated in childhood and examined later in life, a striking similarity in body weight is still seen, although the deviation in this case is slightly greater than that observed in the case of twins brought up in the same household. It is difficult to deny that heredity does indeed play a contributory part in the etiology of human obesity, but the comparative importance of this factor in individual people remains to be evaluated. If it should become possible one day to classify human obese patients on the basis of some sort of physiological analysis, it is safe to predict that genetic predisposition will prove to be a more important contributory factor in some types of the disorder than in others.

If one permits one's fancy to move about freely, it is easy to imagine many ways in which genetic factors *could* influence the success or failure of an individual to maintain himself in energy balance. Available space does not permit extended speculation on this subject. The interested reader is referred to a pertinent essay in which an attempt is made to state the problem in terms of possible mechanisms (Tepperman, J.: Etiologic factors in obesity and leanness, Perspectives in Biol. & Med. 1:293, 1958).

METABOLIC ABNORMALITIES IN THE OBESE HUMAN SUBJECT

There have been many reports of a variety of chemical abnormalities in "uncomplicated" human obesity. The occurrence of abnormal glucose tolerance curves has been well known for some time (see Newburgh and Conn, p. 206), as is a high frequency of insulin insensitivity. The obese subject frequently does not exhibit as pronounced ketonemia on fasting as does the normal, and the response of serum FFA to fasting may be diminished. The serum insulin response to a glucose load may be exaggerated, whereas the serum growth hormone response to induced hypoglycemia or to fasting may be blunted. The urinary excretion of 17-OH corticoids may be increased in obesity.

An important unanswered question is the following: were any or all of these abnormalities present *before* the development of the obesity or do they represent adaptive changes which occur with overeating? With the exception of the serum growth hormone response, all of the findings listed above have been seen in experimental animals with either surgically or chemically induced hypothalamic obesity. Moreover, in one case at least—that of impaired glucose tolerance—a return toward normal is seen on weight reduction. As yet there is no well-authenticated finding of a well-defined biochemical abnormality in any group of human obese subjects. It may be that one day we will have one or more biochemical markers for human obesity similar to the superfluous glycerokinase in the adipose tissue of the obese hyperglycemic mouse, or to the glucose-6-phosphate dehydrogenase deficiency in the red cell of the primaquine-sensitive individual. At present, no such markers exist. Moreover, some of the abnormal responses summarized above are so variable and inconsistent that they can only be studied fruitfully by extremely critical investigators.

⑨ Environment

Obviously, powerful environmental forces interact with physiological mechanisms and hereditary influences to affect the success or failure of any individual person in achieving energy balance. In order to see the problem in perspective, it is essential to consider a few of the ways in which these forces act.

One of the most ancient cliches in biology states that the organism and its environment represent a continuum. In the case of the human species, the individual exists in many environments that differ almost qualitatively in kind. First, there is the *physical environment,* comprising temperature, humidity, oxygen supply, water supply, food supply and so on. Energy balance is more compatible with high food intake in cold environments than in warm ones. High temperatures are more tolerable at low humidity than at high humidity. The general availability of food can disturb energy balance in either direction. When, during World War II, whole populations existed on 1500 calories per day per person, obesity disappeared. In countries which produce an excess of food that is widely distributed, the incidence of positive energy balance is very high, partly due no doubt to the fact that in many of these countries it is possible to live at levels of extremely low energy expenditure.

In addition to the physical environment there is a complex *psychological environment,* or an environment of interpersonal transactions carried on at many different levels of intimacy. There is no doubt that forces which arise from the interaction of the individual with this environment affect energy balance. The husband who is absorbed in his job is far less likely to eat inappropriately large amounts of food than is his bored wife who is constantly surrounded by readily available goodies. On the other hand, the husband whose work requires him to entertain lavishly on an expense account may succumb to insistent gastronomic temptations. A psychological factor which operates in the opposite direction is the standard of beauty that is accepted by large populations. The promotion of the Hollywood starlet ideal of beauty has doubtless stimulated many teen-age girls to make a conscious attempt to keep themselves from getting fat and unattractive, and sometimes this battle is fought at enormous emotional cost. In other cultures as, for example, among the Banyankola people of East Africa, girls were prepared for marriage by forced feeding and activity restriction, and the more obese they became, the more desirable they were considered as brides. This is an example of cultural relativism in relation to energy balance.

As the example just cited well illustrates, the psychological environment is quite inseparable from the *social, political, cultural,* and even *moral* environment. Food habits differ from one culture to another. Industrial civilizations tend to be characterized by low physical activity levels. In many countries, small numbers of people are paid to take exercise for the pleasure of millions who sit and watch them. The effect of the widespread influence of television viewing on the collective energy balance problem of this country is difficult to assess, for this pastime is characterized not only by minimal physical activity but also by maximal temptation in the form of nearly irresistible advertisements for food and beer. This combination taxes the capacity of the best physiological energy balance-regulating equipment imaginable.

Thus, nature and nurture collaborate to influence men as they have affected the destinies of all the other species since the historic replication of the hypothetical Primordial Macromolecule. The fact that man has (superimposed on the biological mechanisms he shares with other species) an imagination and languages, enormously complicates the environmental forces that play upon him, both as an individual and as a member of a small or large group. The epidemiology of energy balance problems is only one example of many that could be cited to illustrate the important point that the integrative physiology of the individual occurs in ever-widening circles of social integration (or disintegration) and that the thoughtful physician cannot permit himself to oversimplify the problem of living at any level of biological organization.

Long-Term Repercussions of Obesity

We have examined the biological problem of energy balance from a number of points of view and at levels of organization from biochemical to social. Obesity, which can be regarded as the result of prolonged positive caloric balance, has been presented as a resultant of many contributory forces, and the suggestion has been made that different individuals may become obese for different reasons. Whatever the reasons, obesity —particularly of long duration—carries with it great risks of morbidity and premature mortality. Figure 10-1 shows that the largest penalty for overweight is paid in the currency of premature death in the third, fourth and fifth decades of life. In Figure 10-8, some of the principal causes for death among men and women rated by an insurance company as substandard risks for overweight are shown as percentages of the death rates of persons accepted for standard insurance. Although other data may differ in detail from that shown here, this figure represents a fair estimate of the cost in mortality of overweight. It does not show another estimate which is practically impossible to make, namely, the cost in serious morbidity or man-days lost due to incapacitating illness in which obesity was a contributory factor. Surely, this cost must be monumental.

Just as obesity itself is a complex disorder which has no readily identifiable single cause, but rather is due to the interplay of many contributory factors, most of the causes of death listed in Figure 10-8 are themselves similar diseases of multiple etiology. Most of them represent the end result of very complicated pathophysiological processes, and many are clearly influenced by hereditary and environmental factors. It is not surprising, then, that there are often differences of opinion concerning the importance of the contributory role of obesity in some of them.

The disorders indicated as "principal cardiovascular-renal diseases" include, for the most part, diseases of the heart, brain and kidneys in which atherosclerotic vascular disease is a common denominator. This raises the whole difficult question of the etiology of atherosclerosis and how chronic overnutrition could contribute to it. There is now fairly wide (but by no means unanimous) agreement that a long-standing elevation of the serum cholesterol and triglycerides predisposes to the subintimal precipitation of this material and the development of atherosclerotic plaques. In all forms of experimental obesity studied so far, a mild to moderate increase in serum cholesterol has been described. The increase is more striking in mice with hereditary

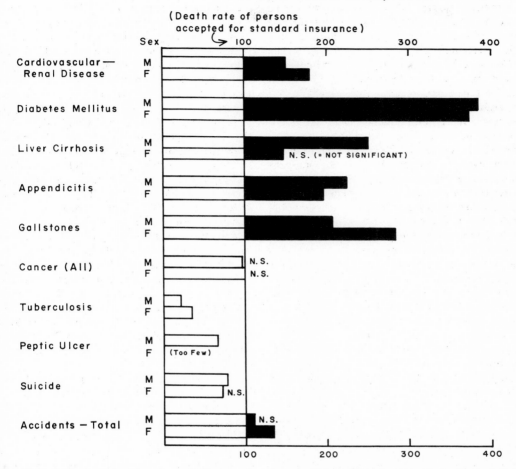

DEATHS —
Per cent actual of expected

(Death rate of persons
accepted for standard insurance)

Fig. 10-8.—Effects of obesity on susceptibility to various diseases. Black bars represent increased susceptibility in overweight individuals. (After Marks, H. H.: Bull. New York Acad. Med. 36:15-31, 1960.)

obesity-diabetes syndrome than it is in obese rodents with hypothalamic lesions. While some degree of fatty infiltration of vessels has been seen in obese rats and mice, members of these species show an extraordinary degree of resistance to atherosclerosis and truly definitive experiments of this sort with atherogenic diets remain to be done in order to evaluate the importance of hyperphagia in the etiology of atherosclerosis. The observation that overfeeding, or periodic overfeeding (tube-feeding), causes a remarkable adaptive change in the rate of fat formation from carbohydrates suggests that the overfed animal or the periodically force-fed one virtually places its tissue on a high-fat metabolic mixture even when they eat a high carbohydrate diet. Furthermore, newly synthesized fat is certainly saturated fat of animal origin and therefore (according to one prominent school of thought) it is the most villainous kind. Cohn has demonstrated that in the chicken (a species which is highly susceptible to dietary atherosclerosis) periodic overfeeding results in far more extensive atherosclerosis than does feeding the same amount of the same diet in small amounts through the day. Walker has described a striking elevation in serum cholesterol and triglycerides in normal men who force-fed themselves twice their usual caloric intake. The blood lipid pattern returned to normal when they resumed their control period intake and, significantly, neither cholesterol nor other lipids rose during force-feeding if a sufficient amount of hard muscular work was done during the experimental period. Although we cannot give a neat mechanistic explanation of the impact of obesity on the development of vascular disease, experiments of the sort that have been described help us to begin to ask pertinent questions.

A high incidence of gallstones is also associated with hypercholesterolemia, and no doubt when we understand the relationship between hyperphagia and atherosclerosis better than we do now, we will also have a better comprehension of the gallstone problem. The statistics in Figure 10-8 are somewhat complicated by the fact that obesity may predispose to gallstone formation, but it also enormously complicates the anesthetic and surgical procedures that are often demanded by the presence of such stones. The latter complications are probably responsible for the fact that obese patients with appendicitis did poorly in the series cited in Figure 10-8. It is often difficult for the anesthesiologist to maintain an airway in obese patients, and anesthesia induction time and recovery time are likely to be abnormally long in such individuals. Fat deposits and problems of muscle relaxation tax the surgeon's technical skill, and postoperative complications such as thromboembolic phenomena are more likely to occur in the obese.

The high incidence of cirrhosis of the liver among the obese correlates well with the results of animal studies, for all known kinds of experimentally obese animals that have been examined so far have shown fatty infiltration of the liver—frequently a precursor of cirrhosis. Actual cirrhosis has not been seen in obese rodents (Hartroft), but it has been described in obese dogs following the induction of hyperphagia by means of hypothalamic lesions (Graef and Ralli). Zelman has described abnormal liver function in a large number of patients with apparently uncomplicated obesity.

The striking association between obesity and diabetes mellitus is apparent in Figure 10-8. There was almost a 4 to 1 ratio of deaths in diabetic patients among the overweight group as compared with the normal weight control group. Middle-age onset of diabetes mellitus occurs extremely frequently in association with obesity.

A possibly pertinent animal model of this phenomenon was described by Brobeck et al. who prepared partially pancreatectomized rats which were aglycosuric postoperatively. Such rats are analogous to patients who have low-reserve insulin-producing equipment on an hereditary basis. When obesity-producing hypothalamic lesions were placed in these animals, profuse glycosuria appeared; when food intake was restricted to control levels, glycosuria disappeared. These experiments were suggested by the observations in patients of Newburgh and Conn, who showed that when obese middle-aged diabetic patients were reduced to average weight by caloric restriction, glycosuria and the characteristically diabetic type of glucose tolerance curve disappeared. Recently, Hamilton and Brobeck (1965) have given a striking demonstration of the accelerating effect of overeating on the development of diabetes mellitus. Working with a strain of monkeys which shows a high incidence of diabetes as they become old, these investigators showed that the establishment of surgically induced hypothalamic obesity in the young animal greatly telescoped, in time, the appearance both of diabetes and of a number of associated vascular abnormalities. The most satisfying explanation we can now give of this phenomenon is as follows: Overeating constitutes a more intense and prolonged stimulus to the β cells of the pancreatic islets than does eating only enough for the maintenance of caloric balance. Many people (and the rodent with an intact pancreas) have sufficiently resilient β cells to adapt to these demands. Those people who have an inborn tendency to develop diabetes fail to compensate and diabetes develops. Recompensation—quite analogous to recompensation of the heart following a bout of heart failure—occurs when the work load imposed on the β cells is reduced. The most significant contribution that a physician can make in this circumstance is to identify potentially diabetic individuals and make every attempt to help them prevent obesity in themselves (see Chapter 9).

The cancer problem is complicated by the fact that while there is no clear relationship between obesity and all diseases that are classifiable as cancer, certain experimental and clinical findings suggest that there is a relationship between chronic overnutrition and some specific kinds of cancer. In the laboratory, Waxler has clearly shown that the induction of ATG obesity not only causes an earlier appearance of mammary cancer in a high incidence strain of mice but also results in larger and faster growing tumors. He has also made similar observations on the effect of overeating on the development of primary hepatomas. In the clinic, there is evidence to suggest a relationship between obesity and two types of cancer in women, namely, breast cancer and endometrial cancer. The mechanisms involved in these associations are not now understood. The feeding of high-fat diets has been found to have an accelerating effect on certain experimental cancers. If, as we have suggested, the tissues of the overfed animal are on a high-fat metabolic mixture even when the animal is fed a high carbohydrate diet, perhaps observations on obesity and fat feeding are somehow linked.

Energy balance problems reach into every corner of medicine—even into the office of the orthopedic surgeon. The high incidence of accidents among overweight women has many conceivable explanations. Possibly fat women simply cannot move fast enough to avoid accidents. Perhaps their view of the ground or floor is sufficiently obscured to cause them to trip and fall more than people of normal weight do. Whatever the cause, susceptibility to accidents is another penalty of obesity.

Recently a respiratory difficulty has been asso-

ciated with severe obesity. It is characterized by dyspnea, marked exercise intolerance, somnolence and, in some instances, cyanosis, and it is sometimes referred to as the Pickwickian syndrome because Dickens' description of the Fat Boy appears to some observers to have anticipated the modern recognition of this disorder. The impairment of respiration is due to the fact that the respiratory movements of the thoracic cage are inhibited by the weight of subcutaneous fat deposits while the downward excursion of the diaphragm is limited by large intra-abdominal accumulations of fat. When the difficulties in gas exchange are added to the fact that increased oxygen is required to move and manipulate a heavy body, the relative pulmonary insufficiency becomes even greater. In severe cases, these unfortunate people can manage to do little more than move their tidal air back and forth with rapid, shallow, ineffectual respirations. When this disturbance occurs in elderly people it may be associated with arteriosclerotic heart disease which contributes an additional component to the dyspnea.

The *lower* incidence of tuberculosis, peptic ulcers, and suicide among obese patients apparently is not sufficiently heartening to insurance companies to cause them to write insurance at ordinary rates on obese applicants. Chronic overeaters must maintain food in their upper gastro-

Fig. 10-9.—Life expectancy of previously obese individuals re-rated after weight reduction. Note that weight reduction improves life expectancy in previously obese individuals. (After Marks, H. H.: Bull. New York Acad. Med. 36:15-31, 1960.)

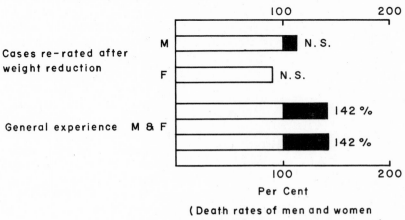

Per cent actual of expected deaths

(Death rates of men and women accepted for standard insurance)

intestinal tracts for a larger fraction of the day than do people who eat maintenance amounts of food, and therefore even an excess of gastric acid and pepsin would be less likely to be free to attack the mucosa of the stomach or duodenum in the former group. It is beyond the scope of this account to discuss the apparent "protective" effect of obesity against tuberculosis and suicide.

One might argue that the coincidence of obesity and many other diseases implies no cause-effect relationship but merely a concurrent genetic or environmental susceptibility to two unrelated illnesses. There is good evidence to support the view that obesity does indeed play a contributory role to the etiology of some of the lethal diseases enumerated herein. For when experience with a large number of people who were re-rated after weight reduction was compared with that of a similar group of individuals who had not lost weight, a highly significant reduction in mortality was seen to occur in the re-rated group (Fig. 10-9).

REFERENCES

Anand, B. K.: Nervous regulation of food intake, Physiol. Rev. 41:677–708, 1961.

Anderson, B., and Larsson, S.: Physiological and pharmacological aspects of the control of hunger and thirst, Pharmacol. Rev. 13:1–16, 1961.

Booyens, J., and McCance, R. A.: Individual variations in expenditure of energy, Lancet 1:225, 1957.

Brodoff, B. N. (Conference Chairman): Adipose tissue metabolism and obesity, Ann. New York Acad. Sc. 131:1–683, 1965.

Craig, R. L. (ed.): Symposium on the prevention of obesity, Bull. New York Acad. Med. 36:5–112, 1960.

Deter, R. L., and Liebelt, R. A.: Goldthioglucose as an experimental tool, Texas Rep. Biol. & Med. 22:229–243, 1964.

Goodridge, A. G., and Ball, E. G.: Lipogenesis in the pigeon: In vitro studies, Am. J. Physiol. 211:803-808, 1966.

Hollander, F. (ed.): The regulation of hunger and appetite, Ann. New York Acad. Sc. 63:1–144, 1955.

Jeanrenaud, B.: Dynamic aspects of adipose tissue metabolism: A review, Metabolism 10:535–581, 1961.

Kleiber, M.: *The Fire of Life. An Introduction to Animal Energetics* (New York: John Wiley & Sons, Inc., 1961).

Knittle, J., and Hirsch, J.: Infantile nutrition as a determinant of adult adipose tissue metabolism and cellularity, Clin. Res. 15:323, 1967.

Mayer, J., and Thomas, D. W.: Regulation of food intake and obesity, Science 156:327-337, 1967.

Renold, A. E., and Cahill, G. F., Jr. (eds.): *Adipose Tissue*, Section 5 (Washington, D.C.: American Physiological Society Handbook, 1965).

Stevenson, J. A. F.: The hypothalamus in the regulation of energy and water balance, Physiologist 7:305–318, 1964.

Tepperman, J.: Adipose tissue: Yang and Yin, in *Fat as a Tissue*, Rodahl, K., and Issekutz, B. (eds.) (New York: McGraw-Hill Book Co., 1964).

Tepperman, J., and Brobeck, J. R. (eds.): Symposium on energy balance, Am. J. Clin. Nutrition 8:527–774, 1960.

Wertheimer, E., and Shafrir, E.: Influence of hormones on adipose tissue as a center of fat metabolism, Recent Prog. Hormone Res. 16:467–495, 1960.

11

The Parathyroids

Calcium Ion Homeostasis

THE MAINTENANCE of a constant calcium ion concentration in the extracellular fluid is essential for the functional welfare of many tissues of the body. Thus the parathyroid hormone, which regulates calcium ion homeostasis in the body fluids, performs a most crucial integrative function. The importance of the parathyroids in the vital economy of the whole animal and their relationship to calcium has been appreciated for many decades (see chronology, p. 210) but the recent renascence of interest in this subject which culminated in the isolation of pure peptide substances with full hormone activity promises additional exciting discoveries in the near future. Very recently another calcium-regulating hormone, *thyrocalcitonin,* has been shown to play a role in calcium homeostasis.

Normally, the concentration of calcium in plasma is about 10 mg%, and this figure remains remarkably constant. Moreover, the variation in it from individual to individual is astonishingly small. About half of the plasma calcium is in the ionized form; the rest is bound to protein or (very small amounts) to citrate and similar complexing agents. There are only negligible amounts of calcium in the blood cells.

Deviations from the normal calcium concentrations in either direction produce profound alterations in function of many tissues and organ systems of the body. In the *heart,* a high ionized calcium level of the blood may cause successively bradycardia, ventricular arrhythmias and even ventricular fibrillation. The earliest electrocardiographic changes associated with these effects are flat or inverted T waves and modification of the P waves. Calcium effects on the heart are of particular practical importance in people who receive cardioactive glycosides of the digitalis type, for calcium and digitalis tend to act synergistically. The excitability of *skeletal muscle* is increased in low calcium media and depressed by an excess of calcium. These effects probably depend on changes in the region of the end plate. *Smooth muscle tends* to be inhibited if the calcium in the extracellular fluid deviates markedly from the normal in either direction.

Analysis of the effect of calcium on *neuromuscular excitability* (which is the basis of parathyroprivic tetany and convulsions) has revealed that the threshold for the electrical excitation of neurones is lowered by a decrease in ionized calcium. The tetany of hypocalcemia persists, however, after motor nerve section, but the persisting tetany is stopped by curarization. Curare, an alkaloid with which certain South American Indian tribes tipped their poison arrows, works by blocking neuromuscular transmission at the motor end plate. Thus, hypocalcemic tetany can be regarded as a state of hyperexcitability of neurones and motor end-plates brought about by a low calcium concentration of their bathing fluids. The intimate mechanism by which these effects are accomplished is not known, but it is possible that alterations in calcium ion concentration influence the permeability of membranes generally to sodium and potassium and thus

Some Landmarks in Parathyroid Chronology

Date		Investigator
1880	Anatomical description of parathyroids	Sandstrom
1884	Fatal tetany after thyroidectomy in cats and dogs, *not* rabbits	Schiff
1891	Proved parathyroids must be removed with thyroid to produce tetany	Gley
1900	Removal of parathyroids, leaving thyroid intact, results in convulsions and tetany	Vasali, Generali
1909	Calcium salts after parathyroidectomy prevents tetany	MacCallum and Voegtlin
1911	Parathyroidectomy reduces urinary phosphate excretion	Greenwald
1924–1925	First active parathyroid gland extracts	Hanson: Collip
1929	Renal theory of parathyroid hormone action	Albright
1934	Direct effect of parathyroid extracts on bone in nephrectomized animals (histological)	Collip *et al.*
1942	Calcium content of blood signal for parathyroid hormone secretion	Patt and Luckhardt
1948	Parathyroid tissue grafted adjacent to bone had a local, direct, decalcifying effect	Barnicot
1955	Tissue culture experiments confirmed Barnicot's observation	Gaillard
1957	Unilateral effect of parathyroid hormone or phosphate excretion by chicken kidney	Levinsky and Davidson
1959	Pure parathyroid hormone peptides prepared	Rasmussen; Aurbach

modify the processes of depolarization and repolarization. Hypocalcemic tetany is seen in untreated hypoparathyroidism, and it is characterized in its early form by muscle spasms, marked hyperreflexia and a positive Chvostek sign, that is, a twitching of the facial muscles in response to tapping over the facial nerve at the angle of the mandible. It may progress to generalized convulsions and respiratory death due to spasm of the diaphragm. Cautious intravenous injection of calcium gluconate or another calcium salt may be lifesaving in this circumstance.

The serum calcium concentration is maintained at a constant level despite the fact that it represents the vector of a number of forces which tend to raise or lower it. In this, it is similar to all other blood constituents which tend to be maintained at equilibrium concentrations. The parathyroid hormone plays an important role in the regulation of the level of equilibrium, and it has effects on all three tissues which participate most prominently in the maintenance of the serum calcium level: bone, kidney, and intestine. There is no known pituitary trophic hormone for the parathyroid glands, and the participation of these structures in the maintenance of serum calcium homeostasis is therefore a more direct transaction than are the complicated neural and humoral systems of signals which are operative in the case of the adrenals, gonads and thyroid. A diagrammatic summary of some of the factors involved in the regulation of serum calcium is given in Figure 11-1.

In all three structures most intimately con-

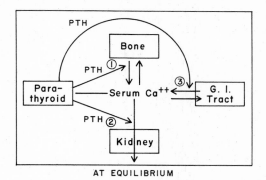

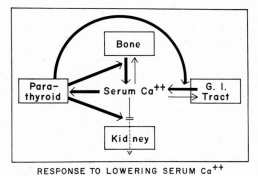

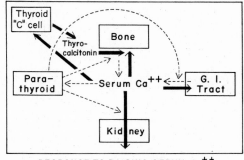

Fig. 11-1.—Serum calcium ion homeostasis and the parathyroid glands.

cerned with maintenance of serum calcium concentration, calcium movements occur in the absence of the parathyroid hormone, indicating that the biochemical machinery for effecting these movements is present and operative. The *rates* at which calcium is transported out of bone, across the intestine and into the urine are influenced by the parathyroid hormone. For example, the bone acts as a calcium bank, calcium ions are added to the blood when their concentration is low and they are abstracted from the blood when their concentration is high. This process occurs in the absence of parathyroid hormone, but when it does, the serum calcium level is set at a concentration of 7 mg%. In the intact animal with a normally functioning set of parathyroids, the setting for the serum calcium is 3 mg% higher, or 10 mg%. It should be recalled that the calcium which is so essential for the vital economy of the soft tissues represents only 1% of the total body calcium. The other 99% is in bone. The remarkably rapid and efficient restoration of serum calcium level following a sharp lowering of the concentration is shown in Figure 11-2. The effect of hormone deprivation on the "set" of the equilibrium concentration is well illustrated.

Absorption of calcium from the intestine is partly an active process—a calcium movement against a concentration gradient—and partly a passive one. The active component of the process is adaptive; when the calcium intake over a period of days or weeks is low, the capacity of the intestine to absorb calcium increases, an effect which can even be demonstrated in isolated loops of intestine incubated in vitro. This adaptation can occur in the absence of the parathyroid hormone, although the magnitude of the adaptation is somewhat greater in the presence of the hormone. It cannot occur, however, in the absence of vitamin D, and we must therefore conclude (tentatively) that vitamin D availability is essential for the integrity of the active calcium-absorbing system in the intestinal cell. Indeed, Wasserman (1967) has isolated a calcium-binding protein which is present in extracts of intestinal mucosa of normal rats but not in those of vitamin D-deficient animals. Treatment of the latter with vitamin D results in the appearance of the pro-

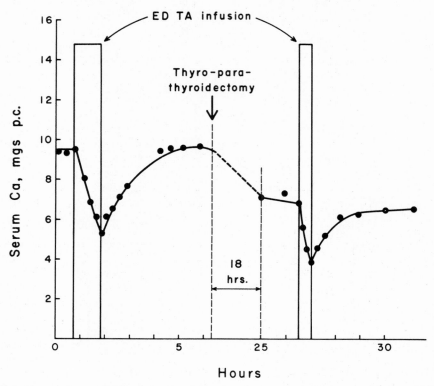

Fig. 11-2.—Serum calcium homeostasis before and after parathyroidectomy in the dog. **EDTA** (ethylenediamine tetraacetic acid) lowers the ionized calcium in the serum by forming a complex with it. Note that the equilibrium level following recovery from an acutely lowered calcium level differs in the intact and parathyroidectomized preparation. (Redrawn from Copp, D. H.: Am. J. Med. 22:275-285, 1957.)

tein within 10 hours. Wasserman believes this protein to be a component of the intracellular transport mechanism for calcium.

The renal excretion of calcium by the kidney is determined by a threshold. In the parathyroid-deprived animal, this threshold is set at a lower level than it is in the intact animal, and the administration of the hormone raises the urinary threshold for calcium.

Other effects on calcium balance may occur in special physiological circumstances, most notably in pregnancy and lactation. In pregnancy, a considerable amount of calcium is necessary for the growing fetus, and in lactation, there may be an appreciable loss of calcium into the milk. These losses are factored into the over-all, continuing calcium profit and loss statement, and it is fair to regard them as the equivalent of a low calcium intake for the mother. The calcium content of the milk may be influenced by the parathyroid status of the lactating rat.

Chemistry of Parathyroid Hormone and Bio-Assay

After the preparation of the first stable parathyroid extracts in 1924–1925 by Hansen and (independently) Collip there were sporadic attempts to purify the hormone. It was not until 1959 that Aurbach, working with phenol extracts, and Rasmussen, who used acid extracts, prepared pure peptides with extremely high activity. Aurbach and Potts' best preparation is a single polypeptide chain with a MW of 8500. It is an 84 amino acid peptide for which a tentative amino acid sequence has been proposed. The 20-amino acid sequence at the carboxyl end of the chain is active both biologically and immunologically.

In the course of purification, the activity was followed by a number of bio-assay procedures which are based on the two most readily observed effects of the hormone (1) its ability to raise the serum calcium level and (2) its ability to interfere with the renal tubular reabsorption of phosphate and thus cause a lowering of blood phosphate and an increase in urine phosphate. The traditional dog assay method involves measurement of the blood calcium rise 18 hours after injecting the test material. One unit has been defined as 1/100 the amount required to raise the blood calcium of a 10–12 kg dog 1 mg% 18 hours after a subcutaneous injection. This is the sort of procedure that makes physicists and physical chemists shake their heads in glassy-eyed disbelief. Nevertheless, although this assay lacks precision and is somewhat inelegant, it is a useful one.

More precise and discriminating methods of assay which involve the detection of effects in parathyroidectomized rats have been developed. In one, the critical parameter is a rise in serum calcium in the parathyroidectomized rat on a calcium-free diet; in the other, the crucial measurement is urinary phosphate excretion by parathyroidectomized rats. None of these methods is sufficiently sensitive to measure fluctuations of the hormone level in body fluids. In collaboration with Potts and Aurbach, Berson and Yalow have devised a very sensitive radioimmunoassay method for parathyroid hormone. With this method, it has been possible to detect a rapid fall in hormone concentration in the blood during infusion of calcium salts and a rapid rise after administration of EDTA.

The recent preparation of parathyroid hormone in pure form has settled one controversy. It has been claimed from time to time that there are two parathyroid hormones, one for calcium and the other for phosphate. The blood calcium-increasing and phosphaturic effects are so nearly parallel in the pure hormone that there can be little doubt that a single substance has both effects.

Parathyroid Hormone and Calcium and Phosphate Balance

The effects of parathyroid hormone deficiency and excess may be summarized as follows:

	Deficiency	Excess
Blood calcium	Decreased	Increased
Blood phosphate	Increased	Decreased
Urine calcium	Decreased	Increased
Urine phosphate	Decreased	Increased

A chronic excess of parathyroid hormone, particularly as it is seen in the disease hyperparathyroidism, may result in such extensive decalcification of the bony skeleton that pathological fractures and bone deformities may occur. When large amounts of calcium are withdrawn from bone, metastatic calcification of the soft tissues may occur, particularly in the kidneys. In such circumstances calcium salts may precipitate in the pelvis of the kidneys and in the ureters; in fact, kidney stones may constitute the first clue to the presence of a state of hyperparathyroidism. Disturbances in renal function may mask the serum phosphate lowering effect of an excess of parathyroid hormone, and the serum phosphate may be paradoxically elevated due to phosphate retention. Chronic renal disease unrelated to hyperparathyroidism may cause a form of secondary hyperparathyroidism which is the result of a line-of-duty response to a signal by the parathyroid glands. Renal insufficiency is characterized by the retention of phosphate ion, among many other substances, and the elevation in serum phosphate causes a lowering of serum calcium concentration (see following section). This, in turn, triggers the parathyroids to produce more and more parathyroid hormone, for the built-in capacity of these glands to respond to the stimulus of hypocalcemia is such that they cannot make an etiological diagnosis of the *cause* of the hypocalcemia. The resulting secondary hyperparathyroidism has the effect of raising the serum calcium to normal levels, but not to supernormal ones. Since the deleterious effect of hyperparathyroidism on the kidneys is associated with hypercalcemia, secondary hyperparathyroidism does not add to existing renal damage.

Control of Parathyroid Hormone Release

The thyroid and the steroid hormone-producing glands are controlled by pituitary trophic hormones which, in turn, are released in response to chemical signals that reach the gland by way of the hypophysial portal vascular system. The parathyroids resemble the islets of Langerhans in that both are stimulated to produce their respective hormones by the fluctuation of a prominent blood constituent: calcium in the case of the former and glucose in the case of the latter. It has been known for some time that low calcium diets lead to hypertrophy and hyperplasia of the parathyroid glands. Patt and Luckhardt (see chronology, p. 210) were the first to show that the perfusion of the parathyroids of a dog with calcium-free blood resulted in the appearance of a calcium mobilizing material in the effluent from the glands, and this has been confirmed and extended more recently by Copp. Raisz and his colleagues, by means of ingeniously designed organ-culture experiments, have demonstrated an inverse relationship between the calcium concentration of their incubation media and PTH production by explanted parathyroid glands.

It has been recognized for many years that the concentrations of Ca^{++} and PO_4^{--} in plasma are reciprocally related; i.e., they behave, in general, as if $CA^{++} \times PO_4^{--} = K$. Although there are some exceptions to this general rule, increasing the plasma phosphate causes a decrease in serum calcium (as we have seen), and vice versa. The existence of this relationship has tended to perplex investigators who have attempted to separate effects of hypocalcemia from those of hyperphosphatemia, for it is not easy to design experiments in which one or the other of these parameters can be changed independently of the other. Although one cannot ignore the possibility that fluctuations in serum phosphate may play a direct role in eliciting parathyroid secretion, the best evidence suggests that the physiological signal for the parathyroid glands is either a low or falling serum ionized calcium concentration.

① Parathyroid Hormone and Bone

Bone consists of an organic matrix of ground substance in which calcium salts are deposited in very small crystals. These crystals are chiefly hydrated calcium phosphate, and they are arranged in a systematic lattice structure similar to that seen in certain minerals called hydroxyapatites. Certain ions in addition to calcium and phosphate may participate in the construction of the lattice or may be adsorbed on its surface. Carbonate is invariably present, and bone-seeking minerals, such as strontium (stable or radioactive), lead, radium, and others, can also be deposited in bone. The crystals are bathed in a shell of water which is continuous with the extracellular fluid of the body, and therefore they are readily and quickly available for exchange transactions with the body fluids in either direction. Due to the small size of the crystals and their great number, the surface available for exchange is enormous; it has been estimated at about 100 acres for a 154 pound man. When one looks at a preserved skeleton in an anatomy laboratory, it is difficult to imagine that this stony structure was once part of a complex dynamic equilibrium with its bathing fluids.

The exchange function is carried out most effectively by the most recently formed bone, for older bone, having lost some of its water of hydration, has less calcium immediately available to the body fluids. In growing bone, new calcium deposits are laid down in the growing areas, while local resorption may be occurring at the same time in other sites of the same bone. The sites of resorption can then become sites of new bone formation. This constant remodeling, or business-as-usual-during-alterations activity, also takes place in adult bone which is not increasing its aggregate mass, and it may be influenced by many nonhormonal factors, of which the most prominent are those related to circulation, weight bearing, and nutrition. Long-continued bed rest may result in decalcification, and so may the paralysis of a limb. The architectural competence of a bone may be determined, to some extent, by the act of weight bearing which, apparently, has marked effects on lines of stress, especially in long bones. Vitamin D has a profound effect on bone by facilitating the absorption of calcium from the gastrointestinal tract, and probably in other ways as well. McLean has suggested that the constant remodeling of bone may be teleologically related to the need to maintain a continuing supply of newly deposited crystals throughout life in order to insure a large exchange surface for quick regulation of calcium levels in the body fluids. The process of remodeling continues in the absence of the parathyroids, but at a slower pace.

The cellular elements in bone appear to be very busy indeed under the microscope, but it is difficult to tell what they are actually doing, even though an osteoclast may look for all the world as if it had just bitten off a fragment of bone. The resorption of bone is always associated with the appearance of osteoclasts, while osteoblasts are seen in large numbers in areas of bone-building. Osteocytes may also be involved in bone resorption. All of these cells probably rep-

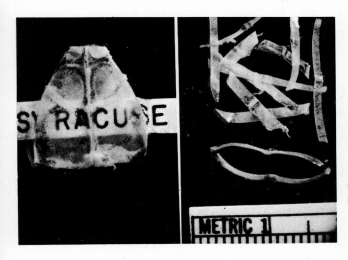

resent variants of a single cell type. The ways in which cells can conceivably participate in the movement of bone constituents to and from bone will be considered in a later section.

In 1929, Albright suggested that the effect of parathyroid hormone on bone was secondary to its effect on promoting phosphate excretion by the kidneys. The calcium-phosphate product relationship simply required mobilization of calcium when the serum phosphate concentration decreased. This suggestion stimulated many investigators to look for direct effects of the hormone on bone with the result that no one now doubts that such effects occur. In experiments on nephrectomized dogs given parathyroid extract (PTE), histological changes associated with hyperparathyroidism were seen when there could have been no stimulated phosphate excretion. Similarly, a hypercalcemic response to injected PTE can be produced in nephrectomized animals under certain conditions. Others have devised methods of keeping the serum phosphate concentration constant and have shown effects of PTE on serum calcium in the absence of phosphate fluctuations. In a famous experiment, Barnicot transplanted a fragment of skull bone into the brain of a rat with a parathyroid gland immediately adjacent to it, a kind of in vivo tissue culture experiment. After several weeks the bone showed clear evidence of dissolution in the vicinity of the parathyroid graft, and signs of bone proliferation on the side of the bone opposite the graft. Other kinds of tissue similarly transplanted (pituitary gland, for example) did not show this effect. Similar experiments have been done by Gaillard on bone in tissue culture. Recently Raisz and others have demonstrated that when baby rats were parathyroidectomized or injected with PTE and when thin strips of their skull bones (Fig. 11-3) were incubated in appropriate solutions in vitro, the calcium concentration of the buffer at the end of the incubation period perfectly reflected the parathyroid status of the donor rat (Fig. 11-4). It should be emphasized that no consistent effects could be observed on bone when PTE was added in vitro in this experiment. More recently, however, Raisz has demonstrated a direct effect of parathyroid hormone added in vitro to organ cultures of Ca^{45}-prelabeled fetal bone.

There is no doubt that old bone (i.e., bone labeled with radioactive calcium during the period of rapid growth of an animal) is readily mobilized under the influence of PTE in the adult animal. Since the bone remodeling process is stimulated by PTE, and since this results in a net addition to the readily exchangeable calcium pool, the hormone also has an effect ultimately on this calcium compartment. It does not seem likely, however, that the hormone's earliest effects involve the readily exchangeable pool. An ultimate solution to this problem must await elucidation of the mechanism of action of the hormone. Many workers have suggested that the hormone may have an effect on the ground substance of bone as well as on its calcification, for there is an increase in the mucopolysaccharide level of the blood following PTE treatment. In

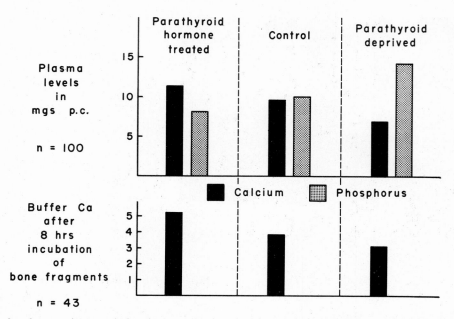

Fig. 11-4.—Serum calcium and phosphorus, and calcium concentration of incubation medium after incubation of skull bone fragments of parathyroid hormone-treated, normal and parathyroidectomized rats. All differences shown are significantly (P<0.001) different from control values. (Data of Raisz, L. G., Au, W., and Tepperman, J.: Endocrinology 68:783-794, 1961.)

harmony with this suggestion, Carnes found that osteoid (i.e., noncalcified bony matrix) of rats fed a low calcium and phosphorus diet for 4 weeks showed resorption after PTE treatment, which indicates that the hormone may have an effect on the nonmineral elements of bone. If this turns out to be the case, it will go a long way toward explaining how PTE appears to have more readily demonstrable effects on resorption of old bone than on readily exchangeable bone.

② Effects of Parathyroid Hormone on Kidney

PHOSPHATE EXCRETION

Within the first hour after the administration of parathyroid hormone phosphate excretion in the urine increases and serum phosphate concentration may fall. These effects have, in fact, been used as the basis for several bio-assay methods for the hormone. As we have seen, the new pure polypeptide hormone shows parallel activity both in producing phosphaturia and in elevating serum calcium concentration, and there is no doubt that the hormone can accomplish both of these effects. Phosphaturia has been demonstrated in

PTE-treated men (Fig. 11-5) as well as animals and the reverse experiment—i.e., the observation of a decrease in phosphate excretion on hormone withdrawal—has been done successfully on patients following surgical removal of hormone-producing tumors of the parathyroids.

The increased phosphate excretion is due to decreased tubular reabsorption of the ion. Changes in renal blood flow and glomerular filtration rate have been discussed from time to time, but these do not now seem to be importantly involved. Renal physiologists have not yet decided whether or not phosphate ion is secreted into the tubular urine in the mammalian kidney, and until they do the question of an effect on this process of PTE (claimed by some) cannot be profitably considered.

While the chicken kidney is undeniably useful to the chicken, it appears to have been designed secondarily for the purpose of clarifying problems in renal tubular physiology. Material injected into the leg traverses the renal portal system of blood vessels that bathe the tubules; thus, by studying the function of the two kidneys simultaneously after an injection has been made on one side only, one can observe renal tubular

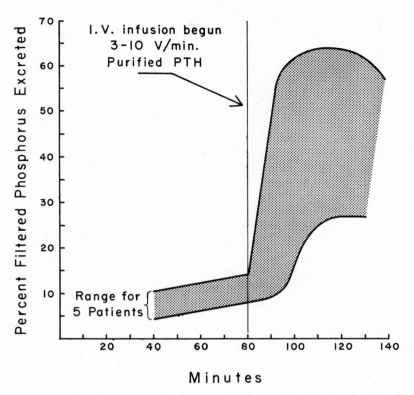

Fig. 11-5.—Urinary phosphate excretion in 5 human subjects injected with highly purified parathyroid hormone. (V/min = Units/min.) (Redrawn from data of Hor-with, M., et al. in The Parathyroids, Greep, R. O., and Talmage, R. V. (eds.) [Springfield, Ill.: Charles C Thomas, Publisher, 1961, p. 418].)

excretion or hormonal effects on this process. A direct effect of PTE on phosphaturia has been observed by means of this technique. Similar results have been obtained in the course of split renal function studies in dogs which were unilaterally injected with purified PTE into the renal artery on one side.

It is interesting to reflect for a moment about the shifting attitudes of students of parathyroid physiology toward the phosphaturic effect which, it will be recalled, was observed as early as 1911 by Greenwald. According to the Albright hypothesis, which was based on the time sequence of parathyroid hormone effects then known, the phosphaturia and hypophosphatemia were the primary events from which those on serum calcium and bone dissolution were secondarily derived. When the direct effects on bone were demonstrated, the Albright hypothesis was relegated to the attic as heuristically interesting but no longer useful. Within very recent years, there has

been a movement to bring it down from the attic, refinish it and put it back on display. For while the phosphaturic effect may not be the primary one of the hormone, it appears to be a significant *part* of the over-all effect, for it cannot be denied that a lowering of the serum phosphate permits more calcium to be added to blood, and that new bone salt deposition is inhibited when the serum phosphate concentration is low. Thus, a lowering of serum phosphate would have the effect of diminishing the rate of calcium removal for this purpose and thus help raise serum calcium by partially blocking one route of its removal from the circulation.

CALCIUM

There is little doubt that parathyroid hormone exerts an effect on calcium excretion as well as on that of phosphate, for recent experiments on both animals and men have revealed a rapid decrease in calcium excretion very soon after the administration of the hormone. This is accompanied by a rapid increase in serum calcium which occurs too soon to be accounted for on the basis of mobilization from bone. This effect is obscured later because of the massive outpouring of calcium from bone. The load of calcium filtered at very high serum concentration is such that an *increased* amount of calcium appears in the urine of the hyperparathyroid patient or the PTE treated animal in spite of the fact that the hormone increases the kidney's ability to reabsorb calcium. Whether or not the effects on raising the calcium excretion threshold and decreasing phosphate reabsorption are related at the cellular level is not now known.

③ Nonskeletal and Extrarenal Effects of Parathyroid Hormone

Bone and kidney effects of parathyroid hormone have been studied most extensively, but those on other tissues are receiving more and more attention. Of special interest is the effect on intestinal absorption of calcium referred to previously. The active transport of calcium is markedly increased on low calcium diets, and the full expression of this adaptation seems to require the presence of the parathyroid hormone. One of the few immediate effects of parathyroid hormone directly on tissue has been reported by Rasmussen, who observed increased transport of calcium across an isolated loop of intestine after one of his pure parathyroid peptides had been injected into a parathyroidectomized rat from which the intestinal sample was obtained. The effect of an accelerated rate of calcium absorption is in the direction of increasing the serum calcium. The quantitative significance of this effect remains to be evaluated.

Munson's observation of a decreased calcium content of the milk of lactating rats treated with PTE represents a serum calcium-elevating effect similar to the increased urinary threshold for calcium; i.e., serum calcium tends to be raised when its routes of egress from the circulation are blocked.

There are recurring suggestions that parathyroid hormone may have effects on the soft tissues of the body generally and that it may participate in the regulation of phosphate distribution between the intracellular and extracellular fluid compartments. The evidence on which this hypothesis is based is indirect and controversial. In the least complicated experiment of this type, it was found that the increase in urinary phosphate induced in patients given PTE was not great enough to account for the observed loss of phosphate from the extracellular fluid. It was inferred, therefore, that phosphate had migrated into the intracellular fluid compartment under the influence of the hormone.

In summary, all of the effects of PTE on the intestine, mammary glands, lens and, possibly, soft tissues are consistent with its well-known serum calcium-raising effect either by promoting calcium absorption, inhibiting calcium egress, or lowering the serum phosphate concentration which would have the secondary result of permitting more calcium to be mobilized.

Mechanism of Action of Parathyroid Hormone

The mechanism of action of parathyroid hormone is unknown. Truth would not be well served if this statement were allowed to stand without further comment. In a very real sense, the flights of imagination of physiologists are a part of the cumulative historical record. Neuman speaks of theories as vehicles for the design of experiments and suggests that when they begin to show signs of breaking down or when shiny new models become irresistible they should be traded in without sentimentality. Discarded theories of the mechanism of action of the parathyroid hormone would fill a medium-sized used car lot.

We have already seen how the first unifying hypothesis, Albright's renal theory, was found to be inadequate. McLean's feedback hypothesis was concerned exclusively with blood-bone calcium equilibrium, and simply described the fact that an equilibrium level of serum calcium is set at about 7 mg% in the parathyroidectomized animal, but that the parathyroid hormone affects the events in bone in such a way that the equilibrium level is maintained at 10 mg%. Talmage pointed out that the elevation of the renal threshold for calcium that is seen after hormone administration constitutes a contribution to the serum calcium-increasing effect of the substance and reduces the amount that must be mobilized from bone in order for the equilibrium level to be restored.

Rasmussen has constructed a collage of the views of many other workers and has made the additional interesting suggestion that the renal and intestinal responses are quick while the bone response to the hormone is delayed, possibly because, as Copp reported, the rate of blood flow through bone is extremely sluggish compared with the rapid flow through such structures as the kidneys. It now seems likely that the bone response may also be much more rapid than had been believed, for the presence or absence of thyrocalcitonin has been found to influence the time of onset of a perceptible rise in serum calcium after PTH administration. Thyroidectomized animals respond much more quickly than do those with intact thyroids. In fact, now that we know about a second calcium-regulating hormone (see section below), the interpretation of many experiments with PTH on intact animals becomes very difficult indeed, for one does not know whether an observed effect was due to the PTH or whether it was modified by thyrocalcitonin secretion elicited by the rising serum calcium brought about by the PTH.

Not only is the cellular mechanism of action of parathyroid hormone unknown, but we do not even know with certainty which cells are under its control. The most obvious candidates are (1) osteoclasts, (2) renal tubular cells, (3) intestinal epithelial cells, (4) mammary gland cells and (5) possibly other unspecified soft-tissue cells, such as muscle.

Parathyroid hormone-stimulated osteoclasts *could* cause mobilization of calcium and dissolution of the matrix of bone in three possible ways: they could secrete a metabolite which would have the effect of "solubilizing" bone mineral; or they could secrete an enzyme which would depolymerize or otherwise break up some crucial substance in the organic matrix; or they could actively transport some critical material from the bone to the blood, which would have the effect of mobilizing bone salt. For a while, citrate was considered as a possible "solubilizing" metabolite on the basis of suggestive evidence, but the citrate theory, which had undeniable charm, is no longer accepted. Nevertheless, the idea on which the citrate hypothesis was based cannot yet be abandoned.

There are a few observations which are consistent with the enzyme-secretion hypothesis. The hormone apparently does have a mucopolysaccharide depolymerizing effect in the animal, for the mucopolysaccharide levels in the blood of hormone-treated animal rises. The fact that hormone treatment results in a dissolution of bone matrix as well as bone salt suggests that some lytic process is operative in the organic substance of bone. The significance of the increase in both alkaline and acid phosphatase that has been seen in hormone-treated animals is not understood. The former has sometimes been regarded as an index of osteoblastic activity, while the latter often increases when osteolysis is dominant. At the moment, these are guesses, and the role of parathyroid hormone (if, indeed, it has one) in the production and release of these enzymes is not known.

There is no evidence that the cellular elements of bone perform specialized transport functions. The suggestion that they may do so may be an expression of a wistful hope for a truly unifying hypothesis of the mechanism of action of parathyroid hormone, for transport functions appear to be involved in the action of the hormone at the intestinal and renal sites. Esthetically, the idea that the hormone may interact with the same biochemical machinery in all three tissues is a satisfying one. Future work may supply the missing common denominator.

Little is known about the effect of parathyroid hormone on the metabolism of cells beyond the facts that (1) it enhances aerobic glycolysis (i.e., increases lactic acid production) in bone fragments in vitro, and (2) pieces of bone removed from parathyroidectomized and PTE-treated rats continue to manifest differences in the bone-medium calcium equilibrium even when the tissue is incubated under anaerobic conditions. The stimulation of lactic acid formation that occurs on aerobic incubation may have local bone-mineral-mobilizing effects, but this is highly speculative. The evidence of persisting hormonal effect in a nitrogen atmosphere makes it unlikely that the hormone requires functioning oxidative machinery for an expression of its action.

Recently, Borle and Neuman, as well as Tenenhouse, Meier and Rasmussen, have reported on a remarkable in vitro effect of PTH on two improbable target cells (1) a mouse ascites tumor cell and (2) the HeLa cell, originally adapted to tissue culture and cultivation in ascites form from a human tumor. Treatment of the mouse ascites tumor cell with PTH results in the production of a heat-stable substance which has the ability to release Ca^{45} from prelabeled, dead bone powder in vitro. Of course, one cannot extrapolate from this model to the mechanism of action of the hormone in bone in the living animal, but neither can one dismiss the model as absurd. It has been proved that, whatever the bone-dissolving agent is, it is not citrate. The possibility of its being an enzyme is not ruled out by its heat stability, for certain colleganases are, in fact, heat stable. There seems to be little doubt that PTH has an effect on the HeLa cell, for one can actually watch the cell change its shape under the influence of the hormone. It is not unheard of for a tumor cell to retain hormone responsiveness (for example, see the accounts of the hormonal manipulation of prostate and breast cancer in Chapters 4 and 5), and it is entirely possible that the HeLa cell unaccountably "remembers" what to do when it is stimulated by PTH.

EFFECTS OF PTH ON MEMBRANES

A large and bewildering literature has accumulated on the subject of the effect of PTH on the translocation of ions across the mitochondrial membranes. While it is difficult to understand the physiologic significance of these studies, certain undeniable facts have been established:

(1) Parathyroid hormone added in vitro in concentrations about 100 times those found in blood causes a release of preaccumulated Ca^{++} from intact mitochondria.

(2) At the same time, it stimulates the uptake by mitochondria of phosphate, potassium and magnesium.

(3) Mitochondrial respiration and pyridine nucleotide oxidation by mitochondria are stimulated by the hormone.

Some investigators have suggested that PTH stimulates the activity of ion pumps which involve the participation of the mitochondrion. The specificity of these mitochondrial effects of PTH now appears to have been established, but it is still difficult to relate them to the physiologic action of the hormone.

The importance of the studies of PTH effects on mitochondria goes beyond considerations of the mechanism of action of PTH. For, as Rasmussen has correctly pointed out, these experiments are concerned with the compartmentalization of ions *within the cell,* and the possible effects of intracellular ion movements on metabolic activities in the various micropools of fluid in the cell. It is well known that enzymic activity is strongly influenced by the ionic environment in which it is measured. Perhaps, one day, we will be able to describe changes in ion concentration within cell compartments as a metabolic control device. We can look forward to kinetic studies of changing "Gamblegrams" in mitochondrial water, cytosol water, intraendoplasmic reticular water, etc.

Another potential membrane site of action is suggested by Vaes (1966) who raises the interesting possibility that intracellularly sequestered (lysosomal) enzymes which destroy the cartilaginous matrix of bone may be released under the stimulus of PTH. It is possible to construct a unified hypothesis of the action of the hormone only in fantasy. However, one can conceive of PTH interacting with critical cell membranes in such a way that all of its observed effects could be accounted for, i.e., (1) ion translocation, (2) release of (highly specialized) lysosomal enzymes from osteoclasts and (3) metabolic changes associated with the production of organic acids which would have a solubilizing effect on bone mineral.

Parathyroid Hormone and Vitamin D

In vitamin D deficiency, the active absorption of calcium by the intestine is impaired, and the adaptive increase in the rate of calcium absorption that occurs on low calcium intakes is not demonstrable. The vitamin may play a permissive role for the action of parathyroid hormone on bone, and there is now much interest in the possibility that it may play a similar permissive role at the other tissue sites of action of the hormone; namely, intestine and kidney.

Vitamin D is also important in the very practical enterprise of treating hypoparathyroid patients. At this time, the purified hormone is still in very short supply and is used only in clinical and laboratory investigation. Until it becomes more readily available (and, very possibly, after as well) the accepted treatment doubtless will continue to be vitamin D in large doses. The normal daily requirement of this vitamin for an adult is approximately 500 I.U. per day. Treatment of hypoparathyroidism is initiated with doses of 400,000–1,600,000 I.U. (10–49 mg); the maintenance dose is 120,000–200,000 I.U. This calcium-mobilizing effect of vitamin D can be controlled by having the patient examine his own urine for calcium by means of a simple chemical test which is known as the Sulkowitch test. The employment of the patient as his own laboratory technician and his autoregulation on the basis of a laboratory analysis are reminiscent of a similar kind of autoregulation performed by the diabetic who analyzes his own urine for glucose. In both cases, the close supervision of a physician is essential. A sterol called dihydrotachysterol (formerly widely known by the code A.T.10) can be substituted for vitamin D in the management of hypoparathyroid patients. Its calcium-mobilizing potency is approximately 5 times as great as that of the vitamin, and the dose is therefore one-fifth as much as that given above, or 2–8 mg. It offers no advantage over vitamin D, and its use has diminished rapidly in recent years.

It is sometimes confusing to students to meet vitamin D as a calcium-mobilizing agent just as they have become accustomed to think of the vitamin as an agent which promotes calcification of bones. The antirachitic effect of vitamin D requires the pre-existence of a deficiency for its demonstration, for in rickets rarefaction of bone is secondary to a critical decrease in rate of absorption of calcium and phosphorus from the gastrointestinal tract. When the deficiency is corrected, bone mineral is deposited. In hypoparathyroidism, vitamin D elevates serum calcium concentration by effects at all three loci of parathyroid hormone action: intestine, bone and kidney. Calcium absorption is promoted, bone calcium is mobilized and urinary phosphate excretion is enhanced. The mechanism of these effects is not known, nor is it known that they are accomplished by influencing the same mechanisms which are involved in the biochemical action of parathyroid hormone.

Another aspect of the relationship between parathyroid hormone and vitamin D is discussed in Chapter 12.

Thyrocalcitonin

From the results of a series of ingenious cross-perfusion experiments, D. H. Copp and his colleagues (1962) brilliantly deduced the existence of a second hormone involved in serum calcium homeostasis. This hormone, named *calcitonin,* had the effect of lowering serum calcium, and the stimulus for its release appeared to be an elevation in serum calcium concentration. Copp originally believed that calcitonin was produced by the parathyroid glands, but Foster and his colleagues (1964) concluded that the thyroid gland, rather than the parathyroids, was the probable source of the hormone. Hirsch, Munson and their colleagues (1963, 1964) found serum calcium-lowering activity only in thyroid gland extracts and not in those prepared from parathyroid glands. Moreover, Pearse (1966) has identified the thyroid "C" cell as the cytologic source of the hormone. A large number of other investigators were stimulated to explore the implications of these interesting findings.

In a remarkably short time, thyrocalcitonin (TCT) has been purified and isolated as a homogeneous protein in gel electrophoresis systems. At first, a MW of 8,700 was reported, but, more recently, it has been estimated at about 6,000, with the possibility of an active 3,000 MW sub unit. Amino acid composition and sequence are under study. It is assayed by its ability to lower the serum calcium concentration of the conscious rat during continuous jugular infusion of the test material. As little as 1 microgram of purified material can lower the serum calcium of an assay rat. The successful purification of the material led to the development of a radioimmunoassay by Arnaud and Rasmussen (see Tenenhouse *et al.,* 1966). Thus the cycle from postulation of hormone to radioimmunoassay took about 3 years for TCT. In the case of insulin, the corresponding time lag was about 60 years.

At first, there was some skepticism about the physiological significance of thyrocalcitonin, but now no one seriously doubts that the hormone plays an active role in calcium homeostasis and may some day prove to be useful as a therapeutic agent in certain disease states. Hirsch *et al.* showed convincingly that parathyroidectomized rats exhibited the expected fall in serum calcium. If, after stabilization at the low level had occurred, the thyroid gland was removed, there was a significant elevation in serum calcium. Similar experiments, in which the protective effect of the thyroids against intoxicating doses of parathyroid hormone, also point to a teleologic role for TCT in serum calcium homeostasis. One of the most impressive demonstrations of the responsiveness of the TCT-producing mechanism was the demonstration by Rasmussen's group (Tenenhouse *et al.*, 1966) that a small increase in serum calcium concentration results in an almost instantaneous appearance of substantial quantities of radioimmunoassayable TCT in the serum of pigs. The rise in serum TCT is abolished by thyroidectomy.

There is now general agreement that TCT works directly on *bone*. In the experiments of Friedman and Raisz (1965), in which embryonic bone prelabeled with Ca^{45} was grown in organ culture, TCT inhibited the release of Ca^{45} from both untreated and parathormone-stimulated bone. Similar results were reported by Aliapoulios *et al.* (1966). In other related studies, TCT was found to decrease hydroxyproline excretion in the urine in parallel with its effect on serum calcium (Martin, 1966). This is interpreted as indicating an inhibition of (bone) collagen breakdown by TCT.

As yet, little is known about the biochemical mechanism of action of TCT on bone, or even about the cellular locus of action. Its rapid onset of action and the fact that it can lower serum calcium when RNA synthesis is inhibited by actinomycin D suggests that its bone-stabilizing effect does not require the synthesis of new RNA (Tashjian, 1965).

A few tentative attempts to relate these interesting experimental findings to human disease are being made. Already, the serum calcium-lowering effect of TCT has been demonstrated in patients with idiopathic hypercalcemia (Milhaud, 1966). One hopes that TCT will prove useful in the management of postmenopausal osteoporosis, although it would be preferable, perhaps, if we could invent a way of preventing that disease. It could be useful in a number of conditions which are characterized either by hypercalcemia or negative calcium balance. Certainly, the pharmaceutical industry in the United States and abroad is betting that this substance will prove to be of therapeutic importance, for large scale production facilities for its manufacture are now being built.

Hyperparathyroidism

Calcium homeostasis may be seriously disturbed in man when an excess of the parathyroid hormone is continually produced. The condition of hyperparathyroidism may be caused by a single adenoma (80–90% of cases), by multiple adenomas, by primary clear-cell ("wasserhelle" cell) hyperplasia, or by carcinoma. Not only is surgery the treatment for hyperparathyroidism; surgical exploration is often a part of the diagnostic investigation of the patient.

The incidence of both hypoparathyroidism and hyperparathyroidism is low, but recently there has been an *apparent* increase in the incidence of both of these disorders, probably because diagnostic acumen has become more incisive and more people are being seen in circumstances in which a suspicion of the diagnosis can be followed up with appropriate chemical tests. The presence of either condition is easy to detect if the deviation from normal is extreme, for the clinical and laboratory findings in hypoparathyroidism resemble those in a parathyroidectomized animal, while hyperparathyroidism represents the effect of a chronically autoinjected overdose of parathyroid hormone. The smaller the deviation from the normal the more difficult the diagnostic problem becomes. The availability of a radioimmunoassay for PTH is a boon to diagnosticians.

There are two important clues to the diagnosis of hyperparathyroidism (1) the occurrence of kidney stones, which occurred at one time or another in approximately 75% of one large series of proved cases of the disease, and (2) peptic ulcer, which occurred in 20% of the patients in the same series (Howard). The kidney stones are secondary to the chronic hypercalcemia which is caused by an abnormally rapid rate of mobilization of bone salts. In some patients, renal dysfunction, first manifested by polyuria and polydipsia, may be precipitated by the hypercalcemia. The reason for the remarkable coincidence of peptic ulcer with hyperparathyroidism is not known. Both kidney stones and peptic ulcer are extremely common diseases and hyperparathyroidism is a rare one, but the coincidence of these disorders is sufficiently high to warrant the suspicion of hyperparathyroidism and the estimation of serum calcium in subjects who have renal lithiasis or proved peptic ulcers.

It is not appropriate here to discuss the differential diagnosis of parathyroid disease. It is sufficient merely to point out that disturbances in serum calcium homeostasis occur in a wide variety of clinical conditions which are not primarily due to parathyroid dysfunction. Some of the hypercalcemic states can be differentiated from hyperparathyroidism by the fact that adrenal steroids restore patients in the former category to the normocalcemic condition, while similar treatment fails to reverse the hypercalcemia of hyperparathyroidism. Many cancer-bearing patients are in this category. One of the most difficult diagnostic problems is presented by the patient with lung cancer but without visible bone metastases, whose hypercalcemia is not reversed by adrenal cortical steroids.

When hyperparathyroidism was first described, the emphasis was on the dramatic rarefaction of bone, skeletal deformities and advanced renal insufficiency. We now realize that these were the final stages of a pathological process of long duration. At present, the diagnosis of hyperparathyroidism is often made long before the stage of osteitis fibrosa cystica, or even before there is any very obvious rarefaction of bone. Once it was taught that the manifestations of the disease in a wine-drinking country such as France were mainly skeletal, while those in a milk-drinking country such as the U.S.A. were largely renal. This too neat generalization, with its implicit attribution of a bone-sparing effect of a high calcium intake, is no longer accepted uncritically. It seems much more likely that the earliest stages of the disease are characterized by few radiologically apparent bone changes simply because the bone formation process is able to compensate for the increased rate of bone destruction. No doubt, hyperparathyroid patients vary both in the severity of the disease and in their ability to compensate for it and, therefore, in the extent of demineralization of bone.

REFERENCES

Arnaud, C. D., Tenenhouse, A. M., and Rasmussen, H.: Parathyroid hormone, Ann. Rev. Physiol. 29: 349-372, 1967.

Aurbach, G. D., and Potts, J. T., Jr.: Parathyroid hormone (Editorial), Am. J. Med. 42:1–8, 1967.

Bauer, G. C. H., Carlsson, A., and Lindquist, B.: Metabolism and homeostatic function of bone, in *Mineral Metabolism,* Comar, C. L., and Bronner, F. (eds.) (New York: Academic Press, Inc., 1961), vol. 1, pt. B.

Gaillard, P. J., Talmage, R. V., and Budy, A. M. (eds.): *The Parathyroid Glands* (University of Chicago Press, 1965).

Geschwind, I. I.: Hormonal control of calcium, phosphorus, iodine, iron, sulfur and magnesium metabolism, in *Mineral Metabolism,* Comar, C. L., and Bronner, F. (eds.) (New York: Academic Press, Inc., 1961), vol. 1, pt. B.

Greep, R. O.: Recent advances in the study of the structure, composition, and growth of mineralized tissues, Ann. New York Acad. Sc. 60:541–806, 1955.

Greep, R. O., and Talmage, R. V.: *The Parathyroids* (Springfield, Ill.: Charles C Thomas, Publisher, 1960).

Marshak, R. R.: Calcium and phosphorus metabolism in man and animals with special reference to pregnancy and lactation, Ann. New York Acad. Sc. 64:279–462, 1956.

Pearse, A. G. E.: The cytochemistry of the thyroid "C" cells and their relationship to calcitonin, Proc. Roy. Soc. 164:478–87, 1966.

Rasmussen, H.: Parathyroid hormone, Am. J. Med. 30:112–128, 1961.

12

Hormones and Protein Synthesis

Effects of Hormones at the Cellular Level

IT IS STILL IMPOSSIBLE to give a precise biochemical description of the mechanism of action of any hormone.. As we have seen repeatedly, many major advances have occurred in our understanding of this area, particularly those associated with Sutherland's "deputy" hypothesis (Chapter 8) and the many instances in which hormones have been shown to influence the translocation of water or solutes from one side of a membrane to another. Examination of Figure 12-1 reveals why the analysis of hormone action at the molecular level is such a difficult problem.

Any hormone-sensitive cell contains at least one enzyme (E) which catalyzes a rate-limiting reaction. In Figure 12-1, I have tried to suggest a few of the many conceivable ways in which a hormone could affect the catalytic activity of enzyme E. It could provide E with more substrate either by facilitating its transport through the membrane ① or by freeing it from a bound form within the cell ②. It could have as one of its effects the provision of some co-factor, such as ATP, ADP, a pyridine nucleotide coenzyme, coenzyme A, a metal or some similar material required for reaction E (③, ⑨, ⑤). Several years ago, there was a brief flurry of interest in the possibility that certain hormones, particularly estrogens, might function as coenzymes in critical reactions ④. While this theory is no longer popular as an explanation of the mechanism of action of estrogens, it would be premature to discard it

entirely, for, as we shall see, there is now much concern about specific steroid-recognizing proteins, and the presumption is that the receptor protein-steroid hormone complex can do something which the protein itself cannot do. This is certainly reminiscent of an enzyme-coenzyme partnership. The same set of possibilities exist for a hormone's effect on the mitochondrion ⑧.

Until this point, it has been possible to imagine the reaction catalyzed by E to be accelerated without postulating an actual increase in the quantity of apoenzyme E protein. The relationship specified by ⑥ describes a circumstance in which an enzyme can exist in an active and an inactive form. While the total amount of inactive plus active enzyme does not change, the activity of E depends on what proportion of the total is present in the active state. The phosphorylase activation by 3', 5' cyclic AMP is the best model we have of paradigm ⑥.

In recent years, largely under the stimulus of microbiologists, students of mammalian cell control mechanisms have become fascinated by the well-known concept of allosteric activation and inactivation of rate-limiting enzymes. It is now perfectly clear that the activity of many enzymes is probably modulated by many kinds of small molecules—nucleotides, substrates, substrate fragments—which have the property of affecting the catalytic activity of a protein by binding to it at a molecular site some distance from the active sites, i.e., the substrate and co-enzyme sites. The three-dimensional shape of the enzyme can be changed by these allosteric modulators so that the

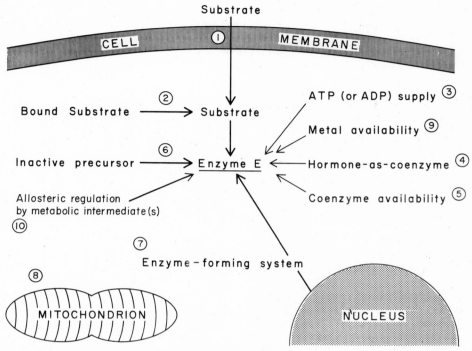

Fig. 12-1.—Some of the suggested mechanisms of hormone effects on cells. The reaction catalyzed by Enzyme E represents one or more rate-limiting steps which govern the over-all rate of metabolism of the target cell.

Effects at sites **1-10** could all modify the velocity of the reaction at **E.** For a more complete discussion of this scheme see Tepperman, J., and Tepperman, H. M.: Pharmacol. Rev. 12:301-353, 1960.

substrate and coenzyme sites are either approximated (activation) or separated (inhibition). Again, this type of control mechanism requires no change in the total amount of enzyme protein.

There is, however, one kind of control device which influences the rate of the reaction at E by increasing the amount of apoenzyme protein E, that is to say, by stimulating an enzyme-forming system to produce more E ⑦. It is the study of this aspect of biochemical endocrinology that has engaged the attention of many enterprising and industrious investigators during the past several years.

Many hormones other than somatotrophin are growth hormones, although the tissues in which they stimulate growth may be highly specialized ones. Thyroxine is a growth hormone, for failure to grow is an outstanding feature of thyroxine deficiency in young animals. Some hormones elicit the selective synthesis of small amounts of new enzyme protein in certain cells under circumstances in which it is difficult to demonstrate net protein synthesis. Thus, an insistent theme of

protein synthesis pervades all of endocrinology.

It is hardly surprising, therefore, that students of the cellular mechanisms of action of hormones have spent the past few years in attempts to apply the principles and methods of the New Biology (which is largely concerned with protein synthesis) to the problems of hormone action (Fig. 12-2).

The Central Dogma of Molecular Biology is too well known to require reiteration here. It is now almost universally assumed that transcription of the genetic message is achieved by DNA-mediated messenger, or template, RNA (mRNA) synthesis in the nucleus; that mRNA migrates to the cytoplasm in a form not yet agreed upon, but probably in association with a ribosome component; that strands of mRNA unite single ribosomes into teams of polysomes. The molecules that *translate* the DNA code are called "transfer RNA's" but are sometimes designated as sRNA. Each of these remarkable molecular machine tools has the capacity to recognize two different chemical configurations (1) an individual amino

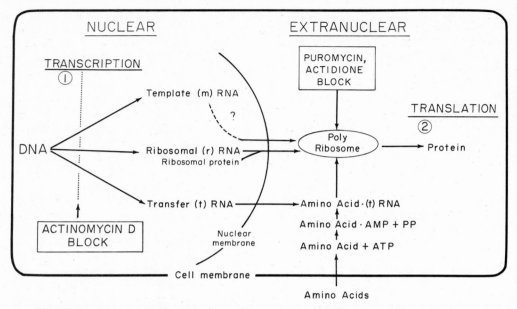

Fig. 12-2.—Mechanisms of protein biosynthesis and loci of action of commonly used inhibitors.

acid and (2) the appropriate "codon," or nucleotide triplet, on the mRNA which serves as a template for lining up the individual sRNA-amino acid complexes in the proper order for peptide bond synthesis to occur. For the purposes of the discussion to follow the simple diagram shown in Figure 12-2 briefly summarizes the essential features of the scheme and illustrates the locus of action of inhibitors which have been widely used in the study of hormone action. Again, *transcription* occurs at step ①; *translation* occurs at step ②.

Actinomycin D is widely assumed to block DNA-mediated RNA synthesis. While this is true, it may have other effects as well (Honig and Rabinovitz, 1965; Tomkins, 1965). Actinomycin D inhibition is often equated with suppression of messenger RNA synthesis, but nucleolar (ribosomal) RNA synthesis is even more susceptible to inhibition than is messenger. The antibiotic probably inhibits the synthesis of all species of RNA—messenger, ribosomal and transfer. It exerts its effect by binding to guanine residues in DNA and thus prevents the production of complementary RNA. The inhibition is competitive and can be overcome by the addition of excess DNA. *Puromycin* interferes with the assembly of protein molecules at the ribosomal site. It apparently acts as a sort of counterfeit transfer RNA and binds to template RNA in such a way that incomplete peptides with puromycin at one end "peel off" the assembly unit. *Actidione* also inhibits at the ribosomal assembly level. In doses ordinarily used, actinomycin D does not materially affect the assembly process and neither puromycin nor Actidione affects RNA synthesis. However, all experiments with inhibitors in intact animals, or even on isolated tissues, may have unrecognized effects on the systems under study which have nothing to do with their presumed biochemical loci of action. In spite of this, much valuable information has been obtained with these inhibitors. The approach has been to study a hormonal response in the presence and absence of one or another inhibitor. If the response persists in the presence of the inhibitor, the reaction blocked is presumed not to be involved in the response. If it disappears, the blocked site is thought to be essential for the hormonal response.

All of the information about hormone effects on genes has not been obtained by the use of inhibitors. The study of reconstructed ribosomal protein-synthesizing systems prepared from the tissues of hormone-deprived and hormone-treated animals has added valuable information. Experiments on the rates of synthesis of various species of RNA, including presumed template, have yielded interesting results. Studies of the effect of hormone treatment on the activity of crucial enzymes in the system, such as RNA polymerase, have been revealing. Isotope studies on the time course of incorporation of various precursors into critical cell components following repair of a hormone deficiency really set the stage for many later developments. Moreover, a recent experiment suggests that hormone-induced RNA may have many of the effects on a deprived tissue seen after treatment with the hormone itself. The technique of radioautography has been used imaginatively in the analysis of these problems. The striking fact is that as soon as a potentially useful method is developed someone quickly uses it in an analysis of hormone action.

ECDYSONE

One source of the present widespread vogue for analyzing hormone effects on genes was the study of insect metamorphosis. It had been observed that the giant chromosomes of salivary gland cells in certain insect larvae show the phenomenon of "puffing," i.e., a localized enlargement at a very precise location with "blurring" of the chromatin material at the site. Radioautographic studies labeled RNA precursors have demonstrated that "puffs" are sites of vigorous RNA synthesis. Clever and Karlson (1960) found that the injection of extremely small amounts of the steroid hormone *ecdysone* into larvae resulted in the appearance of two critical "puffs" which, apparently, were then able to generate a sequential series of signals for the appearance of new "puffs" in a definite, predictably scheduled pattern. The appearance of these "puffs" could be correlated with the process of moulting.

Karlson formally presented the suggestion that many hormones, but especially steroids, may exert their effects by acting directly on the chromosomes in such a way as to activate specific gene sites to produce messenger or template RNA. Thus, the genetic code for the production of hormones obviously was contained in the DNA of the hormone-producing cell; the hormone itself was presumed to act primarily by "turning on" specific gene sites in the hormone-sensitive cell. It should be noted that this hypothesis requires a distinctive attribute of the hormone-sensitive cell

which also was originally encoded in the cell's DNA, i.e., a hormone-recognition mechanism. The question that has been raised by the vast amount of work done in this area in the past few years is simply this: how close to the gene is the hormone-recognition mechanism? That is, does the primary transaction between the hormone and its receptor occur very near the chromosomal sites or can it be remote from these? The answer will probably turn out to be different for each hormone. In the case of ecdysone, there is evidence to suggest that "puffing" induced by the hormone may be secondary to a primary hormone-receptor interaction that may generate a signal (such as a change in electrolyte environment) some distance from the gene site (Kroeger, 1964), but the proponents of a primary nuclear site of action refuse to concede that this is so. They (Sekeris, et al., 1965) have shown that isolated nuclei respond to ecdysone with increased rate of synthesis of nuclear RNA which shows very active template activity when it is tested in a reconstructed cell-free protein-synthesizing system. In fact, nuclear RNA from ecdysone-treated *insects* can direct the synthesis of insect dopa-decarboxylase by *rat* liver ribosomes!

The details of the postulated interaction between ecdysone and a nuclear component are not known. Karlson suggests that the hormone may "unmask" segments of DNA by combining with specific histone proteins which repress or "insulate" them. This would have the effect of activating existing RNA polymerase and stimulating the production of template RNA.

ALDOSTERONE

If the salivary gland of the insect larva goes down in history as a crucial source of inspiration in our understanding of the mechanism of action of hormones, the isolated toad bladder will be honored in its own right. For recent exciting work on the mechanism of the enhancement of sodium transport by this preparation when aldosterone is added in vitro has captured the imagination of biologists. I. S. Edelman and colleagues (1965) showed that the stimulatory effect of aldosterone on sodium transport by the toad bladder (an effect which takes place only after a 60–90 min lag period) disappears when the isolated bladders are treated in vitro with either actinomycin D or puromycin; and that tritiated

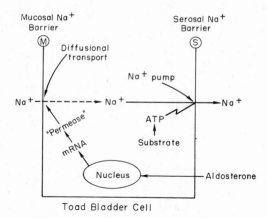

Fig. 12-3.—The mechanism of action of aldosterone on the toad bladder cell according to Sharp, G. W. G., and Leaf, A.: Physiol. Rev. 46:596, 1966.

aldosterone is taken up almost to capacity within 30 min and can be shown by radioautography to be preferentially concentrated in the nuclei of the cells. The specificity of the inhibitor effects was shown by the fact that actinomycin D-treated bladders retained their responsiveness to vasopressin, a hormone which also increases sodium transport in this preparation.

In other studies, the sodium-retaining effect of aldosterone on rat kidney has been shown to be inhibited by actinomycin D and an increased rate of synthesis of RNA has been demonstrated in aldosterone-treated animals. On the grounds that toad bladders treated with aldosterone show a significant increase in ATP content just before the rise in rate of sodium transport occurs, Edelman suggests that the protein or proteins synthesized in response to aldosterone treatment may be involved in an ATP-generating system, a suggestion consonant with the fact that the aldosterone works only in the presence of utilizable substrates.

Sharp and Leaf (1966) agree that new protein synthesis is essential for the action of aldosterone, though no one has, as yet, demonstrated the synthesis of a new protein in aldosterone stimulated tissue. However, they found that when the mucosal side of the toad bladder was treated with an antibiotic called amphotericin B the tissue was capable of transporting Na^+ as rapidly as if it had been stimulated with aldosterone. Moreover, this stimulation of sodium transport occurred immediately on the addition of substrate, which suggests that the energy-yielding systems supplying

the Na^+ pump were equal to the task of transporting the ion at rates required by aldosterone stimulation. Sharp and Leaf have proposed the model illustrated in Figure 12-3 for the action of aldosterone. As a result of treatment with the hormone, the synthesis of new messenger RNA is elicited. This, in turn, serves as template for the synthesis of a hypothetical "permease," which then modifies the properties of the mucosal Na^+ barrier in the direction of permitting more Na^+ to diffuse into the cell. The existing metabolic machinery and serosal Na^+ pump then dispose of the Na^+ through the serosal Na^+ barrier if substrate is available for ATP production. Clearly, some features of this model have not yet been precisely worked out, but, in general, it fits the experimental facts as they are presently known. In view of the fact that aldosterone was discovered only in 1953, investigators of the mechanism of its action deserve our admiration for the progress they have made.

ESTROGENS

Recent studies on the mechanism of action of estrogens illustrate the speed with which new ideas and new methods are currently being applied to the problem of hormone effects at the cellular level. The pioneer work of Mueller and the studies of Gorski, Szego, Hamilton, Segal and many others have not only clarified our understanding of estrogen action but have also served as a model for the analysis of the effects of other hormones. Since no convincing demonstration of an effect of estrogen on estrogen-sensitive tissue in vitro has been made, the strategic plan has been to inject the hormone into a castrate or immature animal and to test the biochemical performance of the uterus by means of a variety of techniques either in vivo or in vitro. Some of Segal's work (to be described later in this section) combines some of the features of in vitro and in vivo experiments, since he has studied effects of inhibitors and other preparations in contact with cells in situ.

Mueller and his school described a large variety of changes in the uteri of estrogen-injected castrate rats. One obvious approach to understanding the primary mechanism of action of the hormone is to arrange all of the effects on a *time scale* on the theory that the earliest changes seen may be more closely related to the primary action of the hormone than later ones. For example, significant net DNA synthesis (signifying cell division) does not appear until 24 hr after hormone injection. At 12 hr, there is a net increase in the protein content of cells and in dry weight of tissue, but at 6 hr there is a perceptible net increase in RNA. Although this kind of evidence is obviously circumstantial, it would lead one to the hypothesis that the 6-hr event may have played a role in initiating the 12-hr event and that the changes at 12 hr may have participated in the generation of a signal complex which resulted in cell division.

There is reason to believe that all of these changes may have had their origin in still earlier ones, for even at 1 hr the rates of many biochemical processes are strikingly increased over those in the untreated uterus of the ovariectomized animal. By that time, there is generalized hyperemia of the uterus and the water content of the tissue has increased. (According to one hypothesis, these effects may be mediated by the local release of histamine in the tissue.) Also, within 1 hr, there is an increased rate of activation of amino acids to their adenylates, an increased rate of incorporation of various labeled precursors into RNA and an increase in the rate of incorporation of P^{32} into phospholipids. Within 30 min, there is an increase in DNA-directed RNA polymerase activity, a finding which emphasizes the possibility that the early stimulation of RNA synthesis may be a crucial event in the hormone's action.

Time scale studies of this sort are useful, but the mechanisms involved in the sequence of responses can be elucidated further by the technique of *inhibitor analysis*. Some of the earliest and neatest inhibitor studies of this sort were done by Mueller and his colleagues on the estrogen problem. A few of their collective results can be summarized in the following table:

	Effect on Estrogen Stimulation	
Process	Puromycin	Actinomycin D
Glycine → protein	↓	↓
Early RNA synthesis	↓	↓
Phospholipid synthesis	↓	↓
Water imbibition	↓	Partial ↓

From this sort of evidence, it was inferred that RNA synthesis plays an important role in the action of estrogen but that, since puromycin as well as actinomycin blocks early RNA synthesis, the hormone may induce the formation of some critical protein(s) which may be related to the initiation of RNA synthesis. Very recently, Gorski has described the increased incorporation of a radioactive amino acid into a very specific, single uterine protein displayed in a gel electrophoresis system following treatment of an immature rat with estrogen.

Talwar and Segal (1963) also showed that the local application of actinomycin D to the vaginal epithelium of a castrate rat prevented the usual

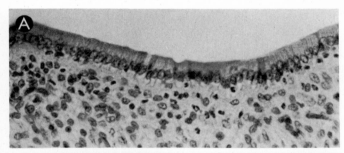
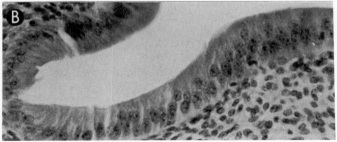

Fig. 12-4.—**A,** epithelium of uterine horn perfused with RNA extracted from nuclei of estrogen-treated uteri. Extract preincubated with pancreatic RNAase. **B,** contralateral uterine horn after 48 hours of perfusion with same RNA extract as in **A** but without prior inactivation. See text for additional details. (Reproduced with permission from Segal, S. J., Davidson, O. W., and Wada, K.: Proc. Nat. Acad. Sc. 54:782-787, 1965.)

cornifying effect of injected estrogen on the epithelial cells. Then Segal and his colleagues prepared ovariectomized test rats in such a way that solutions could be infused periodically and separately through tiny polyethylene tubes into the open ends of the two uterine horns and drained through the vagina. They perfused one horn with crude nuclear RNA extracts (q. 4 hr, 1 or 2 days) prepared from the uteri of estrogen-treated castrate rats; the other horn was perfused with a control solution which varied with the experiment. The two uterine horns were then removed, sectioned side by side and examined. The "RNA"-treated horn showed marked stimulation of growth of the epithelial cells (Fig. 12-4), whereas little or no effect was seen on the contralateral side when the perfusate was (1) physiological saline, (2) RNAase-treated active "RNA" preparations, (3) similar "RNA" extracts prepared from indifferent, non-estrogen-sensitive tissues and (4) "RNA" extracts prepared from uteri of castrate rats. The active preparations were proved to be completely estrogen-free. Although some critics have reservations about the design of these experiments (see especially Hechter and Halkerston, 1965), I find them provocative and important, for they suggest that estrogens work by first eliciting the synthesis of new messenger RNA which can then initiate the sequence of events that we recognize as a highly complicated and integrated response to the hormone without further participation of the hormonal trigger substance. Some features of Segal's experiment have recently been confirmed by Mansour and Nice (1965). In a 1967 Federation Proceedings abstract, Fujii and C. Villee describe very similar experiments on the effect of RNA extracted from tissues of androgen-treated rats on growth and protein synthesis of the seminal vesicle and prostate.

Following Jensen's description of the selective binding of estradiol by estrogen-sensitive tissues, an intensive search for a specific, estrogen-recognizing receptor protein has been conducted in a number of laboratories, notably in those of J. Gorski, of Jensen and of Talwar. Talwar (1964) has described an estradiol-binding protein isolated from the uteri of castrate rats, which inhibits DNA-mediated RNA synthesis by a reconstructed Escherichia coli RNA polymerase system. Similar material isolated from the uteri of estrogen-treated rats failed to inhibit the system. Other workers in this field tend to be somewhat wary of too enthusiastic acceptance of Jacobian-Monodian bacterial models in the analysis of hormone action, but no one can deny that they have considerable charm.

Gorski's estrogen-binding protein appears to be a highly specific substance, present in both cytosol and nucleus, which not only binds estradiol 17β but diethylstilbestrol as well, while it scorns estradiol 17α. In a word, it does everything one would wish it to do on the basis of in vivo effects of the substances. At the moment, there is no very satisfying cept, macro or micro, for describing the events that occur between the initial binding of the hormone to its receptor molecule and the opening of gene sites for transcription. J. D. Wilson has described radioautographic localization of estradiol 17β at fairly specific loci or loops of the lamp brush chromosome of the newt. This is entirely analogous to the ecdysone story, and, again, one wonders about the possibility of steroid hormone interacting with a histone or other masking protein to release a gene site for transcription. The fact that Gorski finds a considerable amount of his estrogen-binding protein in the nuclear fraction is consistent with this possibility.

TESTOSTERONE

A testosterone-deprived seminal vesicle cell, or prostatic cell is small, lacking a nucleolus and cytoplasmic basophilia and biochemically dormant. Treatment with testosterone results in the appearance of a large nucleolus, all sorts of basophilic machinery in the cytoplasm and the recovery of a whole battery of lost enzymes. Since this response is so similar to that of an estrogen sensitive cell confronted with estradiol and since estrogens and androgens are so similar chemically, it is not surprising that a common theme runs through investigations of both kinds of sex steroids.

In studies on rat seminal vesicles (Wilson) and in mouse kidney and accessory sex glands (Kochakian), a defect in protein synthesis was demonstrated in tissues of castrate animals. This defect was reparable with replacement doses of testosterone and "supernormal" rates of incorporation of labeled amino acids into protein could be induced with large doses of androgen. Kochakian observed very large increases in the RNA content of cells following testosterone treatment and inferred that these increases probably involved all species of RNA: messenger, ribosomal and transfer.

Williams-Ashman and his colleagues, in an admirable series of experiments, have proved that prostatic cells of the castrate animal are deficient in messenger RNA activity and that treatment of a castrate animal with testosterone stimulates the synthesis of new RNA with the functional capacity of template, as well as new ribosomal RNA. These investigators isolated ribonucleoprotein particles from rat prostate which were able to incorporate labeled amino acids into a protein fraction. Similarly prepared particles from the prostates of castrate animals performed poorly in the test system. In order to eliminate the possibility that androgen deficiency might have affected either amino acid transport or activation, the investigators charged rat liver transfer RNA with one C^{14}-labeled amino acid and 19 other unlabeled amino acids in the presence of amino acid-activating enzymes. They then isolated the 20 amino acid-transfer RNA complexes and added them to the reconstructed protein-synthesizing system. Under these conditions, the defect in protein synthesis persisted in the system perpared from the castrate. Treatment of the castrate animal with testosterone restored the activity of the system to normal. Moreover, the addition of synthetic messenger (Poly U) to the "deficient" system restored the incorporation of labeled phenylalanine to essentially normal levels, but did not increase that of the control system to supernormal levels. The inference that the tissue of the castrate rat was deficient in template or messenger RNA was strengthened by the later finding that the messenger RNA activity of nuclear RNA obtained from the prostates of castrates is low when tested in a messenger RNA-depleted E. coli ribosome system. Treatment with testosterone restored the messenger activity of nuclear RNA to normal in the same system. These experiments point to messenger RNA synthesis as a critical locus of action of the male hormone, but, of course, they do not indicate precisely how this effect is achieved. Currently, there is much interest in DNA-directed RNA polymerase activity, and many of the speculations about androgen effects converge with those suggested for the estrogens. There is some evidence that androgen is selectively bound by nuclear chromatin in cells of the androgen-sensitive preen gland, an organ which is located in the rear end of the duck (J. D. Wilson). This again constitutes a sort of *a posteriori* argument for an ecdysone-like action of androgens on some nuclear component.

THYROID HORMONE

We often think in terms of the effects of excessive amounts of thyroid hormone on animals and men. We tend to associate thyroxine and triiodothyronine with hypermetabolism and with the dramatic picture presented by the patient seriously ill with Grave's disease. Hyperthyroxinism, whether of endogenous or exogenous origin, is a study in toxicology—the word "thyrotoxicosis" is a very apt descriptive term for the condition. It may contain elements of the fundamental biological effect of thyroxine, but they are distorted and overshadowed by features which probably have nothing to do with the critical function of the hormone.

As we have seen, the thyroactive substances have effects on brain, a tissue in which metabolic rate does not fluctuate with thyroid status. In the thyroid-deprived animal, one can demonstrate a growth effect at dose levels which do not increase the metabolic rate significantly. In amphibia, the whole complex process of metamorphosis is initiated by very small doses of thyroid hormone which, apparently, can cause a catabolic response in one part of the animal (the tail) and a highly differentiated growth response in other parts (the limbs). Certain enzymes, particularly those of the Krebs-Henseleit urea cycle (studied by P. P. Cohen and colleagues), suddenly appear in the livers of metamorphosing animals. It is of some interest that pharmacological hyperthyroidism, as we can produce it in rats, for example, cannot be demonstrated in the adult amphibian. The emphasis in these species is on *differentiation,* and this focuses our attention on a possible effect of thyroxine on gene expression. Consider the possibility that thyroid hormone may function in the tadpole as a sort of amphibian ecdysone; that it may "turn on" a few selected gene sites, possibly by eliciting the production of specific messenger RNA's; and that the subsequent orderly process of differentiation requires the presence of the hormone for its successful completion. The growth of the young animal to the adult size is a continuation of the differentiation process. During this phase of development, thyroxine is neces-

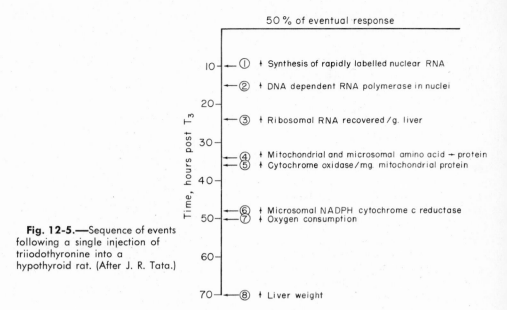

Fig. 12-5.—Sequence of events following a single injection of triiodothyronine into a hypothyroid rat. (After J. R. Tata.)

sary for the maintenance of the differentiated state, for removal of the hormone results in a metabolic regression of many cells of the body.

The biochemical mechanism of action of thyroid hormones has been studied extensively, but we still cannot do more than give a description of some of the events that occur when a hypothyroid cell is confronted with a single dose of thyroxine (T_4) or triiodothyronine (T_3). In Tata's analysis of the sequence of events in the liver following the administration of a single dose of T_3 to a hypophysectomized rat (Fig. 12-5), one is immediately struck by the fact that T_3 is a comparatively leisurely hormone. The well-known increase in oxygen consumption, for example, does not begin until 36 hr after the administration of the hormone and reaches the 50% response level only after 2 days. With gradually increasing knowledge of protein synthesis, it was possible to ascertain that many readily detectable changes precede the appearance of a calorigenic response. The earliest response recorded by Tata was an increase in the rapidly labeled fraction of nuclear RNA which was first detectable 4-5 hr after the injection of T_3 and reached the 50% response level at about 10 hr. Shortly after this, a measurable increase in DNA-dependent RNA polymerase activity of nuclei became manifest. By the 24th hr, a substantial increase in ribosomal RNA had occurred, and by the 36th hr, increased rates of incorporation

of amino acids into the protein of the microsomal and mitochondrial fraction were demonstrable. An increase in liver size was only seen after 70 hr. This time scale is clearly different from that of ACTH, epinephrine or insulin, not to mention aldosterone and the sex steroids.

That the action of thyroxine involves gene expression is quite clear. However, the mechanism by which a selective synthesis of specific enzyme and, possibly, structural proteins is accomplished is far from clear. Moreover, it is not certain that the mechanism of action of the hormone when it *replaces* a deficiency is necessarily identical with the mechanism of its effect when a toxic dose is administered. If it functions by neutralizing repressor molecules are there different T_4-recognizing proteins in the liver from those in the resorbing tail? In the former tissue, new Krebs urea cycle enzymes are elicited, while in the latter, hydrolytic lysosomal enzymes appear in profusion.

In any case, it is now quite clear that new protein machinery must be made during the expression of thyroxine's major biologic effects. Simultaneous treatment of an animal with thyroxine and a protein synthesis inhibitor such as puromycin prevents both thyroxine-induced hypermetabolism as well as increases in certain specific enzymes which are usually elicited by the hormone—particularly mitochondrial α glycerophosphate dehydrogenase and cytosol TPN malic enzyme, both of which increase up to 10-fold in activity in animals treated with toxic amounts of T_4 or T_3. In addition, T_4-induced metamorphosis of the tadpole tail, an event which can be observed in the amputated structure, is blocked by actinomycin D.

ACTH

The mechanism of action of ACTH, recently reviewed by Hilf (1965), has been discussed on page 113. The results of recent inhibitor studies (Garren *et al.,* 1965) should be mentioned at this point because they raise the question of a hormone effect at the level of the translation process rather than on the transcription mechanism. Garren and his colleagues estimated the steroidogenic response of the adrenals in the rat by means of an adrenal vein cannulation technique. They were able to test the effect of prior administration of inhibitors on both steroidogenesis and on the protein synthetic activity of the adrenal. In confirmation of previous work, actinomycin D failed to block the stimulatory effect of ACTH on adrenal steroidogenesis, suggesting that newly synthesized messenger is not required for the response. Puromycin or chloramphenicol, however, blocked both steroidogenesis and protein synthesis in parallel. The authors interpret their results to suggest that a protein with a very short half-life and a very stable messenger RNA must be continuously synthesized in order for steroidogenesis to continue and that ACTH may elicit the synthesis of this

hypothetical protein. Ferguson (1963) had previously suggested that concurrent protein synthesis is essential for the action of ACTH and had pointed out that stimulation of steroidogenesis by either ACTH or 3′, 5′ cyclic AMP is blocked by puromycin. The cyclic nucleotide may be a more immediate signal for the synthesis of "trigger protein" than ACTH itself. In any case, "trigger protein" is synthesized when messenger RNA synthesis is blocked; therefore, the signal for its production may operate on some phase of the transaction among the molecular species which enter into the assembly of the protein at the ribosomal level.

In Figure 12-6, I have combined several theories of the mechanism of action of ACTH into a scheme which fits many of the experimental facts as we know them. The essential feature of this scheme is the fact that the initial transaction of ACTH with the cell occurs with adenyl cyclase at the cell membrane. The 3′, 5′ cyclophosphate which is generated as a result of this transaction then carries a message to many different proteins in the cell so that a beautifully integrated response occurs. This is reminiscent of our discussion of the effect of TSH on the thyroid cell. In Figure 12-6, I have attempted to give an idea of the simultaneity of the events. The molecular "deputy," 3′, 5′ cyclic AMP, may influence membrane permeability ①, the rate of translation of a pre-existing template RNA into a specific, evanescent protein ②, and the hydrolysis of cholesterol ester to provide free cholesterol as hormone precursor ③. In addition, as Roberts has suggested in the

Fig. 12-6.—A composite hypothesis of the mechanism of action of ACTH. This scheme includes features adapted from the ideas of Haynes, Koritz, Peron, Hechter, Ferguson, Roberts and Garren.

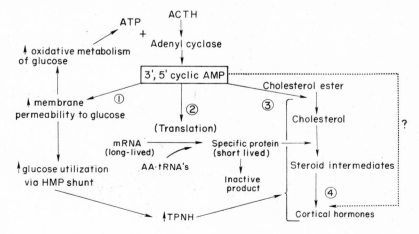

case of 11-β-hydroxylase ④, other enzymes or structural proteins in the cell may be affected by the nucleotide. The role for the hypothetical short half-life protein suggested in Figure 12-6 is in the realm of fantasy.

The membrane effect seems to me to be a crucial part of the over-all response because it provides for a continuation of the response, i.e., a continuing generation of ATP for the cyclase and TPNH for the steroid hydroxylation reactions that occur during hormone biosynthesis. G. Sato (1966) has described a mouse adrenal tumor cell which he has succeeded in adapting to tissue culture and which responds to ACTH by greatly accelerating its rate of producing steroids. Under the influence of ACTH in vitro, these cells change their shape drastically within 30 min—from polygonal, fibroblast-like cells to round cells with few projecting processes. No more dramatic evidence that the cell membrane is affected by ACTH can be found, for, in this instance, one can literally see a hormone acting on a cell before one's eyes!

In July 1967 (Biochemistry 6:2052), R. V. Farese described the in vitro induction of a protein factor in quartered (i.e., largely intact cell) rat adrenals incubated with ACTH. This factor, present in the 60,000 G supernatant, enhanced steroidogenesis by *homogenates* of rat adrenals and, in fact, brought about cholesterol side-chain cleavage when it was incubated with adrenal mitochondria, which contain a large amount of cholesterol. Farese also demonstrated a side-chain cleavage inhibitory factor in the supernatants of control rat adrenals. Whether or not the stimulating protein, whose production is blocked by puromycin, is identical with the short half-lived protein postulated by Garren remains to be proved. Also, it is unknown whether it stimulates glucocorticoid production directly or by removing an inhibitor. In any case, the stimulation of steroidogenesis in a cell free system represents an important advance, for it has never been possible to accomplish this feat by adding ACTH itself to adrenal homogenates.

GROWTH HORMONE

Only a few years ago, much of the emphasis in analyses of the mechanism of action of growth hormone was on the fact that the hormone accelerated the concentrative transfer of certain amino acids into cells (Fig. 12-7). While this response is

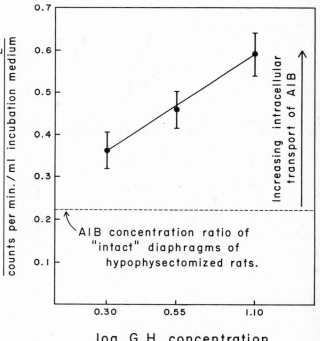

Fig. 12-7.—Effect of pituitary growth hormone (GH) on concentrative transfer of α AIB (α aminoisobutyric acid, a non-utilizable amino acid) by "intact" rat diaphragm in vitro. A significant effect is obtainable in this system with as little as 0.15 μg. of GH/ml of medium. (Courtesy of J. L. Kostyo, Duke University, unpublished. See also Christensen, H. N.: Perspectives in Biol. & Med. 2:228-242, 1959.)

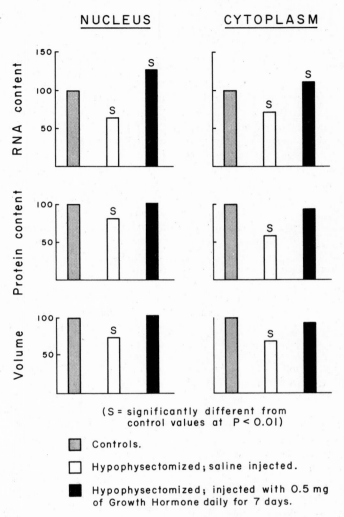

NUCLEUS   CYTOPLASM

(S = significantly different from
control values at P < 0.01)

▨ Controls.

☐ Hypophysectomized; saline injected.

■ Hypophysectomized; injected with 0.5 mg
   of Growth Hormone daily for 7 days.

Fig. 12-8.—Effect of hypophysectomy and growth hormone replacement on RNA, protein and volume of liver cells. (Data of DiStefano, H., et al.: Endocrinology 51:386-393, 1952.)

readily demonstrable, it is by no means clear that it is the main one by which the hormone achieves its effect. It is now essential to attempt some sort of reconciliation between amino acid transport effects of the hormone and other interesting effects at various sites in the protein biosynthetic machinery of the cell.

The changes summarized in Figure 12-8 still represent a fair point of departure in a discussion of the cellular mechanism of action of somatotrophin. These data were obtained by means of the Caspersson technique of microspectrophotometry which permits the quantitative estimation of nucleic acids separately in the nuclei and cyto-

plasm of cells. Hypophysectomy causes a marked decrease in cell size, nuclear volume, nuclear RNA, nuclear protein, cytoplasmic RNA and cytoplasmic protein. Growth hormone treatment restores all these values to normal or above; the first detectable change by this technique was in nuclear RNA, at 2 days. In general, the changes in the nucleus anticipated those in the cytoplasm by 2 days.

The study of growth hormone by Korner and his colleagues has been inspired by the same advances in the field of protein synthesis that have provided the frame of reference for many of the other arguments advanced in this chapter. Starting with the observation that the tissues of hypophysectomized rats fail to incorporate labeled amino acids into protein at a normal rate and that this failure is correctable by prior growth hormone administration, Korner turned his attention to a study of reconstructed, cell-free systems. He found that the microsomal fraction of the livers of pituitary-deprived rats reflected the protein synthetic deficit seen in intact cell preparations. Moreover, since the defect persisted when ribosomes from hypophysectomized rats were mixed with supernates of homogenates of normal rat liver, it was inferred that the defect could not be attributed to a failure of amino acid supply or activation (amino acid-activating enzymes are in the nonparticulate supernates). The argument for a deficiency of messenger RNA in the liver of GH-deprived rats was based on two findings (1) polysomes isolated from these rats were just as active in incorporating a labeled amino acid into protein as were those of normal animals, but the ratio of polysomes to total ribosomes was smaller in the hormone deficient liver, (2) the stimulation of protein synthesis by the addition of a synthetic messenger (Poly U) was just as great for ribosomes of the deficient animals as for those of normal ones. Attempts to demonstrate that growth hormone deficiency is characterized by an inadequate supply of messenger RNA have yielded inconclusive results. According to one prominent hypothesis, polysomes are bound together by messenger RNA; therefore, in the case of a deficiency of messenger, the ratio of polysomes to smaller units should be decreased. This is indeed the case in the liver of the hypophysectomized rat; moreover, the protein synthetic capacity of the polysomes of this preparation is just as good as that of those prepared from normal animals. The synthetic defect is associated with the presence of a relatively larger population of dispersed ribosomes. However, the addition of synthetic messenger (Poly U) was about as effective in stimulating systems prepared from normal animals as it was in those obtained from hypophysectomized animals. This, you will recall, is quite different from the situation described in a prostatic ribosome system by Williams-Ashman.

Inhibitor analysis has not produced a very tidy resolution of the messenger problem. For, while there is a definite and striking *decrease* in the effect of GH on protein synthesis by liver ribosome systems in vitro, there is still a perceptible stimulatory effect of GH even after prior treatment with rather large doses of actinomycin D. This suggests that some of the GH effect can occur even when messenger RNA synthesis is blocked. In the diaphragm, Knobil has found that puromycin, in doses which will practically completely inhibit new protein synthesis, has no effect on hormone-stimulated amino acid transport.

Obviously, it is not possible at this time to give a definitive answer to the question: how does GH stimulate protein synthesis? Does it work at only one site, or are there multiple sites? If it can work when messenger RNA synthesis is blocked, could it, perhaps, facilitate the *translation* of protein messages by pre-existing messenger in a manner analogous to that suggested by Gross and Cousineau (1963) for fertilized sea urchin eggs? In their system, there appears to be a sort of activation of messenger RNA already present in the egg. Only further work will clarify the nature of the effect of GH on *transcription* (messenger RNA synthesis) *translation* (activation of systems without new messenger synthesis) and *amino acid transport.*

INSULIN

Insulin lack is characterized by breakdown of muscle and other peripheral tissue proteins, increased rate of formation of glucose from amino acids and a negative nitrogen balance. Insulin administration, either to a normal individual or to a diabetic, results in a fall in circulating amino acid concentration and the storage of protein in muscle and adipose tissue. The association between insulin and protein anabolism was made many years ago, but the mechanism by which insulin stimulates protein synthesis is still incompletely understood.

There was early validation of an insulin effect at the tissue level when it was observed that insulin stimulates the incorporation of labeled amino acids into protein when it is added to diaphragm incubated in vitro. At the beginning, the stimulation of protein synthesis was attributed to the fact that insulin stimulated the concentrative transfer of both natural and model (nonutilizable) amino acids into the cell. However, Manchester and Krahl demonstrated (Fig. 12-9) that labeled keto acids, which could be incorporated into protein only after intracellular transamination, also appeared in protein to a greater extent in insulin-

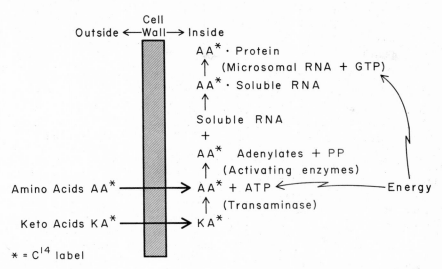

Fig. 12-9.—Observed effects of insulin on protein synthesis in the absence of added glucose in the incubation medium. The rat diaphragm in vitro incorporates more C^{14}-labeled amino acid or C^{14}-labeled keto acid into protein in the presence of insulin than in its absence. (See Manchester, K. L., and Krahl, M. E.: J. Biol. Chem. 234:2938-2942, 1959.)

treated tissues; this tended to disprove the amino acid transport theory. As a result of inhibitor studies, we now know that the amino acid transport effect and the protein synthesis-stimulating effects of insulin are easily separable.

Although it had been suggested that insulin exerts its enhancing effect on protein synthesis by stimulating the production of RNA, it is now accepted that the hormone increases the rate of incorporation of amino acids into protein even in actinomycin D-blocked tissue. Puromycin, however, inhibits insulin-stimulated increases in protein synthesis. Neither inhibitor interferes with the stimulation of glucose or amino acid transport that is characteristically seen in insulin-treated muscle or adipose tissue. Conversely, the protein synthesis-stimulating effect of insulin can be demonstrated readily in tissues in the absence of substrate amounts of either glucose or amino acids.

Rampersad and Wool (1965) have succeeded in preparing ribonucleoprotein particles from deoxycholate-treated homogenates of rat heart muscle. These particles satisfy all of the criteria for ribosomes: They sediment at 105,000 g, and they can effect the incorporation of C^{14} phenylalanine from sRNA C^{14} phenylalanine into protein in the presence of suitable co-factors; the process is inhibited by ribonuclease and by puro-

mycin and is stimulated by polyuridylic acid, a synthetic messenger RNA for phenylalanine.

Wool and his colleagues have made a careful study of the activity of this heart muscle ribosome system under various conditions of insulin deprivation or insulin treatment of the donor animal. (Insulin addition to the in vitro system had no effect under any circumstances.) It was found that heart muscle of diabetic animals yielded ribosomes which were 60% less effective in incorporating phenylalanine into protein than were those from normal animals. Insulin treatment of the diabetic animal 1 hr prior to preparation of the particles restored the functional capacity of the system to normal. Moreover, pretreatment of a normal animal with insulin resulted in a harvest of "supernormal" ribosomes.

Unlike the situation in the androgen-stimulated prostate system, the counterfeit messenger Poly U stimulated both the "diabetic" and the "normal" ribosomes to the same extent, which suggests that the poor performance of the former was not entirely due to a deficient supply of template RNA.

Wool and Cavicchi (1966) have reviewed all the available inhibitor data as well as their experience with isolated RNP particles and have suggested that the primary effect of insulin on protein synthesis is at the level of translation. The recruitment of new species of template RNA occurs only secondarily, possibly as a result of the synthesis of a mystery protein that is quite analogous to that suggested by Garren in the case of ACTH. In both cases, the protein would have to be short-lived, but its synthesis could be coded for by a durable and persistent template RNA.

Thus, in a variety of cases (ACTH, insulin and somatotrophin), it has been suggested that in hormone deficiency states something is lost in the translation. It is still much too early to characterize the defect at the molecular level, but all of this work underlines the fact that we do not yet know many details of the translation process. It is safe to predict that students of the mechanism of action of hormones will help to develop a more intimate understanding of the translation process, just as they have clarified other problems in metabolic control in the past.

Dissociation of Hormone Effect from Protein Synthesis

While many of the effects of insulin on protein synthesis generally and on the synthesis of specific enzymes appear to involve new messenger RNA, insulin-stimulated enhancement of glucose transport into the cell occurs even in actinomycin D- or puromycin-poisoned muscle preparations. Inhibitor independent effects of other hormones on glucose transport—notably TSH on the thyroid and ACTH on the adrenal—have also been described. These are to be grouped with the slight effect of estrogen on water imbibition seen in uteri under the influence of inhibitors and with the persistence of a vasopressin influence on sodium transport in the actinomycin D-poisoned toad bladder (see p. 227). It is of some interest that all of these can be categorized as membrane effects of one sort or another. This suggests that certain hormones, some of which can obviously influence events deep within the cell, can interact directly or indirectly with membranes in ways which clearly affect rates of translocation of water or solutes.

It was first suggested that actinomycin D prevents the effects of parathyroid hormone (PTH) on serum calcium. It is now recognized that the *early* effect of PTH on bone is *not* inhibited by the antibiotic but that the full expression of the PTH effect over a 24-hr period is not possible in the actinomycin D-poisoned animal. De Luca (1966) has suggested that all of the necessary PTH responsive machinery is present in the cell originally but that, with continued stimulation, there must be *de novo* synthesis of new components of an ion transport system whose synthesis is elicited by vitamin D.

Coordinated Enzyme Responses to Hormones

The responses to all of the hormones we have discussed often involve many discrete enzyme proteins which are synthesized in response to the primary interaction of the hormone with its sensitive cell. We can presume that in the case of the specialized cells which respond to estrogen, androgen, TSH, LH or ACTH the coordinate nature of the response was determined in some way during the target cell's process of differentiation. The hormonal stimulus, then, brings into play just those enzyme-forming systems which are concerned with the performance of those functions which are characteristic of the target cell. Whether the enzyme-forming systems are involved primarily as a result of direct or indirect effects of the hormone has been the subject under discussion in much of the preceding narrative.

There is another type of tissue which, though fully differentiated and highly specialized, exhibits a remarkable plasticity of its enzyme profile in a variety of physiological circumstances. Certain hormones appear to play important roles in changing selectively the amounts of enzymes in liver cells in one direction or another. The enzyme changes seem to conform with the biochemical function of the liver that can be inferred from studying it in vivo by arteriovenous difference techniques or in vitro, either by perfusion or by surviving slice methods. I have used the phrase "biochemical imprinting" to signify adaptive increases in enzyme activities that occur along specific metabolic pathways when there is a large and sustained increase in substrate traffic through them. Thus, the experience of accommodating large amounts of substrate is often reflected in a characteristic imprint on the enzyme pattern of the cell. This is a long-range metabolic control device which is superimposed on other regulatory mechanisms which operate within a much shorter time scale and do not require a change in the actual amount of any enzyme protein.

Although adaptive changes in enzyme pattern have been described in a number of tissues, it is convenient to examine the liver as an example of a tissue which shows a high degree of enzymic virtuosity. As we have seen, when carbohydrate is in plentiful supply, the liver (as well as adipose tissue) is poised to extract glucose from the blood, store it as glycogen and synthesize it into triglycerides. When, in fact, the transition is made from a state of starvation to the fed state, the liver can perform these biochemical functions at "supernormal" rates. If carbohydrate is in short supply, as during starvation, or if glucose cannot readily be phosphorylated, as in diabetes, the liver cell undergoes an elaborate readjustment of its metabolic machinery which permits it to synthesize glucose from nonglucose sources very rapidly and export glucose into the blood stream for use by the obligatory glucose-burning tissues of the body—particularly the central nervous system. One can think of these startling readjustments in enzyme pattern in terms of "work hypertrophy" and "disuse atrophy" of enzymes. The arresting feature of the liver's capacity to adapt to states of glucose deprivation as well as to those of glucose abundance is the apparently coordinate nature of the response to each situation. Enzymes adapt as members of a team which is organized to perform a recognizable biochemical function. There is an *adaptive hyperlipogenesis* team of enzymes which comes into relief during refeeding after a fast—at a time when the *gluconeogenesis* team of enzymes is becoming atrophic.

A few rather tentative principles of adaptive enzyme formation are beginning to be recognized. In general, rate-limiting enzymes in a sequence are those most likely to show an adaptive increase when the pathway is heavily used. Single enzymes which catalyze reversible reactions almost never increase adaptively, but, in several cases, single *unidirectional* enzymes have been shown to exhibit adaptive changes. Adaptive changes are likely to occur at metabolic steps which are controlled by the balance between two discrete enzymes which catalyze reverse reactions. Adaptive fluctuations in enzymes also occur at switch points, i.e., at places where a substrate has to "decide" between two or more alternative metabolic pathways. These arrangements afford many opportunities for the exertion of metabolic control, and, in fact, "acute," or short-range, control devices also operate prominently at these sites.

In Figure 12-10, I have tried to illustrate some of these points. When we look at an ordinary metabolic map we see mainly substrates connected by arrows. Thus, we tend to concentrate our attention on the fuel, and not the metabolic machinery. By coding the arrows I have tried to focus attention on the metabolic device itself. Biochemistry-as-process is not only dynamic when the components of the machine—the enzyme proteins—are present in constant concentrations. There is another dimension of this particular kind of machine that is not shared by inanimate machines, i.e., the capacity to change the concentrations of enzymes, and therefore the tendency to fix metabolic traffic patterns, in response to demands that are made on them.

One can absorb most of the message of Figure 12-10 by looking at it through one's eyelashes. The black arrows represent enzymes which are either non-rate limiting, and therefore do not change adaptively in either glucose deprivation or glucose plethora situations, or they are enzymes which have not been adequately studied from this point of view (21, 22). The white arrows represent enzymes which increase in activity when large amounts of glucose are available to the tissues. These include glucokinase (1), the principal enzyme of entry of glucose; the enzymes concerned with glycogen metabolism (2, 3); phosphofructokinase (5), soluble α glycerophosphate dehydrogenase (6) and pyruvic kinase (7); the enzymes concerned with lipogenesis (10, 11) and the one that acts as a sort of fuel-injector system which continually feeds acetyl CoA to the lipogenic complex, citrate cleavage enzyme (9); and the systems which generate TPNH for fat synthesis (4, 8). The malic enzyme (8), by collaborating with the soluble malic dehydrogenase (20) not only generates TPNH but functions as a component of a transhydrogenase team which makes DPNH available for the reduction of TPN. Note that, according to this system, the four-carbon product of citrate cleavage is continuously salvaged as pyruvate, i.e., *below* the unidirectional reaction from phosphenol pyruvate to pyruvate catalyzed by pyruvic kinase (7). This has the effect of preventing gluconeogenesis at the same time that lipogenesis is being promoted. Note also that α glycerophosphate is being continually generated so that newly

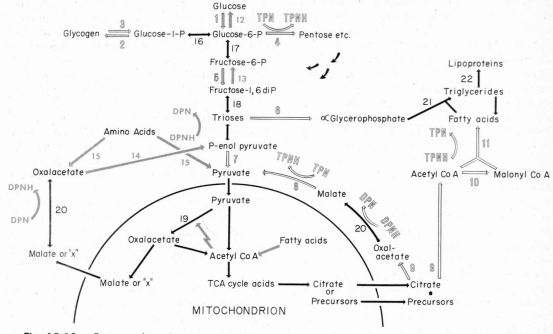

Fig. 12:10.—Enzyme adaptation patterns in adaptive hyperlipogenesis (white) and gluconeogenesis (gray)

Enzyme key:

1. Glucokinase
2. UDPG glycogen synthetase
3. Phosphorylase a
4. Glucose-6-P dehydrogenase
5. Phosphofructokinase
6. α glycerophosphate dehydrogenase
7. Pyruvate kinase
8. TPN malic enzyme
9. Citrate cleavage enzyme
10. Acetyl CoA carboxylase
11. Palmitate synthetase

12. Glucose-6-phosphate dehydrogenase
13. Fructose 1, 6 diphosphatase
14. Phosphoenol pyruvate carboxykinase
15. Transaminase
16. Phosphoglucomutase
17. Phosphoglucoisomerase
18. Aldolase
19. Pyruvate carboxylase
20. Malic dehydrogenase
21. Enzymes of triglyceride synthesis
22. Lipoprotein-forming enzymes

(See text for further information.)

synthesized fatty acids can be esterified to triglycerides, and, therefore, back inhibition of acetyl CoA carboxylase (10) by fatty acids is prevented. While the white enzymes are prominently featured, the gray ones generally decrease in activity.

During starvation, insulin withdrawal or cortisol treatment, the white enzymes wither away and the gray ones increase in activity. In many cases, inhibitor studies suggest that these increases are due to *de novo* synthesis of new enzyme protein. There is an appealing symmetry of the two processes of lipogenesis and gluconeogenesis, for, as Lardy and Krebs have emphasized, the reversal of the glycolytic pathway requires a DPNH-generating system just as lipogenesis re-

quires a continuing reservoir of TPNH. I have tried to suggest in my diagram that gluconeogenesis characteristically occurs when large amounts of fatty acids are presented to the liver for disposal. This has the effect of increasing greatly the acetyl CoA concentration in the cell which, in turn, allosterically stimulates the enzyme pyruvate carboxylase (19) whose activity, as conventionally measured, does not increase—presumably because it is present in adequate supply to accommodate large amounts of substrate. Oxalacetate probably cannot diffuse out of the mitochondrion rapidly enough to support high rates of gluconeogenesis. Therefore, malate or some related substance probably serves as a precursor of cytosol oxalacetate. This is a fortunate occurrence, for the authorities in this field agree that cytosol malic dehydrogenase (20), as it converts malate to oxalacetate, probably serves as the main DPNH-generating system for gluconeogenesis. Phosphoenol pyruvate carboxykinase (PEPCK) (14), is a prominent rate-limiting step in gluconeogenesis and increases greatly in all circumstances in which this process dominates over lipogenesis, i.e., starvation, diabetes, cortisol excess. (The transaminases (15) are also increased in the same circumstances.) It is worth noting that the effect of hypertrophy of PEPCK is to feed substrates into the gluconeogenic pathway *above* the unidirectional enzyme pyruvate kinase (7).

Two enzyme pairs illustrate the principle of regulation that occurs at sites characterized by a counterpoise between two discrete unidirectional enzymes which operate in opposite directions. When gluconeogenesis is dominant, fructose 1,6-diphosphatase (13) gains ascendancy over phosphofructokinase (5), while glucose 6-phosphatase (12) overpowers glucokinase (1). This "set" of the enzyme pattern guarantees that glucose generated from nonglucose precursors will be exported from the liver for use elsewhere in the body. The enzymes of glycogenesis and glycogenolysis (2, 3) appear to adapt in the same direction when glucose is plentiful, but they never recede to such low levels that the processes of glycogenesis and glycogenolysis cannot proceed readily even during starvation. Cortisone treatment during fasting can result in heavy glycogen deposits in the liver, which is probably due to the fact that with large doses of this hormone, new glucose production overwhelms the capacity of glucose 6-phosphatase to pour glucose overboard.

The intimate biochemical mechanisms involved in these enzyme regulations are not known. It is appropriate to introduce them in connection with hormones and gene action because, according to the interesting hypothesis of G. Weber, insulin "turns on" gene sites for the lipogenic complex of enzymes and "suppresses" those for the enzymes of gluconeogenesis, whereas cortisol has precisely the opposite effect. According to this view, these two hormones act like ecdysone with respect to the specific enzyme proteins whose synthesis they elicit. Weber also believes that the coordinate nature of the responses suggests that there is one or only a few operons for gluconeogenesis and a similar small number for hyperlipogenesis. This

is certainly an attractive theory, especially since many investigators have demonstrated marked stimulation of RNA synthesis in livers of cortisone-treated and refed rats. However, it is still too early to extrapolate microbial molecular biology theory into the liver cell. Enzyme regulations in mammalian cells probably involve complexities as yet undreamed of. For example, fructose feeding can result in a sort of hybrid enzyme pattern, half gluconeogenic and half hyperlipogenic, which is difficult to explain on the operon hypothesis. Moreover, there is some evidence that enzyme stabilization may play an important role in setting the levels of certain liver enzymes (Schimke).

Whether the hormone effects are direct or indirect, they must ultimately involve gene expression, for many of the adaptive enzyme increases that I have described can be prevented by protein synthesis inhibitors. There are certain specific enzymes which appear to be particularly responsive to insulin, especially glucokinase (1) (Sols, Weinhouse) and UDPG glycogen synthetase (2) (D. Steiner). These insulin effects appear to be highly selective and precise, and, since glucokinase is so strategically involved in the rate of influx of glucose into the machinery of the liver cell, some of the other adaptations may be secondary to increases in this enzyme. The glycogen synthetase is probably *not* secondary to new glucokinase synthesis for it occurs sooner after insulin administration. However, it *could* be secondary to some sort of activation of glucokinase by insulin.

One argument in favor of a powerful indirect effect of hormones on the processes under study is the fact that changes in the throughput of both pathways can be observed before any enzyme adaptations occur. This is especially true of gluconeogenesis, in both liver slices and isolated perfused liver. This suggests that, prior to any possible participation of genes in the response, a complicated set of signals may "instruct" enzymes at rate-limiting steps in ways that do not require new enzyme synthesis (allosteric activation?) and thereby begin to channel substrates through a pathway. In the case of gluconeogenesis, these signals may include (1) fatty acid oxidation, with its concomitant increase in acetyl CoA concentration; (2) 3′, 5′ cyclic AMP generation, which occurs after epinephrine, glucagon and in the diabetic. Things are admirably arranged so that the very conditions which favor gluconeogenesis—particularly large scale fatty acid oxidation—discourage both lipogenesis and its coenzyme support pathways, for many of the enzymes involved (especially acetyl CoA carboxylase (10) and glucose 6-phosphate dehydrogenase (4)) are inhibited by fatty acids or their thioesters.

Thus, it is convenient to consider these astonishing adaptations of the liver cell as a continuum of change. First, there are acute readjustments of traffic pattern which persist into a phase of new enzyme synthesis—the imprinting of the metabolic experience—progressing until the increased amounts of apoenzyme protein help to determine the substrate traffic pattern. In these complex processes, the hormones play important but, as yet, not clearly defined roles.

REFERENCES

Garren, L. D., Ney, R. L., and Davis, W. W.: Studies on the role of protein synthesis in the regulation of corticosterone production by ACTH in vivo, Proc. Nat. Acad. Sc. 53:1443–1450, 1965.

Hechter, O., and Halkerston, I. D. K.: Effects of steroid hormones on gene regulation and cell metabolism, Ann. Rev. Physiol. 27:133–162, 1965.

Hilf, R.: The mechanism of action of ACTH, New England J. Med. 273:798-811, 1965.

Jensen, E. V.: On the mechanism of estrogen action, Perspectives Biol. Med. 6:47–59, 1962.

Karlson, P.: New concepts on the mode of action of hormones, Perspectives Biol. Med. 6:203-214, 1963.

Lardy, H. A.: Gluconeogenesis: Pathways and hormonal regulation, *The Harvey Lectures, Series 60, 1964-65* (New York: Academic Press, Inc., 1966).

Litwack, G., and Kritchevsky, D.: *Actions of Hormones on Molecular Processes* (New York: John Wiley & Sons, Inc., 1964).

Mueller, G. C.: Estrogen action on genetic expression in *Proc. 6th Pan-American Congress of Endocrinology* (New York: Excerpta Medica Foundation, 1966).

Porter, G. A., and Edelman, I. S.: The action of aldosterone and related corticosteroids on sodium transport across the toad bladder, J. Clin. Invest. 43:611–620, 1964.

Sharp, G. W. G., and Leaf, A.: Mechanism of action of aldosterone, Physiol. Rev. 46:593–633, 1966.

Symposium on hormonal control of protein biosynthesis. J. Cell & Comp. Physiol. vol. 66, supp. (part II, no. 2), 1965.

Tata, J. R.: Biological action of thyroid hormones at the cellular and molecular levels in *Actions of Hormones on Molecular Processes*. Litwack, G., and Kritchevsky, D. (eds.) (New York: John Wiley & Sons, Inc., 1964).

Tepperman, J., and Tepperman, H. M.: Some effects of hormones on cells and cell constituents, Pharmacol. Rev. 12:301–353, 1960.

Tepperman, J., and Tepperman, H. M.: Adaptive hyperlipogenesis–late 1964 model, Ann. New York Acad. Sc. 131:404–411, 1965.

Toft, D., and Gorski, J.: A receptor molecule for estrogens: Isolation from the rat uterus and preliminary characterization. Proc. Nat. Acad. Sc. 56:1574–1581, 1966.

Weber, G., Singhal, R. L., Stamm, N. B., and Srivastava, S. K.: Hormonal induction and suppression of liver enzyme biosynthesis, Fed. Proc. 24:745–754, 1965.

Williams-Ashman, H. G.: New facets of the biochemistry of steroid hormone action, Cancer Res. 25:1096–1120, 1965.

Wilson, J. D., and Loeb, P. M.: Intranuclear localization of testosterone-1,2-H^3 in the preen glands of the duck, J. Clin. Invest. 44:1111–1112, 1965.

Wool, I. G., and Cavicchi, P.: Insulin regulation of protein synthesis by muscle ribosomes: Effect of the hormone on translation of messenger RNA for a regulatory protein, Proc. Nat. Acad. Sc. 56:991–998, 1966.

Index